ZURY: THE MEANEST MAN IN SPRING COUNTY

A NOVEL OF WESTERN LIFE

BY

JOSEPH KIRKLAND

FACSIMILE REPRINT
with an Introduction by John T. Flanagan

University of Illinois Press
Urbana, 1956

LIBRARY OF CONGRESS CATALOG CARD NO. 56-8419

INTRODUCTION

"Let only truth be told, and not all the truth," Joseph Kirkland wrote in the Chicago *Dial* in 1893, in a discussion of realism. A year before this pronouncement Stephen Crane had published his *Maggie: A Girl of the Streets,* which is conveniently labeled the first American naturalistic novel; and the very next year Hamlin Garland was to publish his *Crumbling Idols,* the collection of provocative essays in which he called for veritism and sincerity in fiction. Obviously Kirkland's brand of realism differed from that of Crane and Garland. Yet his most important novel, *Zury: the Meanest Man in Spring County,* 1887, had broken with the genteel tradition and had presented a central Illinois farmer in terms quite unfamiliar to the reader of conventional rural fiction. To a twentieth-century audience Kirkland's realism must seem strangely limited, perhaps even as anemic as the contention of William Dean Howells that literature ought to deal only with the smiling aspects of life. But to Kirkland's contemporaries his picture of early Illinois farm life was both authentic and bold.

It is possible that the limits which Kirkland prescribed for realism may have been due to his limited acquaintance with prose fiction. He knew something of Hardy and Tolstoy and certainly had read the work of his American contemporaries. But like Edward Eggleston he came late to the writing of fiction and could not even have been called a literary man until the last decade or so of his life. Before he tried his hand at novel writing he had been a business-man, a soldier, and a lawyer. Railroad accountancy, coal mining, staff work with General George B. McClellan and General Fitz-John Porter during the Civil War, and legal business in Chicago had occupied his time for a good many years. Indeed, his three novels and his history of Chicago all appeared during the closing period of his life. On the other hand, Kirkland's late attachment to literature was not entirely unexpected, since he came from a literary family and his mother, Caroline Kirkland, was not only considered a brilliant woman but was the author of three volumes of sketches of backwoods life in Michigan which attracted unusual attention because of their accurate transcription of speech and manners.

Joseph Kirkland was born in 1830. His father, William Kirkland, a graduate of Hamilton College, was a teacher and school principal who, with his wife, had organized a school for girls and who moved to Detroit in 1835 to conduct a young ladies' seminary. Unfortunately the Kirklands moved west during the height of the Michigan land fever, and it was not long before William Kirkland gave up his Detroit school for the purpose of investing in timber-land and platting a town. For a time the Kirkland family lived at Pinckney in Livingston County — the Montacute of Caroline Kirkland's stories — but William Kirkland was no businessman and in 1843 gave up his experiment and took his family back east. Three years later the father died.

Mrs. Kirkland, however, was quite equal to the task of supporting her young family. Already in 1839 she had published her autobiographical novel *A New Home — Who'll Follow?* under the pseudonym of Mrs. Mary Clavers. This was followed rapidly by *Forest Life* and *Western Clearings,* both of which sketched pioneer life so successfully and so vividly that they won the plaudits of such a severe critic as Edgar Allan Poe. In the east she assumed editorial positions and was associated both with the *Union Magazine* and *Sartain's Magazine*. Following a year's travel in Europe in 1848 she published a book of impressions of the continent and remained active until her death in 1864. The mother's activity and success as a writer were bound to be influential on the son, although it was to be some time before Joseph Kirkland turned seriously to his pen.

No complete biography of Joseph Kirkland has ever been written, and materials for a biography are sparse. Between his departure from Michigan as a youth and his acceptance of a position with the auditing department of the Illinois Central Railroad in 1855, the record is largely blank — although he apparently clerked for a time in the Putnam publishing house in New York and visited England in the late 1840's. But it would be impossible to exaggerate the value to him of his boyhood years in the Michigan backwoods and of his mother's success in converting the family experiences of these years into readable fiction. Both Caroline Kirkland and her son were interested in domestic life, in the speech, manners, and customs of the early settlers. When Mrs.

Kirkland called attention in the early pages of *Forest Life* to the absence of lurid incident and melodramatic plot ("No wild adventures, — no blood-curdling hazards, — no romantic incidents, — could occur within my limited and sober sphere. No new lights have appeared above my narrow horizon."), she was defining a kind of writing to which Joseph Kirkland would also subscribe many years later. Indeed this domestic realism, accurate and perceptive and detailed, is a hallmark of the work of both the Kirklands.

Joseph Kirkland's life following his removal as a man of twenty-five to Illinois is better attested. As a traveling railroad auditor he saw much of the state in the second half of the 1850's. Then in 1858 he resigned his railroad position to enter the coal mining business as an agent of the Chicago & Carbon Coal Company with his residence at Tilton, south of Danville in Vermilion County. His activity was interrupted by the Civil War, however, and he enlisted as a private in an infantry regiment at Danville on April 25, 1861. Elected by his fellow soldiers as a second lieutenant, he went with his unit for war training at Cairo, was advanced in rank, and saw service in various battles. It is this experience, incidentally, which underlies the fiction of his last novel, *The Captain of Company K.* Kirkland's later duties in the Civil War were those of a staff officer in the Peninsular Campaign. He suffered severely from swamp fever and when in 1863 his immediate superior, General Fitz-John Porter, was cashiered from the Union Army Kirkland resigned his commission and returned to Illinois. Coal mining again attracted his attention, and he and his brother participated in strip mining activities in Vermilion County. The natural expansion of the business, however, was abruptly terminated by the Chicago Fire, and it was probably this unexpected reversal which accounted for his entrance into law and journalism as well as for the removal of his residence from Tilton to Chicago.

From about 1875 to his death Kirkland was active in the cultural life of Chicago. He helped to organize the Chicago Literary Club and was one of its most active speakers. He contributed book reviews to the *Dial* shortly after Francis Fisher Browne began that periodical in 1880. He also did book reviewing for the *Chicago Tribune* and, in addition to publishing his own *Story of Chicago* in 1892, edited the first volume of John Moses' book about the city. Stories and articles by Kirkland also appeared in the *Century,* in *America,* in *Scribner's,* and in the *Atlantic Monthly.* To the new literary group which included Eugene Field, Henry B. Fuller, Opie Read, and Finley Peter Dunne, Kirkland was a kind of elder statesman among the Chicago literati.

Obviously Kirkland brought to his first and most important novel a wide experience but little formal literary discipline. Two factors help to explain the writing and the peculiar nature of *Zury: the Meanest Man in Spring County.* One was Kirkland's personal familiarity with rural people, boyhood reminiscences from Michigan and mature observation of Illinois farm scenes. The other was the career of an actual farmer, one Usual H. Meeker, which Kirkland seized upon and used as a model for his own Zury Prouder. To a very large extent the man focused and symbolified the scene. And the fortunate result was the first convincing and full length portrait of a farmer in American literature.

Zury is not a well constructed novel. It reveals none of the concern with technique which distinguished Henry James, and it shows little consistency in presentation. Kirkland moralizes, intrudes, editorializes as circumstances prompt him without regard to the basic structure of the story. He uses exact colloquial terms such as "niggering logs," "horse-shedding," "corn in the milk," and "log rolling" and then pauses to define the phrases. Indeed his concern with rural speech was so great that he supplied a glossary of terms, presumably on the assumption that later readers might not understand his colloquialisms. Moreover, he changes the pace of the narrative, telescopes much of the final action, and sometimes forgets to motivate adequately certain events of the plot. John McVey, for example, is a very convenient character for Kirkland: he marries Anne Sparrow when it is necessary for her to have a husband, and he departs for California, a prelude to his final disappearance, when he no longer has a plot function.

Basically the novel is the story of Zury Prouder, and his character is revealed through a series of episodes on a roughly chronological plan. In the beginning Zury is a lad coming west with his father Ephraim Prouder to a homestead near Wayback City,

Spring County, state of Illinois. Ephraim Prouder is not the best potential settler of a new community, but he has utilized the land-warrant which came to him as a bonus for military service in the War of 1812 to secure a tract of western land, and the Prouder family are wearily making their way toward their new holdings. It is early apparent that only Zury is adapted to prairie life. The younger child soon dies, the mother is sickly and does not survive long, and Ephraim lacks the hardness and determination which a new land exacts of its conquerors. Zury, on the other hand, is dismayed neither by poverty nor by hard work; to him the wilderness area offers the same challenge to create for the future that Rolvaag's Per Hansa experienced on the prairies of South Dakota. Wooden tools can be made to substitute for iron, an axe will serve as a shovel, and a plow can bank dirt around a cabin as well as a spade. Where his father is timid and uncertain, Zury is pragmatic and practical. Perhaps one of his most symbolic acts is his willingness to trade his rifle to neighbor Peddicomb for more hogs so that he and his father could make the best use of the corn they so laboriously raised. In order to improve the farm Zury would cheerfully forego the occasional pleasure of shooting a deer and adding venison to the table. Zury even develops a New Deal philosophy a century before its Rooseveltian apogee: "Borryin' 's a need-cessity, 'n' payin' 's a luxury. We can't 'fford no luxuries yit a spell."

If it was Ephraim Prouder's original decision to leave Pennsylvania and take up land in Illinois, it is

Zury's hard-headedness and indefatigable toil that make the Prouder farm a success. Zury constructs a crude fence by niggering off the trees and dragging them into position. Zury early perceives the necessity of operating the farm on the basic corn-hog economy. Zury forces his father into mortgaging several quarters of the original homestead in order to provide funds for tools, supplies, and inevitably more hogs. With his eye always on the main chance Zury works long hours, and even before Ephraim Prouder dies the son is the real master of the farm. The rural inventory taken about the time that the Soul-sleepers are trying to exact a contribution for their denominational college in Ohio from the reluctant Ephraim is proof of the success of Zury's method and plan: already the Prouder farm has a score of hay-ricks, two thousand bushels of wheat, a hundred acres of corn to harvest, sixty cattle, two hundred sheep, and hogs multiplying almost beyond count.

Once Kirkland has established Zury's success as a dirt farmer, he wisely subordinates that facet of Zury's activity and shows him in other roles. The initial words of the last chapter might serve as a summary of the events of the novel: "We picked up our homespun thread at the Prouder section: we followed it in its windings, knots, and twists to the school, the woods-fire, the riot, the stump, the polls, the machineshop, the mines, and many scenes beside." And, Kirkland adds, now the reader is back at the beginning scene, but with Zury a rich and respected farmer and Anne Sparrow, the third Mrs. Prouder, as mistress of his wide domain.

It would have been an artistic mistake to show Zury only as a farmer, for in that limited role his other qualities could not appear. Zury is "mean," yet his neighbors respect his integrity. He drives a hard bargain, but he will not cheat or lie or underweigh. To him public property is as much of a trust as private property is a possession. He is on the schoolboard, he serves as assessor, and he is elected to two terms in the state legislature because his associates believe in his probity. As one rustic acquaintance puts it with grudging admiration: "He knows haow t' trade, 'n' ef yew don't, he don't want ye t' trade with him, that's all. . . . Better be shaved with a sharp razor than a dull one."

Yet Zury is no paragon of virtue. Practically without education, crude in manners, insensitive to culture and refinement but yet consciously desirous of these qualities in a wife, parsimonious to a fault, wearing coarse clothes and boots not always free from manure, Zury is a backcountry figure who grows up with the region but can never absorb more than a veneer of cultivation. In his maturity he becomes wealthy and clumsily attempts to help others. But his philanthropy is graceless. Avarice sometimes impels him to act impulsively, as in the case of his second marriage, when he weds his sister-in-law in order to keep her property in the family. Sometimes he is even sensitive to his own reputation. The crucial epsisode in the book, the night which

Zury and Anne accidentally spend together in the shaft of the abandoned coal mine, links the two names indiscreetly (although the community is never aware of the real issue of the event) and causes Zury constant embarrassment. In similar fashion even his penury weighs upon his conscience. In a nightmare Zury flings indictments at himself — land-shark!, mortgage-shark!, ignorant old miser! — which he cannot quite refute. Indeed, the one artistic flaw in the characterization of Zury is Kirkland's capitulation to sentimentalism. The man who has married twice in order to secure the dowery and the cheap labor which his wives could bring him suddenly embarks on a romantic quest and constantly risks being given the mitten by the attractive widow, Anne Sparrow McVey. Zury has of course some motivation for his conduct. He is lonely and, again wifeless, is free to pursue the woman he has always admired. Moreover, marriage to Anne would finally legitimate (at least in his own conscience) the twins who, because of a stratagem, bear the McVey name. But there is no doubt that Zury is softened toward the end of the novel, and his Indian summer romance wrenches slightly a fine character portrait.

Kirkland characterizes Zury through action and description, but probably no method is more successful than the careful recording of his speech. Zury's language is coarse, elliptical, solecistic, but earthy and blunt, and phonetically quite exact. His nasal vowels and his telescoped syllables are meticulously given. When Zury uses figurative diction, his examples appropriately come from the farm and the store, and when he employs country proverbs they are the maxims of Poor Richard with an Illinois flavor. In his early years his goal was to fence a quarter section of land: "a mild o' fence, pig-tight, bull-strong, 'n' hoss-high." He believed that a farmer should never "lay by" his corn "until it's growed s' high he can't see his way aouter th' field come night." His advice to Anne about her lodging troubles is wholly proverbial: "Naow ye jest better hold yer hosses. Ye're a-borr'in trouble. Hain't ye never learnt yit not t' cross a river ontel ye come tew it?" And his definition of money illustrates his own pragmatic philosophy as well as his awareness of the level of his audience: "*Money's* a thing that can't be manufactured by a sharp in an office — its suth'n' th't's got t' be dug aouter the graoun' 'n' then traded off fer suth'n th't 's growed a-top o' graoun': corn, hawgs, wool, — suth'n' 'r other th't takes labor."

Zury Prouder is of course not the only character in the novel. Anne Sparrow, the Yankee schoolteacher, is well depicted despite the fact that changes in the 1892 reprinting of the novel indicate some uncertainty in Kirkland's conception of her. Her definite Fourieristic sympathies, her frustrated ambition to create, her desire to bring a touch of beauty and charm to the life of her benighted scholars, and on the other hand her timidity and fear of the dark — all suggest a complex but human character. There is also old man Anstey, whose mortgage Zury eventually assumes, the Peddicomb family, an occasional neighbor and acquaintance. But as the title of the novel implies, it is the meanest man in Spring County with whom Kirkland is most concerned, and it is his portrait which sustains the book. When Joseph Kirkland published his novel, no American writer had created a realistic portrait of an American farmer. Zury's vitality is greater than that of any figure in the books of Hamlin Garland and E. W. Howe, Kirkland's chief contemporary rivals in the depicting of the American rural scene; and he is worthy of comparison with such later farm characters as Ellen Glasgow's Dorinda Oakley, Willa Cather's Antonia Shimerda, and the Joad family of John Steinbeck.

Kirkland subsequently wrote two other novels, *The McVeys,* published in 1888, and *The Captain of Company K,* 1891. Neither is without interest despite the patent inferiority of both to their predecessor. *The McVeys* includes Zury Prouder as a subordinate character but lacks a strong protagonist to replace him. Moreover, the plot action precedes in time the closing pages of *Zury* so that the reader is unfortunately able to anticipate developments. In a sense *The McVeys* is only an episode in the larger chronicle devoted to explaining the maturing of the two children before Anne Sparrow McVey becomes the third Mrs. Prouder. *The Captain of Company K* is largely the result of Kirkland's Civil War experiences and suffers from a lack of concentration and focus. Yet one should not forget that in its frank treatment of the sordidness and horror of war the novel clearly anticipated Stephen Crane's famous *Red Badge of Courage.* Kirkland's condemnation of battle, incidentally, has all the practical, hard judgment of Zury himself: "Whenever it shall become the rule that the man who causes a war shall be its first victim, war will be at an end. War flourishes by what Gen. Scott wittily called 'the fury of the non-combatants.' "

Historians of American literature are prone to dismiss Joseph Kirkland as the mentor of Hamlin Garland, as the man who converted Garland from a dirt farmer to a realistic novelist. Kirkland's influence on the younger man was undoubtedly important, as Garland himself has testified in *Roadside Meetings,* but his achievement is not merely reflected glory. In Zury Prouder he created a major figure who epitomized the passion for wealth in the early days of Illinois as completely as the characters of F. Scott Fitzgerald later symbolized the flamboyance and glamor of the jazz age. Only those who follow in all its ramifications the career of "the meanest man in Spring County" will realize how superbly Kirkland has vitalized a portrait.

Urbana, November 8, 1955 JOHN T. FLANAGAN

BIBLIOGRAPHICAL NOTE

The text used here is that of the original 1887 edition. The most complete studies of Kirkland's life are two unpublished doctoral dissertations, "Joseph Kirkland: Biography and Criticism," by Clayton A.

Holaday, submitted at Indiana University in 1949, and "The Life and Works of Joseph Kirkland, with an Edition of *Zury*," by Clyde E. Henson, submitted at Western Reserve University in 1950. There is a valuable collection of Kirkland manuscripts at the Newberry Library in Chicago. The short *Dictionary of American Biography* article on Kirkland was written by Dorothy A. Dondore. In addition to references to Kirkland's work in the standard literary histories, the reader may be interested in the following special studies:

John T. Flanagan, "Joseph Kirkland, Pioneer Realist," *American Literature* (November, 1939), 11: 273-284.

Clyde E. Henson, "Joseph Kirkland's Influence on Hamlin Garland," *American Literature* (January, 1952), 23: 458-463.

Clayton A. Holaday, "Kirkland's *Captain of Company K:* A Twice-Told Tale," *American Literature* (March, 1953), 25: 62-68.

Kenneth J. LaBudde, "A Note on the Text of Joseph Kirkland's *Zury*," *American Literature* (January, 1949), 20: 452-455.

Benjamin Lease, "Realism and Joseph Kirkland's *Zury*," *American Literature* (January, 1952), 23: 464-466.

ANNE SPARROW AS THE PURITAN PRISCILLA.

"To be sure, her kerchief was figured and her apron cross-barred; but what of that?"—*Page 194.*

ZURY: THE MEANEST MAN
IN SPRING COUNTY

A NOVEL OF WESTERN LIFE

BY

JOSEPH KIRKLAND

BOSTON AND NEW YORK
HOUGHTON, MIFFLIN AND COMPANY
The Riverside Press, Cambridge
1887

CONTENTS.

ZURY:

THE MEANEST MAN IN SPRING COUNTY.

CHAPTER I.

EARLY DAYS IN SPRING COUNTY.

GREAT are the toils and terrible the hardships that go to the building up of a frontier farm; inconceivable to those who have not done the task or watched its doing. In the prairies, Nature has stored, and preserved thus far through the ages, more life-materials than she ever before amassed in the same space. It is all for man, but only for such men as can take it by courage and hold it by endurance. Many assailants are slain, many give up and fly, but he who is sufficiently brave, and strong, and faithful, and fortunate, to maintain the fight to the end, has his ample reward.

"'Spect we must be a-gittin' daown inter Spring River bottom, dad."

"Shouldn' wonder, Zury. This h'yer flat 's the sec'n' bottom. 'Pears t' be a drap jist ahead, — that 'll let us daown t' the low bottom."

Just then, a more than usually vicious jolt

of the wagon beside which they were walking, brought a cry of pain from inside the cotton tilt that covered it. Old Ephraim stopped the team, and poked his head into the opening at the back.

"What 's the matter, Shoog?" (short for "Sugar"). "Did 'ee hurt 'eeself?"

"Mommy's honey knocked her head agin the hoop, when ye slumped inter that blamed old chuck-hole!" said the mother, who had her sick little girl in her arms, assuaging the pain of a hard bump, the latest of many sustained during the past weeks of slow and painful travel.

"Poppy can't ollers shun 'raound th' chuck-holes; the road 's so narrer, 'n' the' 's sech lots on 'em!"

"Chuck-holes" is the expressive Western name for the short, sharp depressions which use makes in unworked country roads, each hole being on the other side of the track from some rock or root that raises a wheel out of its rut.

"Don't li'l Shoog wanter come out 'n' have poppy hold her on the mare fer a spell?"

But the little pale one was too tired, and only shook her head.

"Wal — never mind! Mebbe we 'll git thar come night. Then she kin rest!"

With this blessed, heavenly, almost inconceivably blissful thought, the little procession resumed its laborious progress. It consisted of a "prairie schooner," a groaning and complaining wagon, covered with a cotton tilt stretched over high hoops, and drawn by a span of jaded mares worn down by hundreds of miles of steady pulling, and still further exhausted by two long-legged, shambling colts, that had been their burden and their solace ever since they left the mountains of southern Pennsylvania. Next followed a cow and calf. Next came a fine sheep-dog, evidently in charge of the whole party, and extremely watchful that no man, woman, or child, horse, colt, cow, or calf, or smallest bit of stray personal property, should fall out and get left behind. If a whip should be dropped, Shep would pick it up, and drag it carefully forward until relieved of its long, awkward weight. Even a piece of useless household waste could not be got rid of without its being once or oftener taken away from Shep, while he was sternly given to understand that it must be left behind, — blows being sometimes necessary to his full comprehension, — after which he would consent to abandon it, reluctantly and with many a halt and backward look. Then he would be low-spirited and unhappy for miles, seeming hurt that his humble effort to be useful should be snubbed and nipped in the bud.

The guiding spirit of the caravan was a shabby, grizzled, middle-aged man, worn and bent with toil and self-forgetfulness. He walked beside the mares, sometimes guiding them, but oftener letting them find their own way, with the lines hung up on the hames. Near him, or elsewhere, "here and there and everywhere," traveled a stout, red-faced, well-grown boy, of whom we shall hear so much in these pages that we need not dwell upon him just now. The whole outfit, the "schooner" and its accompaniments, was only one of a million like unto it which have traversed this land, headed westward, in the century past, and will continue to travel for a generation yet to come, until they meet the reflux wave from the Pacific with the message, "No use to go on. Standing room only." Then, as the illimitable tide continues to flow, it must diverge, part up toward the Arctic, to the region of the Saskatchewan, even disturbing the elk, beaver, and wild swans of the mysterious Mackenzie River; part down, down, down, to the Isthmus and beyond. They are good things, these "prairie schooners," the carriers of virtue, honesty, intelligence, and freedom, and an incredible capacity and appetite for toil, — the "Mayflowers of the West."

Now our party reaches another steep declivity, to descend which a wheel has to be chained. Once down, they find themselves in a flat and comfortable bottom-land, formed by the latest river deposits, containing some sand and gravel, and therefore making a better roadway, in dry times, than the clayey upland. Gigantic white-trunked poplars, cottonwoods, and sycamores, and ragged water-elms, with a plentiful sprinkling of splendid black-walnuts, here spring from an almost grassless plain, and climbing up their trunks and stretching from tree to tree are enormous wild grape-vines, — the whole having a look of tropical luxuriance. Up to a certain level, exactly the same on all the trees, there is a gray stain left by the muddy spring floods, which shows the proximity of the river, and graphically indicates the times when it changes from a mere innocent-looking belt of clear water, interrupted by bars and beds and shallows innumerable, to a vast moving lake, — a surging flood of silt-charged fluid, carrying its quota to form the delta of the Mississippi.

So great is the relief of the soft and level road that the little girl falls asleep, and awakes quite refreshed; then, further stimulated by a dose of the inevitable quinine, she is induced to try a short ride on the back of the nigh mare, where her father carefully holds her as he walks.

"Oh, ferever! how funny!" she exclaims, as she looks about on the changed scene. "Ain't this jist *tew* cur'us! Looks 's though th' trees all hed the'r stock'n's on!"

At this bright fancy the others all laughed, — or came as near to a hearty laugh as their kind, grim, grown-up pioneers, ever do come.

"Yew bet!" said Zury. "Pootty dirty stock'n's tew!"

"What 's them long things a-hangin' fr'm th' trees?"

"Them 's swings the trees puts up fer good little gals to swing on tew!"

"Wal, that 's *me!*"

"That 's so, honey! If ever th' wuz a good little gal, it 's mommy's honey. Best little gal on the job."

"Kin I git t' hev a swing?"

"Kin ye? Ye jist kin! 'N' Zury 's the boy that 'll swing ye! Jest 's sure 's we git thar!"

"Thar," the unknown land where all was to be well, where a thousand buds of promise were to blossom and a thousand dreams were to become realities, was a whole section of the public domain, "six hunderd 'n' forty acres o' the finest land th't ever laid ou' doors," which Ephraim Prouder had "entered," paying for it partly with the land-warrant given him as a soldier in the war of 1812, and partly with the entire savings of his lifetime. He had never seen it, but had invested his all in it with the fine and amazing faith of the emigrant, — faith so rarely misplaced, among all the hordes who have taken their lives in their hands and journeyed forth to people the West.

"Ephr'm, ain't it gittin' nigh on ter noon? Better n't we stop and eat a piece?"

"Not hardly, S'liny," said the old man, squinting up at the sun. "Guess we better push on t' the river. Can't be fur naow. Then we 'll hev s'm water fer the stawk, 'n' know whar we be."

Almost as he spoke, the glitter of water appeared between the tree trunks, and they soon reached the river bank, where the existence of a ferry was indicated by a great rope stretched across, each end attached high up on a convenient tree trunk, and the middle hanging down near the water.

"Guess we 'll ongear h'yer, 'n' git acrost afterw'ds," said Ephraim.

"Better hold on till we git over, dad; th' ain't no grass h'yer fer the stawk," suggested Zury.

"Mebbe th' ain't none t' other side nuther, son."

"Mebbe not, but the' can't be any less 'n none, 'n' the' kin be more."

By this time they saw the scow putting out from the further bank and creeping slowly over, aided by the device of attaching its bow to the rope with a shorter line than that which held its stern; so that its flat side was presented slanting to the current. As it approached it did not look large enough to hold the wagon, alone; but nevertheless, the whole caravan was got on board and safely over, — albeit Shep evidently thought the experiment a hazardous one, and felt it incumbent on him to take the most active and anxious care that no accident should be allowed to occur.

The place where they crossed was a mill-pond, made by a dam just below. At the dam were a saw-mill and grist-mill, and near by was a country store, a tavern, and a few other modest structures.

"That 's Wayback, I s'pose."

"Ya-as," answered the ferryman. "That 's Wayback City."

"'Spect the' 's a ford daown below the dam," said Zury.

"Wal, yes, a kinder sorter one," answered the other, after due consideration of the fact that he had his charge safely on board and beyond the possibility of backing out. "Might lose a colt or a calf, 'n' th' ferriage is only twenty cents."

"Twenty cents!" said father and son in chorus. The idea of characterizing such a sum of money as "only twenty cents!"

But there was no help for it; the money was produced with difficulty and paid with pain. The ferryman directed them to a little "rise" where they would find grass, and there they fed their beasts and ate their "piece" in quiet; but the outlay of twenty cents cast a gloom over the occasion.

Afterward the "men folks" went to the tavern to get some accurate directions for finding their new home; they only knew the Section, Town, and Range, and that it was on the edge of the timber six miles beyond Wayback. Then they spent a few more cents in supplies, and started on the final stage of their hegira.

It was the reverse of the descent they had made in the morning. First the low, ragged luxuriance of the bottom, annually enriched with the fine Nile-like deposit of the floods; then the "second bottom," covered with the calmer verdure springing from deposits made centuries ago; then the final climb to the general level.

Spring County is one of those highly-prized and early-sought-for localities where both prairie and timber awaited the settler. Spring River in the course of ages had dug for itself a deep ravine, through which it runs between high banks, — sometimes abutting the river in bluffs, sometimes receding from it and leaving broad bottoms, but oftenest having bluff on one side and bottom on the other. On each bank a belt of country was then (it was in the first quarter of the present century that our scene opens) covered with forest primeval. The timber growth of the near bottoms has been already described. Further up the slopes, elm, oak, maple, hickory, and other hardy growths had braved and checked the prairie fires and equally destructive prairie winds from time immemorial. Outside these timber belts, and crowding them in a stout struggle for the mastery, lies the famous "Grand Prairie." For countless years the soil has lain fallow; crop after crop of prairie grass has grown up in summer strong and rank, and then in winter has lain down and decayed; the result of the process being a soil of great general fertility, suggestive of a thick layer of cream on a gigantic milkpan. Lucky the pioneer who has such woods behind him and such prairie before him at the onset of his battle with the elements.

As the Prouders' caravan emerged from the timber on the open, Ephraim called to his wife, —

"See here, S'liny! Here 's the Grand Paraira at last!"

With haste Selina scrambled out to the wagon-seat, where she sat and feasted her eyes on the long-wished-for sight. There it was, to be sure! Under the warm afternoon sun, which was already sinking in the yellow western glow of a great, cloudless sky, lay an undulating ocean of grass and flowers. In places, where an inequality of the surface brought them into perspective range, the "prairie flowers" (blue gentian) gave to the whole sward a tinge of pale azure; here and there a tall "rosin weed" would raise its spike of bloom; and again, the golden-rod gave the needed "dash of color;" in damp spots there were lady-slippers and other thirsty plants; and mixed with these few examples of nature's gay moods were weeds and flowers of a thousand descriptions and as many shades of color and varieties of form and texture. Among, between, and around them was the persistent, peculiar prairie grass, a hardy, seedless growth that spreads only by pushing out its intricate, interlacing roots; tenacious of life, and resisting drought and even fire with wonderful hardihood, but never deigning to reëstablish itself after its chosen place has been desecrated by the plow. In ground that has been cultivated and then allowed to return to waste, other grasses may be sown, strange weeds may plant themselves in wild waste; but its former proud occupant never returns.

Now it is near nightfall, and the man of the family begins to look out anxiously for some landmark in the woods which for miles back have been skirting, on the right, the prairie road they are traveling. At length he stops the team, and walks off toward a towering oak he has been noticing from afar. The two colts instantly lie down; so do the cow and calf, and the dog; and each of the mares begins to "favor" her weariest foot. The youth climbs into the wagon-seat, and rests there; and the woman, with the child in her arms, emerges from the recesses of the tilt and sits beside him, without a word. The soft rustle of the tree-tops and the music of the tree-toads are the only sounds which break the vast silence. Presently the man returns, tramping through the thick grass.

"Here we be, S'liny. That thar 's the blazed tree. We 're jist abaout on the line 'twixt the tew half-sections, where we stan'."

"This is home, is it? Wal, ferever!"

And Selina looked about her at forest and prairie and sky and solitude. It is impossible to tell whether she meant any sarcasm by her words or not, — probably not. But she heaved a deep, unconscious sigh.

"Zury, the' 's a little branch starts out a ways beyond the blazed tree. You take the pail 'n' see if ye kin git some water, 'n' find a place t' water the stawk."

After Zury, followed by the faithful Shep, had gone on his errand, the man took the harness off the mares, and they walked off a few steps, lay down and took a refreshing roll, and, concluding that they were more tired than hungry, lay still in the luxuriant grass, only nibbling at what they could reach.

"Hand me daown th' old muskit, S'liny, 'n' I 'll see if I kin start a fire."

He gathered a little dry grass and weeds, and, putting a few grains of powder into the gun, fired it into the mass, and soon had a smoky blaze. (This was before the days of the friction match.)

"Why did n't ye make it to wind'ard o' th' wagin, Ephr'm, so 's to keep off the skeeters?"

"Oh, Zury he kin start a little smudge 'raound thar. We 'll need one both sides afore morn'n'."

Then, as Zury reappeared, —

"D' ye find the water? That 's right; 'n' ye brought a chunk fer the fire, — that 's saved me a trip. Naow drive the stawk daown t' the branch, 'n' take th' axe along 'n' cut a couple o' crotches 'n' a pole to hang the kittle on tew."

"Come, Shep; fetch 'em along."

The cheerful leap and bark of the dog starts up the resting quadrupeds, and directs them all toward the place he and his master have just explored. He knows as well as anybody does what is wanted, and accomplishes it better than anybody else could.

When they come back, the mares and the cow are turned out, and allowed to graze at will, being restrained, until they shall get to be "way-wonted," from straying too far in the boundless waste of herbage by the simple device of tethering the colts and calf.

Soon the kettle is boiling, the inevitable and inestimable pot of green tea is ready, a tiny cup of milk is provided for the sick girl, the bread and ham bought at Wayback are made good use of by the others, the additional "smudges" are built, some things are removed from the wagon to make sleeping-room, as has become a nightly custom, and all hands turn in to their familiar wagon-beds and sleep the sleep of the weary.

The whippoorwills keep up their sad and ceaseless calls, the tree-toads their wild chatter, and all night the gentle rustle of the leaves responds to the undying breeze of the Grand Prairie.

As day dawned, the prairie reappeared, covered with a shallow sea of silvery fog ; the night sounds ceased, and from all around, near and far, came the sound of the innumerable prairie-chickens, the miniature crow of the invisible cocks, — "Kitticadoo, cado-o-o-o!"— in ceaseless repetition, now near, now far, in humble imitation of their more belligerent congeners of the barn-yard.

Before "sun-up" Ephraim and Zury were stirring about in the heavy dew, freeing one of the colts which had got entangled in its tether and nearly ruined for life (vastly to Shep's perturbation), gathering sticks and hickory bark for a fire, bringing up water, and so forth. Then, for the rest of the day, and for many days thereafter, the axes of father and son were heard from dawn to dark, felling, trimming, and notching logs, joists, and rafters for the hut. Next, by the help of the now refreshed team, they had to be "snaked" up through the grass to the place selected for a building site. The nearest neighbor was three miles away, the nearest post-office and store six miles.

When the "raising bee" took place, the refreshments for the little band of friendly workers had to be cooked by Selina over a chip fire in the open air. The feast consisted of boiled pork, crackers, molasses and water with a dash of ginger, coffee sweetened with molasses, and, alas! the last of the cherished dried apples they had brought from "home." Not another atom of fruit did they see, except a small remnant of apples kept for "the babe," till next blackberry harvest; barring a few wild grapes in the autumn, the peculiarity of which fruit is that it consists entirely of skin and bone, and very little of them.

After the raising, the rafters had to be covered with "clapboards," split from straight logs selected and cut square for the purpose. These boards were held up by stringers laid across the rafters, and held down by poles laid on them and weighted with sticks and stones; and, to do them justice, a very poor roof they made, after all.

Next, the chinks in the walls had to be filled up with split pieces of wood, and wet clay daubed in all the crevices within and without, and a stick chimney built and similarly plastered. Next — hang up some spare bed-clothing over the door and window openings; and next, move into the floorless, lightless shelter, pile your few household belongings on the bruised sod of the interior, and sit down and be thankful.

A hovel? A palace to those who have constructed it with their own hands, and now occupy it, after having made a covered wagon serve as a home for nearly three months.

All this and a hundred times more, which nobody would read even if anybody could possibly write it, was accomplished by the able and willing father and son, the mother being chiefly occupied with her sickly little one. As soon as the household stuff was discharged from the wagon, a load of boards was hauled from the saw-mill, and a rough door and a rougher window-blind were knocked together and hung in place by hinges made from hickory withes. Later, the window was cross-barred and covered with greased paper, which admitted a little light; and as soon as a two-inch augur could be borrowed, a hole was bored through the wall by the side of the fire, through which small aperture a tiny ray of light could fall on Selina's needles, on those rare occasions when she had time to sit down and devote herself to such mere luxury as knitting. At other times the hole was closed by a plug.

The only individual of the four travelers who will journey on with us all through our story is Zury, the boy. His parents, by some means we wot not of, found for him the name "Usury," pronounced with the accent on the second syllable, which extraordinary prenomen, shortened to "Zury," has played a great part in Spring County life from that day to this, and will bear a proportionally important burden in these chronicles.

Zury had come early — so early that he had forgotten it — to that most thrilling experience in every fine boy's life, the discovery that he, too, is valuable to the little world about him. He was a natural worker, a seeker after chances to be useful, his ambition always outrunning the demands made on him. When he could be lifted on a horse to go for the cows, of course he rebelled against "tending baby;" and when he could plow, he despised milking and the other "chores," but he did them all the same, asking no rest save the rest of change of occupation. Achievement sprang from his mind and muscles like petroleum from a flowing well: the only thing needful was to provide channels for it.

Frontier life was what he needed to grow in. Openings for hard profitable work are there plenty, unmistakable, and tempting. One of the ways in which he showed his enjoyment of the consciousness of power was a natural impatience of control or interference, a brusque self-assertion, a rudeness which in a weaker being would have been intolerable. Some splendid horses will balk if you check or guide them, though at their own speed and in their own fashion they will cheerfully do more than anybody could ask or expect.

So sets out a traveler magnificently equipped with natural gifts. Let us see how circumstances favor, or dwarf, or distort their growth.

Up to this time he still retained a few boyish weaknesses, — not love of play, exactly, except as all work was play to him, but a love for ingenious devices in the work he did, and a busy brain always occupied with thoughts of such devices and of other things. Of course he was an industrious and accomplished whittler; his jack-knife was always at hand and always sharp, and in the intervals of more important avocations always busy. His colts grew up "ready broke," or near it; they began to help him almost as soon as they were weaned. His horses were as tame as dogs, and (up to their limited intellects) as intelligent. As he would say, "Hoss-flesh is cheaper 'n man-flesh. Whenever ye kin dew back-work with hoss-paower, ye 're a makin' money."

Another of his weaknesses was his love for his helpless sister. It was a yearning fondness in direct proportion to his strength and her weakness. If he had grown weaker or she stronger, his affection would have become less absorbing. Of course little whittled playthings were her constant companions on the bed-cover, — the earth-floor was too damp for her, — and mixed with them were lots of vari-colored birds' eggs, exquisitely cleaned by a process devised by Zury.

The first eggs he brought her were of a delicate pale green, and formed her dear delight for days. Her little hands, more delicate than the eggs themselves, fondled them with a tenderness that kept them safe from breaking, but unhappily nothing could save them from natural decay.

"What 's th' matter, Shoog? Don't 'ee cry."

"Oh, my eggies got spile't."

"Nem' mind, Sweety; bub 'll git ye s' more t'morry!"

"No, I want *them.*"

"All right. Shoog sh'll have 'em agin t'morry!"

"Sure enough?"

"Jest 's sure 's shootin'."

So the little sufferer went to sleep comforted.

Zury took the eggs and tried to "blow" them — making a hole in each end, and puffing the contents through with his breath. But they were too delicate, and either the shell broke in spite of all care or the holes were so big that the beauty was lost. He pondered over the problem long and hard, gazing at the egg he held, and trying to overcome the apparent physical impossibility.

"Could n't I poke in suth'n'? Not hardly; th' ain't no room. Lessee naow. Ef I war n't so big, I'd jis' crawl inside 'n' scoop her aout *good!* Lessee — lessee — lessee. Thar! I've got it!"

He made a pin-hole in one end of each egg; and with the first streak of dawn he was up and out hunting for an ant-hill he had before observed, where some almost infinitesimal marvels of industry in formic shape were always busy at their incomprehensible tasks. Here he deposited the eggs, and soon saw the little creatures doing his desired work in a manner delightful to behold.

"Where's my eggies?" asked a sweet little voice when he came in for his breakfast.

"Brer Zury 's a-fixin' on 'em. Wait till noon-spell, then we 'll see!"

"Sure enough?"

"Jest 's sure 's shootin'."

With much difficulty the little one waited, her faith in Brer Zury aiding her to bear the impatience of childhood and invalidism. (Her habit of doing without most of the things she wanted being also a helpful influence, alas!)

At noon-spell again: —

"Where's my eggies?"

"They'm a-comin' along; not quite done yit."

The irrepressible tears would start at this fresh disappointment; so Zury went out and brought in one of the eggs, with a small army of the little toilers still busy about it.

"Oh, ferever! What's them li'l things?"

"Them's ants — leetle bugs that loves eggs, — 'n' they'm a diggin' on 'em aout fer li'l Shoog. See 'em a-runnin' in 'n' aout o' th' hoel? Every one 't comes aout 's got a leetle grain o' stuff, see? He wants t' carry it daown in th' ant-hole t' feed his little sisters, — only sence I fetched it away he can't find the hoel any more."

"Oh, take it back, so the' kin find ther li'l sisters agin!"

So all the long afternoon she pleased herself with thinking of the work going on and the little sisters being fed. At night Zury brought in another, and again the girl was impatient to have it returned. Then when the shells were perfectly cleaned, she took them with a fresh delight, — so pretty and so pure; and so light that she could scarcely feel their weight in her fingers. One poor stray ant that had not been carried back she carefully guarded till Zury took it, with the promise to return it to its sorrowing family, which promise he faithfully performed.

On another day he came with a new plan for the amusement of his darling.

"Brer Zury's fixed up a nice swing fer li'l Shoog."

"A grape-vine swing?"

"Ya-as. Dooz she wanter come aout 'n' swing in the sunshine a leetle?"

"Oh, yes!" said the child; and, wrapped up in all the poor defenses against the air which their limited supplies could furnish, Zury carried her out, and her thread-like fingers grasped the rough vine while Zury swung her in short and gentle vibrations. A very little was enough, and they hoped for more strength on some other day. The next time she was not so eager to make the experiment; and after the third time she said, sweetly smiling, —

"I feel so much better to-day th't I guess I won't hev t' go aout 'n' swing."

And she swung no more.

CHAPTER II.

TRIFLING DOINGS OF LOW-DOWN FOLKS.

"EPHRAIM, could n't we git t' git some stuff fr'm the sor-mill fer a floor, — puncheons er suth'n'?" ("Puncheons," or "slabs," are the side-cuts from logs squared for sawing.)

"Wal, S'liny, ye see, th' way the roads is naow, a load o' puncheons 'd take a day t' haul, 'n' would n't more 'n' kiver th' spot th' bed stan's on, arter all."

"Mebbe the babe 'd dew better ef she worn't right ontew th' bare graound."

The old man sighed wearily, but had nothing to say. Zury shortly afterward stopped his whittling and went out into the darkness; returning soon with his axe and some knotty chunks of hard wood. Then he proceeded to chop and shape them, throwing the chips into the fire as they accumulated about him.

"What ye 'baout, sonny?"

"Makin' some gluts." (Gluts are wooden wedges used in rail-splitting.)

"What fer?"

"Split s'm boards t' lay daown fer a floor."

"The' 'll all warp up."

"Mebbe so, mebbe not."

"The' will, sure 's shootin'."

"Wal, let 'em."

Next morning at early dawn they could hear his axe resounding through the leafy aisles, and before breakfast two trees had fallen victims to his prowess.

"What made ye pick sech small ones, Zury? Sh' thought ye 'd a made a better outin' ef ye 'd a tuk big uns, like the one we got t' rive the clabboards out of."

"Little uns, jest split in tew, 'n' laid bark daown, ain't s' liable t' warp up, I guess."

"Jesso, jesso. Dunno but ye 're right, my son."

"Yew bet I 'm right, dad!"

The trees were felled, cut in lengths equal to the width of the room, hauled up, and split; then laid athwart the hovel in furrows carefully hollowed out of the ground and shaped so as to bring the split sides to something like a level. How beautiful that jagged and splintery surface looked to those four pairs of eyes! No shining tessellated tiles, no noiseless velvety carpet, ever gave more heartfelt delight. The mother thought of the golden pavement of the heavenly streets, but of course she kept to herself the foolish, unpractical fancy.

"Ye 're my boy, ain't ye, Zury?"

"That 's what yew allers 'llaowed, mother, so I 'llaow it 's so."

"Mine too," said a weak little voice from out the bundle of bed-clothes Zury held in his lap before the fire. He laid his rough, bronzed cheek on the pale forehead and damp clinging hair of the suffering child, but did not speak.

About the floor they none of them said much; but they almost hated to go to bed and lose sight of it. They slyly peeped down at it, gleaming in the firelight, during the short interval between their lying down and their dropping asleep; and in the morning they awoke with a pleasurable start at the returning memory that the precious floor was really there, awaiting their feet, in place of the damp earth they had been accustomed to.

"Naow if so be we c'd anyways git t' git th' haouse banked up a leetle, we 'd be pootty well fixéd fer frost."

"Oh, naow, mammy, ye're a-puttin' on scollops! Don't ye want a pie-anner? I spose ye 'llaow the Queen of England has her haouse banked up, besides bein' floored; so noth'n' 'll dew but yew must hev yourn done, tew."

"Ye 're the boy kin dew it, Zury, if ye wuz t' git sot fer it."

"Show me where the' 's a mattick sot fer t' loosen the dirt with, 'n' a spade sot fer t' bank her up with, 'n' I 'd be sot fer the jawb quick enough!"

"If we lived back in God's country, we c'd git t' borry forty matticks 'n' spades."

"Did n't know th' used 'em in heaven; thought likely th' c'd dig the claouds with a hat er a turkey-tail."

The seed of suggestion was sown, however, and the wise mother knew her son well enough to let it take its time to grow. So that very evening Zury brought in a neat thin piece of hard wood, some four feet long, which he proceeded to hew into some kind of rough spade-shape.

"She 'll split, Zury, sure 's ye 're born!"

"Mebbe so, dad, mebbe not."

"Ye 'll see, — right where ye got t' set yer foot, she 'll split square off."

"Yew jes' hold yer hosses."

"Ye can't dig nothin' with that thar slopin' tool, — no place t' set yer foot on, 'n' so all-fired long in the bit."

"Din't I tell ye t' hold yer hosses?"

"Lop-sidedest tool ever I see. One shoulder 'baout six inches higher 'n t'other."

Zury did not deign to reply to this taunt.

"Bain't ye a-goin' t' hew that shoulder daown level with t'other?"

"Guess that shoulder 's 'baout right," answered the youth, who delighted in mystifying his father.

"Wal, ferever!" said the mother.

This was the strongest expression Selina ever indulged in; probably it was a contraction and corruption of "If I ever."

Then Zury got a long iron rod and laid it in the coals to heat, while he went on smoothing, sharpening, and polishing his odd-looking implement.

"Goin' t' brand yer name ontew it, Zury?"

"Yew jest wait 'n' see if I don't put my mark on it so ye'll know it anywher's."

All done, and the iron white hot, he proceeded to burn a hole in the "high-shouldered" side, just the right shape and size, and in just the right place for the digger's foot.

"Wal, ferever!"

"Zury, boy, I b'lieve ye c'd make a clock!"

"Ya-as, with my axe, 'n' my jack-knife 'n' a piece o' hot iron."

"But, arter all 's said 'n' done, that ain't no mattick ner no pickaxe."

"Haow d' ye 'llow t' loosen up the sile, sonny?"

"Wal, the' 's th' old axe."

"Th' old axe! Sho t' man! I 'll 'gree t' bank up in an hour all the dirt th' ole axe 'll loosen up in a day!"

"Tell ye what, dad, if I 'll get th' dirt ready, 'll yew shovel it up?"

"What, get it ready, loose enough t' handle with that thar wooden do-good fixin' o' yourn?"

"Ya-as, good 'n' loose."

"Go ahead; I 'll bank up all yew 'll loosen."

"It 's a whack! Remember, all the dirt I 'll turn up with any tool I 've got, er kin make."

It was a "whack," or bargain struck. So, after covering up the fire with the new shovel, "t' harden the p'int," they went to bed.

Next morning, the parents looked to see Zury "whaling away" with the old axe, laying out a large job of shoveling for his father; but he took things much as usual, did his "chores," and came in for his breakfast.

"Don't 'llaow t' do no bankin' up t'-day, sonny?"

"Oh, yes, mammy; 'llaow t' give dad all the shovelin' he wants t' tie up tew this arternoon."

Then he began to harness the mares.

"Goin' off t' borry a mattick, boy?"

"No; thought I 'd jist hitch 'em up fer a leetle exercise."

The next thing they saw of him he was coming around with the plow; and, drawing furrow after furrow about the house, back and forth and crosswise, he easily provided all the loose soil the banking up needed, and gave his father all the work he could do in the rest of two days.

"Wal, ferever!"

Life was not unbearably hard with them yet. The beasts could get ample food by the simple effort of wandering off for it; the house could be kept quite habitable by the warmth of the open fire; all were well except the ailing girl, and she could still sit up a little and take some interest in things, especially Zury and Shep. But the "pinch of the winter" was approaching. The features of each year shrivel up and grow pale and thin and wrinkled as it nears its end.

"Don't mommy's honey want a leetle apple?"

"I wuz 'feared they wuz all gone."

"Oh, no; *plenty* on 'em left."

Poor Selina! she was afraid there were more of them than her little "honey" would ever eat, though in truth they had dwindled to a mere handful.

"There, mommy 'll hang this one up by the string afore the fire, and honey can take this switch and keep it whirlin' while it cooks."

So the little one would watch the circling and

hissing fruit for long, long spells, and then her mother would make it as tempting as possible to the waning appetite of the invalid.

"Now, remember to save all the seeds fer Brer Zury."

This was an added incentive to stout efforts to eat; for if she did not eat the apple, how could she give the seeds to brother Zury?

"Ephraim, if we could only manage t' squeeze out a leetle pay fer the doctor, mebby he'd come oftener, 'n' bring s'm stronger physic. I kin see the babe 's better every time he gives her suth'n'."

The next time the doctor came, Selina gave him her wedding-ring as a substitute for money. Thereafter he often dropped in, and always left some anodyne, or stimulant, or tonic, to deceive the parents with a show of relief.

"Thar; wha 'd I tell ye! See haow she sleeps! Hain't slep' like that sence last time he wuz h'yer! If we only hed a plenty o' that same stuff, so 's we could keep her right up tew it!"

They did break a little prairie that season, though it was too late to put in any crop. They called it twelve acres, but it was n't. They thought they could get it fenced before frost, but they could n't. They hoped for a mild winter, but it proved a severe one: for years afterward it was remembered, and in bitter jest was styled "the year eighteen-hundred-and-froze-to-death." They felt almost sure of sustaining their beasts till the spring grass should start, but one of the mares died. They resolved not to mortgage any of their land, but they were disappointed.

It was this way: The little girl, who might have lived, and even thriven, in a warm, rich and comfortable city home, could not bear the cruelty of her environments, and died after long, quiet suffering.

How slow Death was in finishing his work that night! Long after the beloved eyes had turned up out of sight, the poor little chest kept on, gasp succeeding gasp, the heart-broken mother praying that each might be the last. Ephraim had fallen asleep by the fire, and Zury had fled out into the pitiless snow-storm — the black fury in his heart outvieing the white blast about his head. At last Selina laid her hand on her husband's shoulder and answered his questioning look with a nod. He called Zury in from the path which his tramping had kept open in the snow, and both men sat by the fireside till morning, while Selina straightened the wasted limbs, put on the poor girl's poor best clothes, tied up the sharp chin and closed the eyes with — something. They had no coins to lay on the lids.

The whole family had not money enough, nor even credit enough, to provide a coffin for the child. Then the poor vanquished father went to the village, and gave the store-keeper a mortgage on one of his cherished quarter sections, and thus established a credit which relieved their direst needs. He drove back home with the little coffin, and in it and around it food and clothing that seemed luxurious in their destitution. The grief-stricken mother did not reproach anybody for that the relief came only after her darling was gone.

There was no funeral. Nobody could reach them through the pathless snow. There was not even a burial until spring thawed the ground so that a grave could be dug. Ephraim tried it, but it was like picking at a bed of sandstone. Then Zury cleared the snow off a little space, and built there a huge fire, to soften the obdurate bosom of mother earth, hardened against thus untimely receiving back her own. He kept it going far into the night; but the wind rose and the snow flew again before morning, so that when day broke there was only a fresh white drift where the fire had been. Then they fixed two crotched sticks against the back of the house, and set the little coffin on them, where it remained until April came, and with it a day sufficiently humane to allow death the rights which even death possesses.

Selina could not get around the house through the drifts; but she learned the place where they had set up the supports, and could go and rest her face against the corresponding spot inside — when no one was looking.

At the death of his sister, Zury's grief was passionate and heart-rending. This surprised the mother, who had not credited him with so much love and tenderness. In fact, it startled her out of some of her own sorrow. She had looked the coming disaster in the face so long as to be better prepared.

A veil must be drawn over the sufferings of that first winter. The reader would resent the tale, if fully told, as being beyond the pale of presentable narrative. After Zury's outburst of feeling, he settled down into a stony hardness. Those tears for his "baby" sister were the last tears he shed for many a year. It was as if the fountain had filled up and run over a few drops, and then frozen solid. All this poverty, toil, and distress, and the terrible need for money, made a deep impression on the forming mind of the youth; and being of a logical turn, he "put this and that together," and drew conclusions fitted to the premises as he saw them. Money was life; the absence of money was death. "All that a man hath will he give for his life;" *ergo* all that a man hath will he give for money.

The axe is the *vade mecum* of the pioneer. As we use it, it is strictly an American tool. Long in the handle, perfectly fitted to the grasp, free and quick in the great curve it makes from far above and behind the head clear down to the ground in front, it has a grace and effectiveness much in advance of the short, heavy "woodman's axe" of other countries. The accomplished Western axeman strikes his blow with an exactness of aim that is literally "to a hair," and a vigor and quickness of repetition delightful to behold.

One inclement day, Ephraim and Zury went to Wayback together, so that one could turn the (borrowed) grindstone while the other held the axes and restored them to the razor-like quality they ought always to possess. The enforced idleness of the season had brought quite a large gathering of men and boys to "the store," and Tom Lackner, the store-keeper, improved the occasion by getting up a chopping contest for the amusement of the public and the benefit of his wood-pile, which consisted of a huge mass of logs of various lengths, all too long and large for use without cutting and splitting.

"See h'yer, boys, I 'bserve ye kin all cut lots o' wood jest a-settin' 'raound the stove 'n' talkin' abaout it; who kin cut the most with an axe?"

Hereupon arose a wordy war, each showing how well he could wield the axe or the long bow.

"Wal, chin-music is cheap, but the longest pole takes the persimmon. I'll give a dollar t' the boy er man that kin cut 'n' split the most wood outer my wood-pile in an hour by the clock. All split wood, mind; no twigs 'n' saplin's."

"Oh, ain't ye cunnin', 'n' ain't ye kind! Haow much 'll th' other fellers git, th't comes aout second 'n' third 'n' so on?"

"Wal, I'll give them day-wages, — a bit an hour."

"Haow 'll ye pay?"

"The dollar man in store-truck, th' rest in cash."

"Good enough! Then all 'll git abaout the same, th' way yew charge fer yer truck!"

At this hit all laughed; but the upshot was that some half a dozen entered into the friendly contest, Zury among the rest. Each selected his log, — such a one as he thought would about last him the hour. Zury observed that all passed by a short, thick black-walnut, too formidable to be attractive. He carefully studied the two ends, measured the diameter with his eye, and called his father into consultation.

"Dad — ye see that thar season-check in the butt-end? Cut daown t' that 'n' she 'll 'most split herself, 'n' one cut threw that lawg 'll gimme tew chunks short enough t' split up. Them long ones, ye got t' make a threw cut fer every chunk ye git aout till ye come tew th' last."

"Kin ye fetch it in an haour, Zury?"

"Kin I? I 'll dew it er die a-tryin'! Yew jest watch me! Take yer axe 'n' hew aout a couple o' gluts; but don't dull th' axe, fer the land's sake! I 'll swap axes with ye when I 'm half done."

"Now, boys!" shouted Tom Lackner, pulling out his watch and affecting to pause for the exact second. "Be ye all ready?"

"Ya-as!"

"Good 'n' ready?"

"Ya-as — ya-as!"

"Then spit on yer hands!" He was laughingly and heartily obeyed. After further jocular delays and disappointments he yelled, "Now GO!"

How the chips flew! The connoisseurs gathered around one contestant or another as sympathy or admiration dictated; but the largest number kept their eyes fixed, admiringly, on Zury and the most able of his rivals.

"Every other pop fetches a chip!"

"Ya-as, 'n' he don't never cut his chips in tew. See haow clean th' edges be!"

"Yew bet! He ain't the feller t' waste three clips on one chip!"

When Zury had cut his log half through he hopped down, seized one of the gluts his father had prepared, set it instantly into the exact spot in the "season-check," struck it a few mighty blows, and the monster log parted in the middle, leaving him a clean place for the remaining cross-cut.

"Some head-work 's well 's hand work in Zury, boys!"

"Ain't he chain-lightnin'?"

"*I'll* bet ye!"

Now with the fresh axe (which his father had rubbed on a whetstone after shaping the gluts), he fairly flew at his work. Faster and faster fell the strokes: he was in a frenzy of hope and emulation. The second cross-cut was complete; the two gluts were set and driven; both axes put in play, one sunk deep in the widening rift until the other liberated it by going in deeper; and at last the second and more difficult "chunk" gave way and lay in two shining aromatic halves of solid black walnut. The rest was easy; the foe, being driven from his stoutest defenses, made but little resistance, and before "time" was called Zury had what looked like a whole cord of solid split black walnut sticks of appropriate length and thickness.

He straightened up and took his eyes off his work for the first time.

"Thar! That 's all I kin dew! If any feller 's done better, *I* can't help it!"

But no one had done better, or as well. The next best man — six feet four, wielding an extra weight axe with an extra long helve — had done more work, but he had not used as shrewd plans to help him, and he made only a good second.

Tom's eyes glistened as he saw the six great piles of cut wood ready for his use, and he paid up his promised guerdons with great good humor. Zury took his dollar in the shape of a grindstone, which would thereafter save him and his father from many a long journey, or, what was worse, many an hour of work impaired by dullness of tools. Tom would have liked to add something to Zury's pay, except that he feared to arouse jealousy in the breasts of others who had also done their best. Luckily his eyes fell upon a bundle of papers which had accumulated in the shelves adjoining the post-office desk.

"Sa-ay, Zury; aour Member o' Congress he 's sent me aout by frank a hull heap o' numbers o' th' 'Republican,' t' dew what I 'm a min' ter with, fer the good o' th' party, 'n' t' help him git reëlected. Folks hez helped themselves all th' wanted tew, but yit the' 's a lot of old numbers left. Don't ye wanter clean 'em aout?"

"Free gratis?"

"Oh, ya-as—'gratuitous distribution' wuz whut he 'llaowed in his letter."

"O. K. Thet 's th' kind o' tradin' suits me."

So he carried home a large bundle of "Republicans," full of tales, continued stories, political articles, news from abroad, advertisements, riddles, jokes, and such like familiar newspaper scraps. The inner sides of the logs of their house were already hewn to something like a flat surface, and Zury, as he found the opportunity, papered the whole interior with the neat, cheap, and cheerful hangings; and afterward, whenever time and daylight served, his favorite pastime was reading the wit and wisdom thus spread about him. He had some sad experiences, as when in the most thrilling part of an exciting tale he came to the dread words, "continued in our next;" and the "next" happened not to have been among those which had been given him! For years one of these unfinished narratives haunted him (he not being a sufficiently experienced novel-reader to complete it for himself), and he would return wistfully to the familiar corner where that tantalizing mystery was stated, never in the world to be solved!

The tale was delightfully commonplace and improbable, one of the old-fashioned simple-hearted kind, that might have been written by machinery, run out by the mile, and cut off in lengths to suit. A boy, "born of poor but respectable parents in the little town of B.," was good, and strong, and willing, and ambitious. But, alas, he could not get any education to speak of because he had to work so hard, and his father was too poor to give him clothes fit for school. The first time he tried schooling, the other boys laughed at his rags; he fought with the biggest and whipped him, — but he never went back to school. He ran away to sea; his ship was cast away on an uninhabited island, where his farming knowledge and his mechanical ingenuity made him the salvation of the whole company including the captain's lovely daughter. "For a full account of his shrewd doings and his ingenious contrivances on the island, the rescue of all hands, his education, his marriage, and the glorious height from which he looked back on his early discouragements, the reader must look to our next." And there was no next!

When Selina saw the rough walls thus decorated and humanized she said, for the first time since her bereavement, —

"Wal, ferever!"

CHAPTER III.

ZURY "NIGGERING" LOGS AND MAKING A CORN-CROP.

"EPHRAIM, what 'll yer crap dew withaout no fence?"

"Dunno."

"No fence, no crap," said Zury. Then after a pause Selina said, —

"Haow much fence 'll it take t' go raound them twelve acres?"

"Th' ain't no twelve acres, mammy; but it 'll take a good half mild of fence," said Ephraim.

"'N' forty acres 'll take a full mild," added the boy.

"Forty acres, sonny!"

"Yes, mammy; I said forty acres, 'n' I meant it, tew! A mild o' fence, pig-tight, bull-strong, 'n' hoss-high."

"A mild o' fence!"

"Yes, a mild o' fence — if the timber holds out." And he gave a jerk of the head over toward the forest where millions of trees were to be had for the hauling.

"Guess ye'll wear yer axe daown tew a penknife 'fore ye split all them rails!"

"Yew 'll see!"

So Zury fell to work at the task of providing a whole mile of fencing material. Part of this was prepared in a way worth describing. He would find a long, prostrate tree-trunk in the woods, dry but not rotten, the victim of some storm or lightning stroke of past years. This he would measure off in about twenty-foot lengths, and at the end of each length he would build a fire, which, patiently attended to and replenished, would sever the log at that point, leaving it in lengths which could be hauled by a stout team over the snow to the place where they might be needed. This method of severing logs is called in the vernacular "niggering them off," whether because of its laziness, or of the blackness of the resulting heads, cannot be certainly stated. It is certainly ingenious and effective. Zury, starting in the morning with his axe and a burning brand, could light and attend to some thirty fires, and so prepare thirty logs, while he would have been chopping only a quarter as many. To be sure, there would be disappointments, as when the fire, through excess of zeal in doing its part of the work, would burn the log all up, while Zury was at home asleep.

Now at once, before the snow failed them, these logs ought to be "snaked" up to the plowed field and laid end to end around it, so that it would be half fenced at once. Then a couple of lines of "stake-and-rider" on top of the logs would make a good barrier against all marauders except the deer, which were still at that day a great nuisance among the scattered cornfields of Illinois, and which could clear any fence. But then, one horse, alone, was helpless. What was to be done?

"Dad, ye better git three more hosses, 'n' gears, 'n' a bob-sled, 'n' another plaow, 'n' some seed-corn, 'n' a saow 'n' pigs, 'n' a stack o' hay, 'n' a load o' mill-feed fer the stawk, 'n' some floorin'-stuff, 'n' — one thing another."

"'N' yew 'llaow t' pay fer 'em, I s'pose."

"I 'llaow t' dew my share."

The old man groaned in spirit, fer he saw that this meant a mortgage on another of his cherished quarter-sections, and he saw that his son was right, too.

"Faoun' a pot o' gold, Zury?"

"Hain't quite faound it yet, mammy, but it 's buried up in the paraira yunder."

"Take a heap o' diggin' t' git it aout."

"With one hoss it will."

"Wha' 'd ye 'llaow t' dew?"

"Snake up the lawgs 'raoun' the hull forty-acre piece, 'n' saplin's enough t' stake-'n'-rider 'em, 'n' git the balance inter sod-corn somehaow."

"Wal, son, ef yew kin stand it, I kin."

So another quarter was mortgaged, and the things Zury wanted were obtained; the swine from a neighbor on credit. The youth felt his responsibility, and worked twelve or fourteen hours daily, even when the daylight was less than nine hours long. The glittering steel-gray light of many a zero-morning found him already at his fires. All day long his axe rang through the frosty air as he felled saplings for the fence and stripped them for fuel for the "niggering" fires, and then it was long after night-fall before he tramped homeward through the deep gloom of the silent woods, the frosty snow squealing loudly under his footsteps.

Old Ephraim was fully occupied with the home duties, — caring for his almost helpless wife and almost perishing live-stock, and providing fuel for the voracious open fire that must be kept going night and day on the hearth to make life even barely possible. He dragged the back-logs up to the door, and even into the house, with a horse. Zury did his timber work, as far as possible, in the woods close to the homestead. In the first place it made less hauling for the heavy logs; then, besides, he reasoned, —

"Th' ain't no better place fer trees th'n whar trees hez growed."

This indicated the wild scheme his long head had in contemplation, — an apple orchard! He had the little pocket of seeds the poor "baby" had saved for him, and some he had himself saved thus: he one day found, in a broken jug on the one board that served as a kitchen shelf, the apples his sister had not lived long enough to eat, — eight shriveled relics. Zury said nothing, but carefully separated the seeds, and adding them to the rest, had nearly four hundred.

"Like enough half on 'em 'll spraout. Seedlings ain't no sure thing t' fetch good fruit, but mebbe some on 'em 'll be O. K., 'n' then we kin graft fr'm them onter th' others. Apples 'll fetch money h'yer. Th' ain't no money, but yet the' 's more money th'n the' 's apples."

Then in building his "niggering" fires he would often please himself with the fancy, —

"That row o' ash-heaps 'll come jest right fer a row o' apple-trees."

Shep was Zury's only companion through these long, cold work-days, and he proved his physical superiority, as compared with his human friends, by keeping fat and happy through it all; catching many a rabbit for his own tooth, and even some for Zury to carry home to eke out the slender stores of the household and vary the fare for the suffering mother. Zury always carried his rifle, and hoped for deer, as the tracks where they scraped the snow for grazing and brushed the trees for browsing were everywhere plentiful. But the sound of his axe and the smoke of his fires tended to keep them at a distance; also the wild turkeys that roamed the woods in great broods, long of limb, fleet of foot, wary and wily.

However, one morning before day, when his snow-muffled footsteps approached the nearest of the fires, he chanced to catch sight of a pair of gleaming eyeballs while he himself was still in shadow. Keeping Shep quiet behind him, he crept cautiously up to where he could rest his rifle on a log, drew his "bead," and pulled trigger. The sharp crack echoed from hill to hill, far up and down the lonely bottom, white and still in the bitter dawn. Shep bounded forward, and, his yelps becoming stationary, Zury guessed that his game was secured. He soon arrived, breathless with haste and hope, at the place where Shep in a passion of excitement was keeping guard over a fine buck, — rather thin, to be sure, but splendid game for an Eastern boy who had never before had a shot at anything more worthy than a rabbit. While he was bleeding the game, dragging it back to his working place, and hanging it up on a convenient sapling, the day broke, and his father came down, having heard the unaccustomed sound of the rifle, and missed hearing the accustomed sound of the axe.

"You Zury! Anythin' the matter?"

"Noth'n' much."

"Wha' 'd ye shoot at?"

"Deer."

"Missed it, did ye?"

"*Yew* missed it! Look a yonder on the saplin'."

"Wal, wal! I *will* say! Better n't I pack it up t' the haouse 'n' skin it afore it freezes?"

"Jest 's yew say 'baout that."

"Better come up noon-spell 'n' have a bite o' venison."

"No. Got my dinner with me."

"Better come up, sonny."

"No time."

So, Zury did not quit work a single minute earlier than usual.

Now came the long, tough job of "snaking"

the logs up to the prairie and around "the forty," a mile in circumference. This was hardly finished before the snow went off, and the ground thawed into deep mud. Then the live stock began to be able to shift for itself, and none too soon, for the little hay they had laid up was gone.

Ephraim proposed a "log-rollin'," — a bee (like the raising-bee), where all well-disposed neighbors might join in a day's work for one, expecting him to reciprocate when any of them had occasion to ask for public aid in the same fashion. (This is the origin of the phrase "log-rolling," used in political slang; the several parties interested in divers men or measures making common cause for the common gain.)

"No, dad. We hain't paid 'em nothin' fer comin' t' aour raisin', 'n' hain't no time t' spare t' be a paradin' raound, anyhaow."

"I don't see, nohaow, what I c'd git up fer 'em t' feed 'em."

"Jesso, jesso, wife; but I dunno 's I see haow we 'm a goin' t' git all them lawgs in line."

"Oh, you 'n' me 'n' th' four hosses 'll be bee enough! We'll roll 'em, or break a leg, — one o' th' tew!" said his son.

Snow or no snow, mud or no mud, Zury worked on, dragging and rolling the logs into place on the fence-line. He would take one horse in the morning and work him till noon, winding the log-chain around each log, and making the horse roll it into its position; then leave that horse to graze or "browse around," while he used another in the afternoon, in the same way. Thus did this one young fellow move weights which several strong men might have "tackled" in vain.

The "chinkin' in" between the ill-matched ends of the "niggered" logs and the setting of the stakes and riders occupied Ephraim and Zury while the ground was getting dry enough to plow. Then the piece they had broken up during the previous fall was plowed, and corn regularly planted, and all the remainder of the inclosed forty was put into "sod-corn," thus: as the plow turned over the ground, one followed behind it and with an axe made a hole at every other step and dropped two or three kernels in the hole and trod it in with his heel as he passed on.

The face of nature softens wonderfully as the sun climbs the heavens in spring, and the lot of all in contact with her softens too as she begins to smile. This softening, however, is not without its drawback, and the name of this drawback is — mud. The more fertile under sunshine, the more fathomless under rain. The fiercest storm that ever blew over the prairie is not so absolute an embargo on travel as is the mud beneath its surface when the spring rains are pouring and the frozen subsoil is thawing. An astonished traveler, accustomed to the gravelly comfort of less fruitful lands, once observed to a resident of Illinois: —

"Well, I've been through your State."

"What! Traveled through Illinois and the roads in this condition?"

"Yes, sir; clear through. Did n't have to travel far, either; just stood still and went down through, sunk through." And in proof of his assertion he pointed to his half-dead steed, covered with mud up to his ear-tips, and to himself shrouded from top to toe in the same black stickiness.

For the Prouders it was high time that life should begin to be easier. If the winter had been as nearly arctic in its length as it was in its severity, it is doubtful if any of the colony would have survived it, except Shep. To the poor bereaved mother it seemed ten years long, and her aged appearance bore out this suggestion. However, she now grew strong enough to attend to some of the slight and simple indoor tasks so that both Ephraim and Zury could work at the farming.

But few plants have changed and improved more by cultivation than has maize. "Indian corn," as the Indians knew it, hard and hardy, small, strong, and poor, would scarcely be recognized in the prairie giant of these days. Even to these emigrants it was a wonderful novelty.

"Look, mammy; h'yer's an ear o' corn sech 's the' raise aout h'yer!"

"Wal, ferever! Looks bloated, don't it? Bloated 'n' then shrunk." (The "dent" which occurs in the top of each kernel produces a withered appearance and gives it the name of "horse-tooth" corn. It is quite different from the smooth, hard, semi-globular grains the Prouders had been accustomed to.)

"Ye 'llaow it's shrunk, dew ye? Naow look a h'yer." He broke the great ear — sixteen inches by three or thereabouts — across his knee, and showed her the fractured ends.

"Wal, ferever! Them kernels is an inch long, I reckon. 'N' the cob ain't nowher's."

"That's what's the matter. Naow look a h'yer." He fitted the ear together again, and shaped a piece of paper about it, so as to make a bag of just its form and size. Then, while his mother held the bag he shelled off the kernels and dropped them in, and they completely filled it, leaving the cob in his hand.

"Naow ain't that a merikle! Th' cob's left over clean 'n' clar."

"Ya-as. That's coz the grains is so big 'n' th' cob's so little; 'n' then we can't pile 'em so close 's they growed."

"I 'xpect that's growed on them mountainious tall stalks we passed 's we come along, 't I could n't see over not when I stood up in th' wagin'."

"Ya-as; th' 'llaow 'raound h'yer aways 's how a man had n't oughter never lay by his corn until it's growed s' high he can't see his way aouter th' field come night."

"Haow soon d' ye 'llaow t' begin plaowin'?"

"Oh, jest 's soon 's we kin see the rows. Th' weeds is a-startin'; good corn-graound is good weed-graound, 'n' they 'll be jest a howlin' afore we git wunst threw, try aour best."

The two plows toiled up and down the long,

quarter-mile stretches from daylight till dark for weeks together. The modern "cultivators," which employ two horses and throw the soil from both sides toward the hill, were then unknown. Only one horse could be used by each driver, and the small plow had to make two journeys between every two rows.

By the time they were "once through" the corn seemed to "catch on to the idea" of what was expected of it. Its broad blades shot up knee-high and assumed the deep, strong, fat green which is the characteristic of prairie corn. (Its growth is often three inches a day at this period.) Again Ephraim and Zury set themselves to tire out each one horse between daylight and noon, and another between noon and night; but, shade of Ceres! how tired they themselves were by "quitting-time!" To pull off the harness and free the horse, to drag one foot after the other as far as the house, to slouch down anywhere and eat anything that was offered them, and then to roll heavily into their rude beds and enjoy utter oblivion until the too speedy daylight started them forth again, this was all they could pretend to do.

Selina did not expect any talk, except a word or two casually dropped at meal-times, always on the absorbing subject of the work in hand. She had, herself, planted a few potatoes in one corner of the field, in rows corresponding with the corn rows, so as to be plowed with the corn; and, on a rainy day, Zury dug up with his wooden spade a little patch on the sunny side of the house. Into it he put his precious apple seeds to sprout for transplanting, and also the seeds of morning-glories, sunflowers, and hollyhocks brought from "home." So there was soon one streak of color, bloom, and brightness about the dreary place.

The last plowing of the corn is the most trying. The inclement sun is at its highest and hottest, and beats down almost perpendicularly on the shadeless intervals between the rows. Green-headed horseflies drive the poor steeds frantic; they would commit suicide if horse-sense were equal to it. The corn is breast-high or higher, and quite impenetrable to the summer breezes. No harvest field is so torrid; nothing short of a "reverberatory furnace" can fairly typify the horror of it.

Then the wise farmer gives up several of the hottest hours of the day to rest or cooler duties; but Ephraim was not wise; he kept at work, and was soon seized with "the shakes." Every other day did he shiver for half an hour, then burn for an hour and a half, and then dissolve in weakening sweats. However, the corn did not lose so much by his illness as one might suppose, for he would work until the fit came on, and as long as he could hold the plow and make the plow hold him, then tie his horse and lie down in a fence-corner (within reach of the pail of tepid water), and wrestle with his dreadful distress, and when it began to leave him, stagger to his feet again, untie his horse, and once more hold the plow and be held by it until it was too dark to work any longer.

He who doubts the accuracy of this picture can easily convince himself that it is not overdrawn.

At last, one Saturday night, Selina was gladdened by the words:

"Corn laid by, mammy."

"Thank the Lord! I begun t' think it would n't never be!"

How they did rest all that night, and all the next day! Before daylight, Zury, impelled by habit, rolled out of bed and stood on the rattling floor of his loft.

"Corn 's laid by, Zury!" called out his mother. Instantly he fell back on his bed and was again asleep before he could fairly voice a "hurrah!" He slept nearly the whole day.

Toward night they all strolled out to the fence. What a sight the great, green forest of rollicking standards presented! The day had been one of intense, still sunshine; one of those when the plant takes its hugest meals of light and soil-juice. The leaves looked slightly wilted as the sun went down.

"Looks 's though suth'n' wuz th' matter on it, don't it?" said Selina.

"Nary! It 's like a hawg that 's jest tired o' feedin' 'n' goes t' sleep t' turn it inter fat."

The others went back to the house, but Zury could not tear himself away from the sight until dark night. Then he went in.

"Ye 'd oughter waited! Ye kin jest hear 'em,

like big boys, three in a bed. Sez they, 'lay over, bub, 'n' gimme room t' grow.'" And just as he climbed slowly to his bed he called down: "Th 'll be a-growin' all night while we 're asleep."

During the week Ephraim drove to town on one of his "well days" to get some medicine and a few other indispensables of life. He came back without them. Zury looked in the empty wagon.

"Wal, dad; made a water-haul, did n't ye?"

"Yes, son."

"Mortgage money used up?"

"Teetotally; the way they charge things! An' the interest on it 's a-comin' dew nex' month."

"Could n't ye git t' git at the store ontel the crap comes in?"

"Nary. Not 'thout I 'd give 'em a mortgage on another quarter."

That evening was a sad one at the log hut. Half the section mortgaged and nothing to show for it but *this.* Not one cent in money, nothing to eat, drink, or wear, a growing crop that might be worth ten cents a bushel three months hence, and a little unsodded grave without even a fence around it.

"Could n't we git t' go back home, Ephr'm?" tearfully asked Selina. Ephraim did not reply. Zury asked him further:

"Wha' 'd the' say, dad?"

"'Llaowed I 'd bit off more 'n I could chaw. Said the' did n't see haow I wuz a-goin' t' pay interest on the mortgages an' git shet of 'em 'thout losin' the place."

"Did, did they?"

"Yes, 'n' offered me a hunderd dollars on another quarter section, er fifty dollars on my crap. I near abaout tuk 'em up on the crap."

"Oh, do!" said Selina, who almost hated the corn crop.

"Oh, don't!" said Zury.

"Better lose the crap than lose the land that 'll fetch craps."

"Ef ye lose the crap, ye 'll lose the land tew."

A long silence followed this, then Zury spoke again.

"Ain't them thar pigs out thar in the woods a-growin'? Jest a-howlin'! Ye kin hear 'em a-crunchin' th' mast 'fore ye git within a mild on 'em."

"Feller I bought 'em of, Peddicomb, he see me in taown 'n' tole me he wuz a-goin' t' sue me fer the pay fer that saow 'n' pigs."

"Sho t' man! Did he so? Wha' 'd ye tell him?"

"Tole him t' come 'n' take 'em, ef he wanted 'em."

"What? Ye don't tell me! That saow 'n' pigs? He don't git 'em!"

"No danger. He said he did n't want 'em. Ye kin buy hawgs fer a cent a paound anywhar's naow."

"Let 's buy 'em, then."

"Buy hawgs, my son, 'n' them sellin' at a cent a paound?"

"Why, mammy; had ye druther buy 'em at a dollar a paound?"

"I 'd druther buy suth'n' 't 'll sell fer suth'n'; that 's ef we had anythin' t' buy with."

"Mortgage another quarter, dad, 'n' buy some o' 'em cent-a-paound hawgs."

"That 'll take th' last quarter but th' one we 're on tew, Zury."

"Mortgage that, tew, if we hev ter. We 're boun' t' swing this thing naow we 're inter it. Swing it fer all it 's wuth. That 's th' way t' keep the hull patch — all four quarters."

"Haow 'd ye 'llaow t' dew it, son? I don't feel t' be wuth much myself t' git us outer this h'yer slough."

"That 's so, dad. Th' way yew look ye won't be wuth shucks getherin' corn come col' weather. 'N' I can't handle 'n' haul no twelve hundred bushel o' corn outer that field 'n' daown t' the store, besides gittin' in th' hay, 'n' fencin' another forty, 'n' breakin' them colts, 'n' diggin' a well, 'n' keepin' mam in firewood, 'n 'goin' t' deestrick scule, 'n' visitin' raoun' amongst th' neighbors, 'n' whistlin' 'n' chawin' gum all t' wunst."

"Law, Zury, quit yer foolin'! Ye 'most make yer ole mammy laugh right aout."

"Who 's a foolin'?"

"My son, ef ye got anythin' t' say, say it, 'n' ef not, go t' bed."

"I 'll go to bed when I git ready. Yew mortgage another quarter 'n' git th' hawgs. They 'll do well on mast all summer, 'n' in fall we 'll gether what corn we kin, 'n' hawg the rest." (To "hog" corn is to turn hogs into the field and let them feed themselves.)

"That don't pay no mortgages."

"Don't, eh? You better believe it dooz. I'll jes' take a load o' them hawgs, killed 'n' dressed 'n' froze, daown river till I find some man as 'll buy 'em, if I have t' tote 'em clean t' Orleens! See ef I don't!"

They did n't settle the matter that night, but soon separated for sleep. As Zury disappeared up the ladder to his roomy and airy bed-loft he called back to his father, —

"Dad, I 'm goin' t' own a mortgage 'fore I die; mind what I say."

"Hope ye will, Zury. Yew 'll have a holt of the right eend of the poker then; 'n' t' other feller he 'll have a holt o' the hot part, same 's we 've got naow."

"You bet! An' it 'll sizzle his hands, tew, afore I 'll ever let up on him."

CHAPTER IV.

MORE WORK, MORE PIGS, BUT NO MONEY FOR A COLLEGE.

ON the following Sunday Zury's mother saw him take down his rifle from its place and start away.

"Son Zury, whar be ye a-goin' — a Sund'y?"

"Goin' fer Peddicomb, the man 't sold us them hawgs, 'n' is a-goin' t' sue fer his pay, dog-gone him!"

"Oh, my son! What ever can you mean?"

"Don't stop me, mammy, I 'm desp'rut." Then seeing that she was really alarmed, he burst into one of his rare laughs, and told her not to be scare't, he was n't going to hurt nobody. Still, she looked after him wistfully. But he was fast becoming the ruling spirit in the household, and nobody presumed to interfere with him much, his mother least of all.

He went over to the farm of Peddicomb, the creditor in the pig-purchase, and introduced the subject. The man was a loquacious person, and went over the case somewhat in these words, which fairly illustrate the hold which the cultivation of maize has obtained on the prairie farmers. It has given rise to a new system of chronology and terminology: —

"Ye see it wuz long afore plantin' that I sol' yer father that saow — afore breakin' if I remember right — 'n' he 'greed t' pay me in a week. 'N' then abaout corn-up I buzzed him fer the money, but did n't git no satisfaction. Then we wuz all pootty busy, of course, fer a spell, but when we wuz wunst through I met him to meetin' 'n' he 'llaowed he 'd done clean forgot all abaout it, 'n' haow he 'd square up when he got his corn laid by. Wal, tosslin' time come 'n' passed, 'n' corn-in-the-milk tew, but he never talked turkey, 'n' come along abaout ros'n-ear I jest upped 'n' told him if he did n't settle fer th' hawgs I 'd sue him. In fact, I did tell Squire Braown t' c'mence suit. Ye see, it 's a gittin' along toward shockin' 'n' getherin', 'n' if I don't look aout fer myself th' storekeeper he may up 'n' clamp daown on the crap, 'n' me a-stan'in' by, suckin' my fingers 'n' whistlin' fer my money."

This quaint local speech, translated into the vernacular, makes the prairie farmer's time-table for the whole year from spring to spring.

"Breakin'" is the spring plowing; March and April, when the frost is out and the ground dry enough to turn over without being made "cloddy." "Plantin'" should begin about May first. "Corn-up" will follow in about ten days. "Wunst through," the completion of the first corn plowing, should be early in June. "Laid by" will follow six or eight weeks later, some time in July. "Tosslin'," when the tassels begin to turn the field from green to yellow, will be before the beginning of August. "Corn-in-the milk," by the middle, and "ros'n' ear," when the milk has coagulated into gluten and the ear may be roasted for the table — say by about September first. "Shockin'," cutting up and placing in "shocks" such portion as is kept for the sake of the fodder in stalks and leaves, takes October, and "getherin'" goes on all winter.

"Dad sez ye won't take 'em back."

"No; thet ain't what I sold 'em fer. I wanted the money, 'n' if I had n't a wanted money more 'n hawgs I would a tried to a worked so 's to a kep' 'em."

"How much wuz it?" (Zury knew the amount as well as he did, but he observed that the other had an interested eye fixed on his rifle, and he wanted to give him time.)

"Seven dollars is the price, if the Squire hain't begun suit, 'n' I don't s'pose he has; he don't never do nothin' 'less ye stan' over him with a club while he dooz it. That 's a good-lookin' rifle ye 've got!"

"I believe ye; that rifle cost over twenty-five dollars."

"Dew tell! I wanter know! Wal, it 's all right fer a rifle."

"Ye d' want no rifle, dew ye? If ye 'd gimme a fair price fer it, ye mought stop out the seven dollars 'n' gimme the rest in money."

"Money! Th' ain't no sech a thing! Hain't set eyes on no money fer a coon's age. Give ye s' more hawgs."

This was just what Zury wanted, so he began to hang back.

"Oh, hawgs is nowhers naow. Ye can't give 'em away."

Nevertheless, he and Shep drove home a fine lot of swine at estimated weights. It happened that as the sharp bargainers were talking, the old doctor rode by, and they got him to "guess them off," he being a noted expert at "guessin' hawgs," which is a great accomplishment in the rural districts, wonderful expertness being attained by long experience and many competitive trials of skill in foretelling from the pig's looks how much the pork will weigh. Zury also carried away a "paper-writin'," showing that on the payment of twenty dollars by New Year's day, his rifle was to be returned to said Prouder, otherwise to be and remain the property of said Peddicomb. (A few unusual phrases add largely to the value and dignity of every transaction.)

"Wal, mammy; Peddicomb he got my rifle away before I got a chance to put a bullit inter any vital part, but I got away some of his best hawgs. Here the' be."

"Look awfle thin!"

"'Course! S'pose I wanted t' pay a cent a paoun' fer fat hawgs? Ef th' wuz fat, we could n't make 'em no fatter 'twixt naow 'n' sellin' time. Thin hawgs is wuth more 'n fat hawgs every time."

"Good plan t' starve 'em most t' death, 'n' then sell 'em back."

"Mammy, ye wuz jest made fer a sculema'am! Know yer 'rithmetick fustrate, 'n' back part o' th' spellin'-book tew; clean over t' where the leaves is all tore out!"

Zury's strong sense and strong will prevailed in the matter of the additional mortgage. Soon the woods were well sprinkled with Prouder pigs, loudly munching acorns day and night, and almost as wild as deer in their forest freedom. Later the ungathered corn was "hogged," and the lantern-jaws of the woods-rovers stood out with fatness by the time they had been six weeks in the corn-field. Then with the first good sleighing Zury set forth, the hay-rack on the "bob-sleds" and twenty good porkers on the hay-rack, besides corn enough to feed his four horses for a month, some bedding, and a bag of bread and ham, half a bushel or so of hard-boiled eggs, and last, but not least, Shep.

In less than a month he was at home again with a hundred and sixty dollars in silver, not having spent one stiver on the road except two eight-cent tolls and a twenty-cent ferriage, and also the cost of an occasional feed of hay for his team when, as he said, they could n't live any longer on "post oats," that is, the fragments they could gnaw off the posts they were tied to while eating their corn.

Did any inanimate treasure ever look more beautiful to its possessors than did those sixteen piles of twenty silver half-dollars each? It was better than the log floor. They gazed at them lovingly for a long, long time. Their shine rested the tired eyes, their jingle charmed the ears unused to pleasant sounds.

"Wal, ferever!" sighed Selina.

"That 'll pay off one of the mortgages, Zury," said his father.

"That won't pay off noth'n', dad, not with my consent."

"'Llaow t' bury it, my son?"

"Yes, mammy; bury it in some stuff t' live on, 'n' a shelter fer the stawk, 'n' s' more stawk, 'n' help t' fence another forty, 'n' some o' th' ready john fer dad t' take when he goes t' buy truck, so 's he wunt hev t' buy from them sharks that holds the money on the mortgages; them a-sockin' on it tew him every time in regard of quality 'n' prices of everythin'."

"Wal; ye 'll git yer gun back, Zury?"

The youth thoughtfully lifted two of the little piles and set them apart from the others, leaving fourteen together. Then he replaced them with the rest, saying stoutly, —

"Noap! I guess not. If ary deer comes araound a-pokin' his nose at me 'n' tryin' t' bite me, I kin borry dad's ole muskit. But I ain't a-goin' t' hev much time a-foolin' raound with no guns. Hawgs 'll fetch pigs a goodle faster 'n rifles 'll fetch deer."

"Zury, th' dew say 's haow th' ain't no better use fer money 'n t' pay debts with."

"Don't ye b'lieve it, dad. Borryin' 's a need-cessity, 'n' payin' 's a luxury. We can't 'fford no luxuries yit a spell. Gimme another year, 'n'

I 'll talk t' ye 'baout clearin' off them mortgages."

"Wal, ferever!"

Zury had brought home with him an individual name Jule. Jule was as black as black could be: "charcoal 'd make a white mark on him."

"Haow on 'arth 'd ye pick him up, Zury?"

"Wal, I seen him nigh t' the steamboat landin' fer a couple o' days, 'n' then agin I missed him; 'n' that night I heerd the boys a-la-aughin' 'n' raisin' Ned 'cause they 'd scared Jule most white by a tellin' on him his ole master 'd come on the boat 'n' wuz a-layin' fer him."

"Wal, ferever! Worn't they a crool, stony-hearted set o' critters! Did n' nobody take his part?"

"Oh, yes; th' wuz a long, lanky feller — Cap'n Abe Linkin — he wuz Cap'n 'n' part owner of th' flatboat th't tuk my hawgs. Sez he, 'Let him alone, boys. Ye onery limbs! Wanter tromp onter a poor cuss when he 's daown?' Some on 'em jest larfed at him; sez they, 'Oho Abe; lookin' aout fer fear yer ole uncle 'll git hurt? Or yer half-brother is he, which?' Ye see, Abe wuz pootty dark complected. Wal, then the' all hooted, 'n' then the Cap'n he jest rared up on his hind legs, long enough t' reach f'm h'yer t' Christmas, 'n' lifted a hand 't looked like the hand o' Providence, 'n' the fellers upped 'n' scooted. The' wuz all scare't of Abe when he wuz riled. But by that time Jule he 'd got aout o' sight up th' road."

"Whar d' ye come acrost him nex'?"

"Wal, nex' day I lit aout fer hum light-footed, 'n' come along on a trot, 'n' I seed suth'n' awful black away ahead 'twixt th' snow-drifts, but when I got t' where it wuz it worn't thar. So 's I, 'Whar is he, Shep?' an' it worn't more 'n a quarter of a minute afore Shep he snooped 'raoun' in the snow 'n' come t' Jule, jest 'buout dead. I went up tew him 'n' sez he, 'I gin up, ma'hse; I 'll go back wi' ye 'n' never run away f'm ole ma'hse no mo'.'"

"Oh, Lordy, Lordy! A runaway slave!"

"Yew bet! So 's I, 'I 'm a-goin' north, 'n' if ye wanter go back t' ole marse, I can't help ye none, but if ye wanter go north'— Then y' oughter jest seen him! He jest got half way up, 'n' crept on his hands 'n' knees t' me, an' of all the beggin'!"

Here Zury's command of language failed him, and he was silent, while his mother shed a tear or two on her sleeve.

"Then sez I, 'Kin ye work?' 'n' sez he, 'Ef I cudd'n' work I doan speck dey 'd want me back s' bad.' That looked kind o' sensible, so sez I, 'I 'll hev t' charge ye ten dollars t' tote ye a hunderd miles up north.' 'N' sez he, 'Goramity, ma'hse, I ain't got a cent!' 'Wal, ye kin work it aout when ye git thar. Dollar a month 'n' yer keep.' 'N' here he is."

It appeared that after being so dreadfully scared poor Jule had walked all night with nothing to eat, and was very near to death's door when Zury overtook him. Zury related that Jule always slept in the sleigh face-downward on the straw, and when asked to explain this habit, he said, "I specks it 's coz my back done ben so'ah mos' all my life, 'pea'hs like." But he laughed when he said it, as if it were rather a good joke at his expense.

Probably Jule had been a "lazy nigger" when working under orders from non-workers. But "industry is catching," as says the Vicar of Wakefield; and Jule must have been more or less than human to fail to work hard when he wielded one axe and Zury another on the same job, often on opposite sides of the same tree. Their lonely situation favored the absolute subjection of the weaker mind to the stronger, and in any case, when ethnic disposition toward shirking seemed to show itself, the remedy was easy, and was unsparingly used. For instance: —

"Chilblains, eh? Wal, Jule, tell ye what it is; ye better light aout 'n' git daown t' whar it 's warmer weather. Ye need n't mind abaout th' rest o' them ten dollars. I 'll let ye offen that."

"Oh, Ma'hse Zury! Doan' ye do it! I 'll git t' wu'hk in 'de mo'hnin', shu'h 's ye 're bo'hn I will. My feet 's awfle, — it 's jest like I wuz a walkin' on my eye-balls, — but I 'll git 'roun' somehow, foah de Lo'hd I will."

And the poor tropical being (whose sufferings were real enough) would swathe his unhappy feet in rags, hay, pieces of deerskin and bark, tied on with rawhide thongs and willow withes, or anything else he could command, and would hobble out and do at least a half-day's work in the fear of expulsion from this poor harbor of refuge. He had run away from one master, but could not be driven away from another, though for the latter he worked harder than for the former, and getting no greater real wages, rather less. But with Zury he was "free."

It was with something like dismay that Selina heard Zury tell his father that he was bound to have a whole quarter section fenced for next year's crop. (They were all sitting around the hearth, Zury whittling as usual.)

"A hull quarter, Zury boy?"

"That 's what I said, mammy."

"Ain't that four forties?"

"Jest exackly; a hunderd 'n' sixty acres."

"Oh, Zury; ye make me tired a-talkin' that a-way!"

"Ef me 'n' Jule kin stan' it, I reckon yew kin!"

"It tuk a mild o' fence t' dew the forty, that makes four mild altogether ye 're a-layin' aout t' dew this winter."

"Mammy, ef I wuz hired aout t' yew I 'd let ye dew the figgerin' fer pay. One mild fer forty, that makes four miles fer four forties, don't it?"

"'Course it dooz. 'N' ye know ye 're all th' chick er child I 've got left! Ef ye kill yerself yer poor ol' mammy 'll be in th' poorhaouse fust thing ye know. Yer dad, he ain't a-goin' t' be no 'caount t' work n' more, so fur 's I kin see!"

Zury did not reply directly, but quickly whittled out eight little sticks of equal lengths.

"Now, look a-hyar, mammy. Ye see that li'l square I've drawed in th' ashes? That's a forty. Wal, it takes four sticks t' go 'raound it, don't it? So each stick 's a quarter-mild long. Naow watch while I draw three other forties — thar; four forties in a square. Haow many sticks will it take t' go 'raound 'em all?"

"Why, haow many?"

"Jest exackly eight. See? Them fust four goes half 'raound, 'n' four more fences it all. See?"

"Wal, ferever!"

"That's jest the diff'rence betwixt wholesale 'n' retail business. I'm goin' t' be a wholesaler all my life, er die a-tryin'."

And he was. Their quarter section of corn, when it was "tossled aout," looked like a half-mile square of green ocean, the tassels making a yellow foam for the wind-swept waves; and then the working of it was easy by comparison, as there are only half as many turns for horses and plows to make in doing the work. On some of the giant western farms the fields are laid out so that the plow, starting in the morning, makes but one turn before getting back at noon, the furrow being long enough (say two miles and a half) to use up the whole time.

There is no need for us to follow every step in the Prouders' fortunes. Each inch gained was won by hard work and held by sordid economy.

Of course, every cent so made looks to its owner "big as a cart-wheel." Zury's acquaintances soon began to say of him that he "would pinch a dollar till the eagle on it squealed." And Zury did not deny it, but gloried in it. He never looked into a book, nor did he in any way (except by using it) add to the slender stock of learning he had acquired before the migration. The newspapered walls of their room was all his library.

He was without associates, ambitions, or objects in life, except, in the first place, "subduing" that farm; in the next place, clearing it of the mortgages; in the third place, increasing its money-making capabilities; and thenceforth and forever adding dollar to dollar, mortgage to mortgage (on other people's farms), note to note, and gain to gain, with all the force of a strong intellect pent into a narrow channel.

As the fine farm grew fat, the old couple who had given their life to it dwindled away. Selina died, murmuring the name of her lost daughter with her last intelligible breath. Zury had long looked for the event, and (being callous from the wound he had received in the death of his sister) was not at all affected by it. Old Ephraim seemed half dead during the rest of his life, as if part of his body and part of his mind had sickened with her sickness and been buried in her grave.

He and Peddicomb had both been connected with the little sect of Christians called "Soul-sleepers," from their individual guess as to the fate of mankind between death and judgment. Old Prouder's easy descent toward second childhood was accompanied by a maundering return of interest in the doctrine of Soul-sleeping. This made Zury anxious, and impatient, and prone to be, as Ephraim phrased it, "hard on his poor old dad." But the veteran jealously kept the old mastery of his property, while at the same time he clung to Zury with touching persistence and confidence. He was as close as ever, or closer: his devotion to the great principle of Soul-sleeping was only such as could be rendered without expense, and usually when Zury was absent and Peddicomb present.

The Soul-sleepers had founded a college at a town in Ohio, the headquarters of Soul-sleeping. The truth probably is, that denominational education would be for them denominational suicide; for when you educate a Soul-sleeper he ceases to be one. But that is their lookout. They had their college, and whether they needed it or not they needed funds for it. An emissary in quest of contributions came to Spring County: the man selected (one Elder Bigration) being, of course, as wise as a serpent at any rate. He showed great devotion to business, — that is, devotion, with an eye to business. His sermon on Sunday was very stirring. He likened faith to an anchor, and remarked that when the tempest-tossed ship was about to founder in the fathomless ocean of despair, then the ungodly soul in his frenzy seized on any frail plank or bit of wreck, in the vain hope of salvation. But what, he asked, did the Soul-sleeping Christian do? He lashed himself to the anchor!

This made a deep impression on all; and on the road home Ephraim ventured to call Zury's attention to the importance of the truth set forth; but Zury only chuckled in his dry way, and said, —

"Wal, — th' Elder he's a talker sure enough. A reg'lar old Blower from Blowtown. But when the ship's a-sinkin', if any feller ups 'n' ties himself to the *anchor*, — why I reckon he's a fool. He'd oughter be bored fer th' holler-horn! Gimme a board t' float on, every time!" (Of course his mind reverted to the wall-paper shipwreck in all its thrilling details.)

Bigration stayed at the Peddicombs, and awakened great interest in the breasts of the three unmarried daughters by his fervor. He would walk up and down before the fire-place by the hour, at intervals groaning out, "What shall I do to be saved?" or some other pious ejaculation. Long and anxious were his talks with Peddicomb — not as to how much brother Peddicomb would give, but how much could be squeezed out of brother Prouder. He aimed to make the former a co-worker, with a double purpose; the second thought being that co-workers give more money, as well as more other help, than the non-workers.

"Pootty poor show of gittin' anythin' out of old Ephr'm!"

"Brother, I shall, with God's help, discharge my duty!" (He said this as if his duty had been a gun.)

At last it was settled that a note, without interest, having a year to run, might seem to brother Prouder a fine investment in the work of grace; and further, brother Peddicomb was to give as much as brother Prouder did; so the latter would feel that he was bestowing on the Cause twice what he paid out, — buying two dollars' worth of grace for a dollar. Privately, the missionary hoped that brother Prouder might take a notion to give such a sum as would be a dreadful pull to brother Peddicomb; to punish the lesser nabob who presumed to challenge him in this manner. (He did n't know Ephraim!)

As Bigration departed on his fearful errand to Prouder's, Peddicomb called after him, encouragingly: —

"Mebbe ye mought git suth'n' aouter him by a-stayin' with him till he thinks yer keep 'll come t' more 'n his subscription."

Toward night he returned, "beat out" as he expressed it.

"Brother Peddicomb, come over and labor with me on brother Prouder. I'm *stalled!*"

"He-he! Wha' 'd I tell ye? Wal, let's have s'm supper, 'n' sleep on it. T'morrer 'll be time enough."

Zury was absent when they called. Ephraim received them cordially, but warily. He did n't "slop over," not he! The meeting opened with prayer by brother Bigration, during which he depicted a happy fate for those who should serve Heaven in the way he pointed out: they were to do well in this world, and better, if anything, in the next; while those who grieved away the Spirit now were to have very bad luck in both. Their store and their bread-basket, however full hitherto, would be empty henceforth and forever! (Proverbs iii. 1–10.)

Old Ephraim groaned in the spirit and in the flesh. Ruin seemed to stare him in the face as the experience of Job was held up before his eyes. The threats chimed in with his natural sordid fears. Times were hard: perhaps his punishment had begun already!

"Hawgs is three cents a paound er less, 'n' beef th' same, and wheat a-droppin' every day. Ya-as, a year's time withaout int'rest is an objick; but then I 'd druther see when th' time comes. I 'll dew full 's well then 's if I gin ye my note naow, mebbe better. Very *likely* better."

"Brother Prouder, the Lord don't require no man t' go beyond his means. Let 's go out and look over your stock and crops a little."

A score of handsome hay-ricks; two thousand bushels of good wheat in the barn; a hundred acres of corn yet to gather; sixty cattle, two hundred sheep, and more hogs than cattle and sheep together; and all marketable by spring. No deduction to be made for family sustenance in the mean while, for there were bee-hives, potato-pits, cabbage-pits, pork in pickle, apples, milch cows, chickens, — in short, provender of all kinds in utter abundance, outside all the salable "truck."

Ephraim's heart did warm up a little as he looked over the splendid show, but then he took gloomy views, and in estimating values took care not to overstate anything.

When they returned to the house Bigration produced pencil and paper and spent some time in figuring. At last he submitted to Prouder a list of the salable truck with valuations. Ephraim could find no fault with it.

"Now, brother Prouder, that property can't fetch less than those figgers. If it's the Lord's will, it 'll fetch more, won't it?"

"Surelye, ef it's his will."

"If it fetches more, ye 'll owe it t' Him, won't ye?"

Ephraim was silent.

"Then, brother," added the emissary, rising and speaking with a heart-moving fervor, "return to Him half the surplus. Stacks may burn, corn may rot, wheat may sprout, cattle may die of murrain, and hogs of cholera; but if the Cause is to get one poor half of the bare *increase* in value on these good things, you are safe to *know* that your other half will be more than the whole gain — or even the whole principal itself — will be if you let this occasion slip by. The Lord cares for his own lest he strike his foot against a stone."

Superstition stimulated cupidity into liberality. When the visitors departed they had Ephraim's sign-manual to a document promising all that Bigration had asked; the document to rest in Peddicomb's hands until the "overplus," if any, was ascertained, when he was to add a like amount, and forward the whole to the struggling institution.

On their way home they met Zury, and Peddicomb, who had begun to feel very uneasy in view of the obligation he had rashly undertaken, revealed the matter to him in the confident hope that he would find means to upset the whole thing. Zury looked very black, but did not make known any plan of interference.

As he proceeded homeward he pondered long over the affair. At first every impulse was against it; but still, the more he thought the more he saw two clear sides to the subject. He had begun to feel keenly the want of education. Here was a lot of money — his earnings — going into an educational institution; could n't he borrow time enough from the farm to attend the school? In all his thoughts about himself (they were few and rare) he was always the boy in that unfinished wall-paper story. The Soul-sleepers' College might be his ship to run away to. The sea was the sea of knowledge, of which he had learned so little. The unhabited island — oh dear! Why did that next paper happen to be nowhere in the world for him? Now that blower — to come and get away a heap of his hard earnings in pay for wind! Should it go for nothing? Not if he knew it!

"Wal, dad, I hear you 've be'n 'n' gone 'n' done it!"

Ephraim, already in something of a panic at

what he had done, sat speechless before his son. His empty jaws fell apart, and his poor old thin face blanched in every wrinkle.

"Son Zury," he began, as soon as he found his voice, "d' ye b'lieve the' kin c'lect anythin' on that thar paper-writin'?"

"C'lect? 'Course the' kin! That thar Bigration he's jest sharp enough t' draw up a bindin' agreement. 'N' ye 're jest fool enough t' sign one!"

"Mebbe — mebbe it 'll pay us, son — mebbe we 'll git more aouter th' truck fer givin' a sheer on it t' th' Cause."

"Ah, yah! Goin' pards with th' Almighty, be ye? I s'pose that 's the kind o' talk the' come it over ye with!"

"It 's only half the overplus, ye know."

"I don't care what ye call it, — half the overplus or a quarter of the underplus, — it 's a good four hunderd dollars, that 's what it is!"

"Four hunderd dollars! Lord a massy on me! But mebbe we 'll git it back. The Lord don't fergit his own."

But the old man shook as if with palsy. He spilt his tea on the way to his mouth; the pot was empty, and he was too stingy to let Jule make him a second drawing. Zury even pitied him.

"Ne' mind, dad. I 've thought of a way t' git even with 'em!"

"Haow 's that, my son?"

"Why, I 'll take it aout in edication next winter."

"But, Zury," the old man screamed in his quavering voice, "it 's 'way off in Ohio!"

"I don't keer if it 's in Jericho! I 'll foller that money 'n' git th' wuth on it somehow."

Zury's short evening passed in fits of grim anger at the extortion that had been practiced on his doting old father, alternating with dim visions of gaining greater money making power through "schooling." Ephraim lay till morning in the sad wakefulness of age. Four hundred dollars! Zury gone, and he alone on the farm all winter! Then bright and early he walked over to Peddicomb's. (The latter had been growing more and more anxious at the prospective obligation so unexpectedly thrust upon him.)

"'Lijah, jest lemme look over that thar paper-writin' a half a minute."

He took it and pretended to scan it carefully, though his dim eyes could not make out a word of it; then he said, —

"Oh, that ain't drawed right at all, — not the way I meant it, ner understood it, nuther!" And he tore it in scraps and threw it in the fire.

So ended the Spring County aid to the Soul-sleepers' College. (The college probably did its work, — the sect seems to have disappeared.)

So, too, passed away Zury's last glimpse of educational progress, except the sordid training forced upon him by his character and circumstances. The ship had sailed without him.

CHAPTER V.

HOW THE MEANEST MAN GOT SO MEAN, AND HOW MEAN HE GOT.

EPHRAIM wanted Zury to marry, but it was with "a sharp eye to the main chance." Property and personal service at no wages might both be secured by a judicious choice. Girls were not plenty, but at the Peddicombs' there were three of marriageable age. Their place was only three miles from Prouder's, and they were still the nearest neighbors. Mrs. Peddicomb had not long survived the birth of her three daughters. She died (as was and is common among farmers' wives) at not much over thirty years of age, just when her life ought to have been in its prime.

She was called a "Come-gals kind of a woman" by neighbors; partly in ridicule of her enthusiasm, and partly in admiration of her energy. It was told of her that she would get up before light on Monday, "fly 'raound," uncover the fire, hang on the kettle, and call up the ladder to the loft, —

"Come gals! *Dew* git up 'n' start in! Today 's Monday, to-morrow 's Tuesday, 'n' next day 's Wednesday; 'n' then comes Thursday, Friday, 'n' Saturday, — the hull week gone 'n' nothin' done."

The two younger girls had been cared for by the oldest, and so had retained some girlish freshness and delicacy, but as for Mary (the caretaker after her mother's death), she was "good-looking" only because she looked good.

On this marriage subject Ephraim took occasion to speak to Zury.

"Mary Peddicomb, she's a likely gal."

"Mary? Why not S'manthy 'n' Flory?"

"Oh, yes; they 're all right tew. Th' ol' man he 's got th' best part of a section. Some stwak, tew; 'n' th' haouse 'n' barn 's fust rate."

"Ya-as. Ef th' haouse 'n' barn worn't so good he 'd have more stawk th't 'd pay him right smart better 'n th' haouse 'n' barn dooz."

"Peddicomb ain't like t' marry ag'in. Mary she 'll have her sheer."

"Any more 'n th' others?"

"Oh, no. All same. But I reck'n Mary she 'd be more of a manager. *She* kin work! I 've watched her ever sence she wuz knee-high to a hoppy-toad, 'n' *I* tell ye she kin work!"

"Ef ye mean more manageable ye mought 's well say so."

"Wal, I dew 'llaow she 'd be full 's little likely t' be uppish 's th' others."

"Ye 'llaow 't humbly and humble goes t'gether?"

"Wal, yes; 'mongst the wimmin folks, substantially. Nothin' sets 'em so bad up 's bein' ha'ans'm. Spiles 'em fer use abaout the place. Th' humbly ones take t' milkin' more willin' like; 'n' I don't see but what the caows give daown tew 'em full 's well 's tew the ha'ans'm ones. 'N' then when ther' looks goes the' 're apt t' kick."

"What, the caows?"

"No, the wimmin."

("Humbly" in country parlance is a corruption of "homely," the opposite of handsome; plain, ungainly. "Humbly as a hedge fence.")

Zury pondered on this shrewd counsel from time to time, but took no step toward marrying.

"Right smart o' things t' think on afore th' 'll be any hurry 'baout a-gittin' marr'd. Th' feller th't 's in an orfle sweat t' marry, he 's li'ble t' be the very feller th't 's behindhand with everythin' else. Takes Time by the forelock 'baout gittin' a wife; 'n' by the fetlock 'baout gittin' suthin' fer her t' eat."

The boy was wedded to his idols quite as faithfully, if not quite so sordidly, as was his father. Their dispositions were much alike. No draft on their powers of endurance and self-denial could be too great.

As to niggardliness, there was a confessed rivalry between them. Each would tell of the money-making and money-saving exploits of the other, and of his efforts to surpass them.

"Dad 's a screamer t' save money! D' ye ever see him withe a plaow-pint ontew a plaow? Give him a hickory grub, 'n' he kin dew it so it 'll run a good half a day; 'n' then withe it on agin in noon-spell whilst th' team 's a eatin', 'n' then withe it on agin come night so 's t' be ready fer nex' morn'n', 'n' keep it up fer a week that-a-way, sooner 'n pay th' smith a cent t' rivit it fast."

"Thasso, thasso, Zury. Hickory twigs is cheaper ner iron any day."

"Ya-as, dad; but then I kin make a shillin' while ye 're a savin' a cent. Look at it wunst. I upped 'n' sold the smith a half an acre, 'n' took a mortgage on it, 'n' made him dew all aour repairin' b' way of interest on the mortgage, 'n' then foreclosed th' mortgage when it come dew, 'n' got th' land back, shop 'n' all. Business is business!"

Ephraim always wanted to buy at the shop where they wrapped up the purchases with the largest and strongest paper and twine, and the harnesses on the farm gradually grew to be largely composed of twine. Zury could buy everything at wholesale, half price, including merchandise, paper, twine, harnesses, and all.

One day Zury came across a poor little boy carrying a poorer little puppy and crying bitterly.

"What 's the matter, sonny?"

"Our folks gimme a dime t' draownd this h'yer purp, 'n' I — I — I — hate t' dew it."

"Wal, ne' mind, bub; gimme the dime 'n' I 'll draownd him fer ye."

Whereupon he took the cash and the pup and walked to the mill-pond, while the boy ran home. Zury threw the little trembling creature as far as he could into the pond. A few seconds of wildly waving small ears, legs, and tail, and then a splash, and then nothing but widening ripples.

But out of one of the ripples is poked a little round object, which directs itself bravely toward the shore. Nearer and nearer struggles the small black nozzle, sometimes under water, and sometimes on top, but always nearer.

"Ye mis'able, ornery little fyce, ye! Lemme ketch ye swimmin' ashore! I 'll throw ye furder nex' time."

At last poor little roly-poly drags itself to the land and squats down at the very water's edge, evidently near to the end of its powers. Zury picks it up and swings it for a mighty cast, but stops and studies it a moment.

"Looks fer all the world like a sheep-dawg-purp."

Whereupon he slipped it into his pocket and carried it home, where it grew up to be a fit mate to old Shep, and the ancestress of a line of sheep dogs which ornament Spring County to this day.

Later, when the same boy, grown older, applied to Zury for one of the pups, he charged him the full price, fifty cents, took all he had, thirty-six cents, and his note on interest for the balance, the dog being pledged as security. The note being unpaid when due, Zury took back the dog. "Business is business!"

Years passed, and it came time for the old man to be gathered to his fathers and the son to reign in his stead. When Ephraim lay on his deathbed, he whispered to Zury: —

"What day 's to-day?"

"Tuesday, father?"

"I hope I'll live ontel Thursday, 'n' then ye kin hev the fun'r'l Sunday, 'n' not lose a day's work with the teams."

He did not die till Saturday night, but Zury had the funeral on Sunday all the same, like a dutiful son as he was, bent on carrying out his father's last request.

After Zury had grown to be a prosperous farmer, Chicago became the great market for the sale of grain. Teams by the score would start out from far down the State, and, driving during the day and camping at night, make the long journey. They would go in pairs or squads so as to be able to double teams over the bad places. Forty or fifty bushels could thus be carried in one load, when the chief parts of the roads were good, and "the ready john" (hard cash), could be got for the grain, at twenty or thirty cents a bushel for corn or wheat. This sum would provide a barrel or two of salt, and perhaps a plow and a bundle of dry goods and knickknacks for the women folks, the arrival of which was a great event in the lonely farm houses.

Zury had now working for him (beside Jule, who kept house and attended to the live stock), a young fellow who became a score of years afterward private, corporal, sergeant, lieutenant, and captain in the —th Illinois Volunteer Infantry in the great war. From his stories, told in bivouacs and beside camp fires, to toiling, struggling, suffering "boys in blue," these tales are taken almost verbatim. (Some of them have already found their way into print.)

"Zury always wanted to get onto the road with farmers whose housekeeping was good, because his own was — well, wuss th'n what we git down here in Dixie, an' there 's no need of *that*. Well, when they 'd halt for noon-spell, Zury he 'd happen along promiscuous-like, an' most generally some of 'em would make him stop an' take a bite. He was good company if he *was* so near. 'N' then a man's feed warn't counted fer much, unless it was some store-truck or boughten stuff.

"But one day they jest passed the wink and sot it up on him, and come noon-spell nobody asked Zury an' me to eat. Zury left me to take care of both teams while he walked up and down the line of wagins. Everybody who had n't 'jest eat,' warn't 'quite ready' yet, an' by the next time he came to those who had n't been 'quite ready,' they 'd 'jest eat.'

"Wal, Zury swallered his disappointment and I swallerd all the chawed wheat I could git away with, and the first settlement we passed Zury went and bought a monstrous big bag of sody-crackers, and we eat them for supper and breakfast. And still we were not happy.

"Next noon-spell Zury said, 'Boys, s'posin' we kinder whack up 'n' mess together.' Wal, the others 'd had enough of their joke, and so they all agreed, and chipped in. Ham, pickles, pies, cakes, honey, eggs, apples, and one thing another. Ye see every man's o' woman knew that when they got together, her housekeep would be compared with everybody else's; so these long drives were like donation parties, or weddings, or funerals,— well fed.

"Of course, Zury's sody-crackers went in with the rest, an' me an' Zury always ate *some* anyhow for appearance sake. I could see the fellers were all makin' fun of Zury's cute dodge of gettin' a dozen good meals for him an' me at the price of a few pounds of sody-crackers. But *then*, they did n't know Zury so well as they thought they did. By an' by the trip was done an' settlin'-up-time came, when each man was called on for his share of pasturage, ferriage, an' one thing another. Zury paid his, but he deducted out twenty-five cents paid for sody-crackers. Said it was one of the cash outlays for the common good, an' if any of the rest of 'em spent money an' did n't put it in, more fools they. Business is business."

So Zury in the soda-cracker episode came out "top of the heap" as usual. The top of the heap was his accustomed place, but still he perceived that he was living under one useless disability, and, with his quick adaptation of means to ends and remedies to deficiencies, he simply — married. In doing this, he was guided by his father's shrewd words; counsel which had lain fallow in his memory for years.

Zury's marriageability had, of course, not been unobserved in the household of the three daughters. Peddicomb had remarked what a good "outin'" the Prouders had made in their purchase of swine from him, and cherished the same kind of feeling toward them that most of us experience when some other person has done better in a joint transaction than we did.

"Them Praouders, the' 'll skin outer the land all the' kin skin, 'n' then sell offen the place all 't anybody 'll buy, 'n' then feed t' the hawgs all a hawg 'll eat, 'n' then give th' rest t' th' dawg, 'n' then what th' dawg won't tech the' 'll live on theirselves."

"Yew bet," tittered Semantha, the second. "That thar ornery Zury Praouder he 'd let a woman starve t' death ef he could. 'N' o' man Praouder wuz th' same way, tew. Th' o' woman she wuz near abaout skin 'n' bone when the' buried her. I seen her in her coffin, 'n' I know."

"Oh, don't *yew* be scaret, S'manthy. I hain't saw Zury a-lookin' over t' your side o' the meetin'-haouse, no gre't," kindly rejoined Flora, the youngest daughter.

"Who, me? He knows better! Not ef husbands wuz scarcer ner hen's teeth."

"Six hunderd 'n' forty acres o' good land, all fenced 'n' paid fer; 'n' a big orchard; 'n' all well stocked, tew." (He added this with a pang, remembering once more the pig-purchase, which by this time had grown to a mighty drove, spite of many sales.)

"Don't care ef he owned all ou' doors. Th' more the' 've got, th' more it shows haow stingy the' be."

Then the meek Mary ventured a remark.

"Mebbe ef Zury wuz t' marry a good gal it 'd be the makin' on him."

"Oh, Mary, *yew* hain't no call t' stan' up fer Zury! Th' o' man he 'd a ben more in yewr line."

"No, Zury would n't want *me*, ner no other man, I don't expect," she answered with a laugh —and a sigh.

One Sunday afternoon Zury rode over to Peddicomb's to get a wife. He tried to decide which girl to ask, but his mind would wander off to other subjects,—crops, live stock, bargains, investments. He did n't much think that either girl he asked would say no, but if she did, he could ask the others. When he came near the house he caught sight of one of the girls, in her Sunday clothes, picking a "posy" in the "front garding." It was Mary.

"Good day, Mary. Haow 's all the folks?"

"Good day, Zury — Mr. Praouder, I s'pose I should say. Won't ye 'light?"

"Wal, I guess not. I jes' wanted t' speak abaout a little matter."

"Wal, father he 's raoun' some 'ers. Haow 's the folks t' your 'us?"

"All peart; that is t' say th' ain't no one naow ye know, but me 'n' Jule 'n' Mac. That makes a kind of a bob-tail team, ye know, Mary. Nobody but Jule t' look out fer things. Not b't what he 's a pretty fair of a nigger as niggers go. He c'd stay raoun' 'n' help some aoutside."

"Whatever is he a-drivin' at?" thought Mary, but she said nothing.

"The's three of you gals to hum. Ye don't none of ye seem t' go off yit, tho' I sh'd a-thought Flory she 'd a-ben picked up afore this, 'n' S'manthy tew fer that matter."

Neither of them saw the unintended slur this rough speech cast upon poor Mary.

"Don't ye think we 'd better git married, Mary?"

"What, *me?*"

"Wal, yes." He answered this in a tone where she might have detected the suggestion, "Or one of your sisters," if she had been keen and critical. But she was neither. She simply rested her work-worn hand upon the gate post and her chin upon her hand, and looked dreamily off over the prairie. She pondered the novel proposition for some time, but fortunately not quite long enough to cause Zury to ask if either of her sisters was at home, as he was quite capable of doing.

She looked up at him, the blood slowly mounting to her face, and considered how to say yes. He saw that she meant yes, so he helped her out a little. He wanted to have it settled and go.

"Wal, Mary, silence gives consent, they say. When shall it be?"

"Oh, yew ain't in no hurry, Zury, I don't expect."

He was about to urge prompt action, but the thought occurred to him that she must want to get her "things" ready, and the longer she waited the more "things" she would bring with her. So he said: —

"Suit yerself, Mary. I 'll drop over 'n' see ye nex' Sunday, 'n' we 'll fix it all up."

Mary had no objection to urge, though possibly in her secret heart she wished there had been a little more sentiment and romance about it. No woman likes "to be cheated out of her wooing," but then this might come later. He called for her with the wagon on the appointed day, and they drove to the house of a justice of the peace who lived a good distance away. This was not for the sake of making a wedding trip, but because this particular justice owed Zury money, as Zury carefully explained.

And so Mary went to work for Zury very much as Jule did, only it was for less wages, as Jule got a dollar a month besides his board and clothes, while Mary did not.

For a year or two or three after marriage (during which two boys were born to them) Zury found that he had gained, by this investment, something more than mere profit and economy — that affection and sympathy were realities in life. But gradually the old dominant mania resumed its course, and involved in its current the weak wife as well as the strong husband. The general verdict was that both Zury and Mary were "jest 's near 's they could stick 'n' live." "They 'd skin a flea fer its hide 'n' taller."

"He gin an acre o' graound fer the church 'n' scule-house, 'n' it raised the value of his hull farm more 'n' a dollar an acre. 'N' when he got onto the scule-board *she* 'llaowed she had n't released her daower right, 'n' put him up t' tax the deestrick fer the price of that same acre o' ground."

So Zury, claiming the proud position of "the meanest ma-an in Spring Caounty," would like to hear his claim disputed. If he had a rival he would like to have him pointed out, and would "try pootty hard but what he 'd match him."

Strange as it may seem, these grasping characteristics did not make Zury despised or even disliked among his associates. His "meanness" was not underhanded.

"Th' ain't nothin' *mean* abaout Zury, *mean* 's he is. Gimme a man as sez right aout 'look aout fer yerself,' 'n' I kin git along with him. It 's these h'yer sneakin' fellers th't 's one thing afore yer face 'n' another behind yer back th't I can't abide. Take ye by th' beard with one hand 'n' smite ye under th' fifth rib with t' other! He pays his way 'n' dooz 's he 'grees every time. When he buys 'taters o' me, I 'd jest 's live 's hev him measure 'em 's measure 'em myself with him a-lookin' on. He knows haow t' trade, 'n' ef yew don't, he don't want ye t' trade with him, that 's all; ner t' grumble if ye git holt o' the hot eend o' th' poker arter he 's give ye fair notice. Better be shaved with a sharp razor than a dull one."

On an occasion when the honesty of a more pretentious citizen was compared with Zury's, to the advantage of the latter, he said: —

"Honest? Me? Wal, I guess so. Fustly, I would n't be noth'n' else, nohaow; seck'ndly, I kin 'fford t' be, seein' 's haow it takes a full bag t' stand alone; thirdly, I can't 'fford t' be noth'n' else, coz honesty 's th' best policy."

He was evidently quoting, unconsciously but by direct inheritance, the aphorisms of his fellow Pennsylvanian, Dr. Franklin.

In peace as in war strong men love "foemen worthy of their steel." Men liked to be with Zury and hear his gay, shrewd talk; to trade with him, and meet his frankly brutal greed. He enjoyed his popularity, and liked to do good turns to others when it cost him nothing. When elected to local posts of trust and confidence he served the public in the same efficient fashion in which he served himself, and he was therefore continually elected to school directorships and other like "thank 'ee jobs."

CHAPTER VI.

A BRAVE GIRL — THOUGH A COWARD.

"TELL ye what, pardners," said Zury one day to his associates on the school board, "Johnny McVey that works to the tavern, he 's hed a letter from a feller he knowed in Massychusetts; a Boston doctor 'n' a good one, tew; askin' ef a gal — a ra-al smart gal — kin git a jawb a scule-teachin' aout h'yer. Sez she 's got a big notion o' comin' West. I told him t' write t' hev her come along. Plenty o' room h'yer fer her t' grow up with th' kedntry. Ef she can't keep school she kin keep company with some o' th' boys. Gals is so paowerfle scuss. It won't matter ef she 's caowhocked, parrot-toed, ewe-necked, 'n' hain't got but one eye, 'n' that one a squinter. Some feller 'll take up with her."

Zury's "pardners," three of the other members of the school board, kept a grim silence until he was out of hearing, then they broke forth: —

"Say, fellers, mebbe th' legislatur 's upped 'n' 'p'inted Zury a guardeen over we-uns, 'n' we ain't never heer'd the news till naow."

"Looks like it, don't it, naow? Him a sendin' fer a gal-teacher unbeknownst t' us! Some stuck-up, white-faced, soft-handed, hifalutin' silk-stockin' th't never went bar-foot ner did a day's work in her life!"

"Ah, yah! Her a-comin' aout h'yer t' keep Deestrick Scule Number Seven! She 'll be onter th' poor-farm afore ye know it."

"*I* believe ye. Set a city gal at that thar jawb that 's beat aout men, ra'al *men*, that 'll aout-weigh three on her!"

"Ye 're mighty right. Thar 's Johnny McVey, he ain't no great shakes fer a man, but he kin lick any gal that 's goin'. 'N' jest see haow th' boys jest massacreed him! Kep' school jest a day, not — hardly that, neither."

"Why, that thar gal won't be but a maouthflē apiece fer Sile Anstey 'n' John Felser; 'n' not a bite left fer the rest t' chaw on!"

"Wal, jest let her come 'n' try it on, that 's all! Zury Praouder! Smart Aleck 'd oughter be his other name!"

The young woman whom McVey had sent for, and who, with all the reckless and splendid courage of New England youth, self-reliance, and inexperience, had taken her life in her hand and journeyed into the unknown wild, is well worth a few paragraphs, historical, biographical, and descriptive.

At the very time when Prouder and his neighbors were wagoning corn all the way from Spring County to Chicago, a young girl named Anne Sparrow was growing up in a Lowell cotton-factory, wearing out her shoes and a clean pine floor by her ceaseless tread, to and fro, behind frames which held hundreds of whirring spindles. As she walked, with a springy, half-dancing step, she kept time to the rhythm of the machinery and sang or whistled, clear and shrill, some pretty air to the same measure. She was handsome in a style of beauty not then in vogue, though highly favored a few years later, a tall, lithe, strong blonde, with red hair, gay, brave blue eyes, and a red-and-white and freckly skin.

The threads twisted by those spindles were constantly breaking, which gave her the duty (backache-y at first, but easy afterward) of leaning over the frames and deftly re-uniting them, which service earned a pretty good living for herself and widowed mother. The widow was intellectual, — even literary in a modest way, — for she edited the local weekly paper which published or declined with thanks the crude offerings of the work-girls of the factory-town. Anne herself grew up with a great deal of desultory knowledge, largely the result of reading the books sent to the "weekly" for review, at first to aid her mother in writing the book-notices, and later to enable her to write them herself.

"My happiest days" (she said, long afterward) "were those when the paper came out containing something I had written. I tried to fancy that it looked like the things in the "Boston Transcript." I was always hoping the "Transcript" would copy something I had written, — but it never did! I would conjure up things as I worked, and then write and re-write them; and sometimes (not often) they looked bright when printed; but it made no difference. Nobody cared whether they were bright or not." (A smiling sigh.)

Among the books she read and reviewed were those to which Fourier gave his name, and she became deeply impressed with the plausible views they set forth. She and her mother were above their business, their neighbors, and their circumstances, — an offense never forgiven by any community since the world began. So the aging and failing mother and the growing girl were essentially alone in the world. When Anne approached marriageable age she saw that no one whom she would marry would ever offer himself.

Society has created a cruel fate for lonely women. Every theory which seems to provide a place for the unmarried millions of the gentle sex finds a natural following of adherents among them. Even Mormonism is not coarse enough to repel the lower orders of the race, abhorrent as it is to the refined. Fourierism aimed at giving every human being an honorable chance to live; no wonder it gained passionate adherents from the ranks of New England women, Anne Sparrow among the rest.

The widow's death soon left the daughter alone and desolate, and she drifted quite into the stream of the most "advanced thinkers." She wrote some articles for the Boston papers, which were always published — until she suggested a little pay for her contributions. Some of the leading people among the "new-lights" learned her name, and wrote kindly to her, — a gleam of light in her darkness. A young doctor, who had attended her mother in her last illness, had a great influence among the "come-outers," and Anne joined their ranks under his guidance.

The whole story of the New England "socialistic movement" has never been told, and probably never will be; certainly not until the generation of its actors shall have passed away. The annals of Brook Farm give only the surface of events. As to Anne's part in it, we need not inquire how far from the beaten track her "broad views" led her. Whatever she did was not done from wickedness; it was in accordance with her honest opinions of right and wrong, and not in violation of them. Her lips are sealed; she had neither praise nor blame to bestow on her former friends at the time when she begins to be connected with our story. That is, when her theories, her independence, her pride, her strength, her weakness, had led her far out into the West, — to Wayback in Spring County, Illinois.

One of her characteristics (mental or physical, it is hard to say which) must be touched upon because it affects her future. By some accident, perhaps an inherited or at least an inborn tendency, she was morbidly sensitive to darkness. As a little child if she awoke alone, after being put to sleep, she would scream "Mother!" at the top of her voice until help came; and later, when the widow tried to reason with her, she confessed that if she were alone at night, and knew the house was on fire, she could more easily be burned in her bed than put her feet on the unseen floor. Her intellect recognized this as a kind of insanity, but it was no more to be conquered than is that of the poor lunatic who kills himself to escape imaginary perils threatening his life.

So it was the rule of the little household that Anne should never be left alone at night. Together she and her mother sat at home; together they went out (though seldom); and together they slept and woke. Then when her mother died —

Poor, suffering, lonesome girl! To die, suddenly, was her nightly longing; but luckily — sometimes afterward she said unluckily — she was sane enough to fear that too.

Among her mother's papers she found a slip which had been made as the record of an incident she herself had forgotten. It was used in an effort to get medical relief, — so the doctor told her when they afterward became acquainted. Here it is: —

"Oh, mother — mother dear — I'm so glad you've come to bed — at last! I heard a noise — and I got afraid I was going to be frightened. And then the bed and the room began to move about like a boat — and I got almost seasick — and then I shuddered, and the goose-flesh came all down my back and on my legs; — just feel them! — and I could hear my hair crawl about on the pillow — and I tried to call out but I could n't! And then you came, and I did n't *quite* get frightened after all."

At the end was appended in another hand (the doctor's) this quotation: "*Comes erectæ stant; vox faucibus hæsit*," and some medical hieroglyphics.

The triumph of the rebellious scholars over their teacher at the last attempted term of the Wayback school made Anne's prospect a very gloomy one. To this threatening danger must be added the prejudice conceived against her by a majority of the school board because Zury had invited her without their advice and consent.

Fancy, now, a meeting of that august body, composed of four farmers all alike in attainments of "book-larnin'," except that three of them could almost read and write, while the fourth could not. The place is the log school-house in the woods between Wayback and the Prouder Farm. (Zury Prouder was unluckily away.) The time is evening, starry on the prairie, but darkness under the giant trees that surround the school-house. The light (material) is one tallow dip; the light (intellectual) consists of the afore-mentioned four members of the school board of Wayback district and Anne Sparrow.

"Miss Sparrer, this h'yer's brother Peddicomb, and this 's brother Sapp, *an'* brother Anstey. My name is Bromwell, Omri Bromwell." (The pronunciation of these sounding syllables was evidently a strengthening exercise, precious as an antidote to any modesty or self-distrust.)

"Brother Proauder and brother Braown, they 're absent, but, as is well known, four is a quorum of six. If we 're all agreed, we 'll now proceed to examine yew as a candidate fer teacher of Deestrick Scule Number Seven."

Anne had no difficulty in "doing" all the little arithmetical "sums" they propounded "up to the rule o' three." Her handwriting was *tolerable.* Spelling was her forte, and she "floored" *phthisic* and *indefatigability* and *incomprehensibility* without murmur. The doughty four began to fear they would have no chance to exercise their unaccustomed authority, — unaccustomed because this was the first time they had ever met without Prouder and Squire Brown, who were the ruling spirits of the board — and also to fear they could not give to Zury the desired "set-back."

But their great hope lay in the "back part o' the spellin'-book." They could not answer the questions, but by painful effort, eyes on line and finger on word, they could ask them; and then by the same process they could compare the spoken answers with the printed ones. Poor Anne felt her courage dissolving into thin air as the grand inquisitors marked question after question "missed" when she had given the sense instead of the words in her answer. If she could only have given the words and reversed the sense she would have been quite safe. Every little while a brother would moisten his fingers with nature's lubricator and snuff the tallow dip which served to show the darkness of the squalid school-room, subsequently cleaning his fingers on his garments in a vain effort to save the page from a little more grime; and on each of those occasions she would see in the sinking candle an emblem of her sinking heart.

At last the fateful four retired outside the door into the vocal silence and lumined darkness of the dewy woods to consult on the candidacy.

The consultation was short, and to a great extent inaudible, but evidently all on one side.

"She got the parts o' grammar Othorgaphy an' Entomology all right; an' Sign Tax after she thort awhile; but she left aout Prosody altogether."

"She did n't seem t' git a-holt on a verb agreein' with its nomitive in number 'n' person, neither: thort they orter 'correspond.' *Agree* 's the word in the book."

"*To* be sure! Ye correspond with a man ontel y' agree with him 'n' then yer correspondence draps."

"Yes, *sir!* 'N' when she tried t' tell what an adverb 'll qualify, she left aout 'other adverbs,' teetotally."

"Ye reckleck brother McVey he answered every question."

"Yew bet! 'N' if *all* the boys had n't a ben able fer to a licked him, brother McVey he 'd a done fust-rate."

So all who spoke were of one mind; each trying to show the others that he had detected a failure on Anne's part,—some glaring and inexcusable and irremediable defect in her education. The poor girl, divining what was going on, was almost hysterical in her discomfiture. Had she come all this way by railroad, steamboat, canal-boat, and stage to find out that she was unfit to teach anything, however simple, to anybody, however ignorant? Had she (metaphorically) descended to the very foot of the social ladder to be told that she must go lower or starve? Poor girl! Alone, homeless, friendless, almost moneyless,—she passed a very bad quarter of an hour.

The mighty tetrapod approached the school-house door to go in and tell her her doom. But now brother Anstey, who not being able to read or write had never before been known to utter a word, put in his little oar. As his disability shut him out from any active part in the oral examination, he had simply sat in the shadow during its progress and scanned the candidate's whitening face, great scared eyes, and quivering lips. Now he said,—

"Brother Bromwell, somehoaw it don't seem t' me 's haow we ain't got no quorum t' act fer keeps, s' long 's brother Praouder 'n' brother Braown ain't h'yer."

"I don't 'llaow t' let brother Praouder 'n' brother Braown have the say-so 'baout everythin'."

"'N' four 's a quorum o' six, every time," added the brother who had laboriously acquired this one item of (inaccurate) parliamentary information, and no more.

"Ef the' worn't but three on us we could n't do nauth'n', but four 's a quorum."

"Oh, four 's a quorum, is it?" said brother Anstey, and then his little eyes twinkled, and he slipped off around the corner of the school-house, chuckled to himself, fought mosquitoes, and peeped in at the window; and this is what he saw.

The three learned worthies filed portentously in, wise as owls, and far more solemn. Said brother Bromwell: —

"Miss Sparrer, we 've considered your case 'n' reached a conclusion; 'n' so 's you kin see that everythin' 's done in *pro formy* 'n' 'cordin' t' law, we will take the vote right here afore ye. Our board 's composed of six, 'n' consekently four 's a quorum by law as you are doubtless aweer. Gentlemen, all as is in favior of votin' t' hev Miss Sparrer excepted 'n' ingaged as teacher of Deestrick Scule Number Seven 'll please signify it by sayin' why wheer 's brother Anstey?"

This oration with its absurd close, all spoken in one breath, was too much for the overcharged feelings of poor Anne, and she burst out laughing. She could n't have helped it if her life had depended on it, instead of simply her living. It turned out all right, however: it made the brothers look foolish, and left her mistress of the situation, — a safer state of things than if they had gone off leaving a crushed fellow-mortal as a gratifying trophy of their power.

"He must a mistook 'n' thought we wuz through. I 'll step t' the door 'n' holler to him."

Then Anne heard, for the first time in her life, the peculiar intonation with which Westerners and Southerners shout aloud, — giving great force to the "Oh!" and slighting the rest of the cry.

"O-H-H-H brother Anstey!"

But of course brother Anstey was n't to be had. He had been moved by some unsuspected and almost unimaginable tender and sympathizing chord in his rough nature to "break that quorum if it cost him a leg!" as he afterward gleefully declared, and so he kept himself well hidden and let the shout echo unanswered over and beyond and around him, and away through miles of silent, shadowy tree-trunks and branches; silencing many a low-voiced forest denizen, making many a night-brooding beast, bird, and insect pause and listen; but extorting no response from him, a hundred feet away, to whom it was addressed.

"O-H-H-H brother Anstey!"

Even old Shep, at the Prouder farm-house, heard the "O-H-H-H," and set up his answering bark; and to him other watch-dogs replied, —

> "Down the coast, each taking up the burden,"

so that, for aught we know, it may have spread on and on, in ever-widening circles, until it reached the Mississippi on the west, the Great Lakes on the north, the Ohio on the south, and daylight in the east. There seems no perceptible reason why, in that quiet, breezeless starlight, inhabited by from a dog and a half to ten dogs per square mile, the chorus should ever come to a halt, — why every dog that heard that shout should not bark;

and every dog that heard that dog, and so on to an extent which the imagination fails to grasp in its monstrous possibilities. (This digression just about measures the delay in waiting for brother Anstey's answer.)

Meanwhile the conviction was deepening and hardening in the little assembly at the schoolhouse, that the august body must ignominiously — go home.

"Zury Praouder ain't no man fer a school-director — away all of his time, buyin' 'n' sellin' cattle 'n' truck, 'n' tradin' hosses 'n' sech-like."

"Miss Sparrer, I 'xpeck we 've got t' git another meetin' t' morrer night, ef s' be ye kin be 'raound — 'n' think it wuth yer while."

"T'morrer 's Sat'd'y; mebbe we kin git t' git t'gether t' th' tahvern t' Wayback, 'n' save Miss Sparrer a-comin' daown h'yer."

Manifestly this was an expedient to "let her down easy" and spare her and them a journey which must, after all, prove fruitless. Still, Anne took it as a sure opening to success, and accepted it joyfully. The hearty laugh had had its due reflex influence on her spirits: she slipped the old spelling-book into her pocket, and simply resolved to learn the whole "back part" by heart during the next day.

"Bid ye good-night, Miss Sparrer, 'n' wish ye well. S'pose ye kin find yer way t' the tahvern — ye can't miss it, 'n' it 's *safe* enough. We don't none o' us happen t' be a-livin' that way, 'xcep' brother Anstey, 'n' he 's gone."

Alone! Were they men? Could they leave her in that black place alone! She is going to be frightened, surely! Oh, horror! Oh, desolation! She must call to them — she must call for help — she must scream out loud to break this dreadful silence! But not a sound will her dry and hollow throat give forth. Once more her old well-known fear of being frightened fell upon her with a force greater than ever before. Her hair took on its horrid independent life and moved audibly and sensibly beneath her hat, and roughening chills shot over her body and limbs.

What were all previous terrors compared to this! The trees were so huge and black! The world was so big — and she so small! The people were all so far, far away! O mother, mother! Your poor little girl — alone — alone — all alone!

She tried the school-house door again and again, but, alas! the boors had locked it after them. Never in her life had she felt such bitter and reproachful anger against any human being as now filled her breast toward those men. And yet it was not just. They could not conceive of such weakness as hers. As to asking her to go home with them — if she had been less unlike their kind they might have done so, might have put her to sleep with the wife while the father turned in with the snoring boys. To the dignity of a spare room none of those prosperous settlers had yet arrived. (This was many years ago.)

Anne felt her way along the ground a little

distance, almost on her hands and knees, but she found herself so much more wretched after she lost sight of the school-house, that she crawled back to it again, and laid her cold cheek against the door. It was smooth; so at least some human hand must once have touched it. She tried to whistle, but her poor, parched whistle would n't whistle; or, if it did, it was so faint she could n't hear it through the ringing in her ears.

What new horror is that? Her hair is getting up again, — she did not know it had lain down. A light, by itself, moving noiselessly, mockingly, from side to side, and coming nearer; a ghost, — a corpse-light! Black Dread has found her at last, and is coming to seize her in his claws!

"O-h-h-h!" and she uttered a shriek which might have startled the echoes and the dogs again, only that it was confined to the crack of the school-house door by her two bent hands, one pressed against each side of her eyes and temples, while her feet beat tattoo on the stone outside.

"Why Miss Sparrer! Be ye scare't? It's only old Anstey. I started aout t' meet ye on the road, but I could n't find noth'n' on ye, so I come 'long clean h'yer!"

For the first and last time in his life that old man had his gnarled hand kissed!

"Oh, I came so *near* being frightened! But you came at last. Oh, take me somewhere!"

"Wal, I 'llaowed t' take ye t' our'us ef so be ye c'd put up with poor folks' doin's over-night. I jest went hum 'n' raouted aout th' ole woman 'n' told her her 'n' me we'd take a shake-daown up garret so 's ye c'd hev a night's rest—ye look t' need it—traveled so fur, 'n' had sech bad luck wi' yer 'zam'nation 'n' all!"

"Oh-I 'll-sit-by-your-fire-all-night-and-not-trouble-you-at-all-and-not-let-you-give-up-your-bed-nor-your-wife-either-if-you 'll-only-take-me-out-of this—*wilderness!*" and she paused for breath, and then resumed faintly, but more deliberately, "And thank you as long as I live! Oh no, don't take away your hand! Let me hold it while we walk—there—so."

"Why—you—poor—creeter!"

So he led her gently along, happy, almost gay, in her revulsion of feeling, and half inclined to put her arms around his corrugated neck and kiss his weather-beaten and toil-marked old face. The moonlight silvered his uncouth outlines, and he looked, in her eyes, more like an angel than he had ever looked to human eyes before—unless to his mother's when he met her earliest gaze—or than he would ever look again, in this world.

"I jest sot it up on them fellers 'baout right. Tell me! I dunno much, but I know 's haow *yew* know a heap. Thet thar ornery Omri Bromwell, he dunno enough t' know haow much yew *dew* know! What yew dunno ain't wuth a-knowin', 'n' I know it! Takes a blind man t' see some things!"

"Oh, I knew you were my friend all through." (The fib was unconscious, but even if it had been deliberate, who could have blamed her?)

"Sho now! Did ye, though? Wal, thar! Ef I ever did! That shows 's haow ye 're quicker 'n a-mink-trap 'n' sharper 'n a tack! Wal, I warn't a-goin' t' let them fellers come no snap jedgment on ye, not by a long chalk! I jest broke the four-um a-purpose."

"Did you? Oh, you dear man!"

"Did I? Wal, you better b'lieve I did! Them t' come a snap jedgment on *yew!* 'N' Zury Praouder away! I 'termined t' break that four-um ef it cost me a leg! 'N' I did it, tew!"

And the old man swelled with pride at his prowess. All alone he had broken a quorum! Not having any idea what a quorum was, — not even its name, — all unaided he had attacked the mighty chimera and shattered it at a blow.

"Yes you did, indeed! No man in the world could have done it more quickly or better!"

"Jest let 'em wait ontel Zury Praouder gits a-holt on 'em 'n' he 'll fourum 'em!"

"Who 's Zury Prouder?"

"What! dunno Zury? Wal, come t' think, 'course ye don't! Oh Zury, he 's a hull team 'n' a hoss t' spare, 'n' a dawg under the wagin! He 's lightnin', Zury is! Ain't noth'n' th' matter o' Zury. Jest let him git a-holt on them fellers wunst, a-tryin' t' run things 'n' him gone, 'n' they 'll look 's though an elephant 'd tromped onto 'em! I 'd druther deal with Zury Praouder, *near* 's he is, then a hull bilin' o' such misable ornery truck 's Omri Bromwell! A man 's more li'ble t' cut his chin with a dull razor ner with a sharp one. If ye deal with Zury, ye know whar ye be, but dealin' wi' them, whar be ye?"

Anne was unable to answer this conundrum, though disposed to think that, dealing with such truck, you were lost. And lightening the way with such amiable conversation (as Bunyan says) they arrived at the humble abode of her guide. There were a few embers just glowing on the hearth, and they showed by their fitful light an empty bed in one corner of the only room. Two things were most fortunate, — one that the firelight was too dim to show her how unattractive were the sleeping accommodations offered her, and the other that the light of knowledge in the old man's mind was too dim to show him the same thing. He thought, innocent old soul, that that was "a pootty fair of a bed," as he would have expressed it. And so he bade her good-night, and clambered up the ladder with a comfortable glow of gratified pride of hospitality in his heart, and Anne heard him and his "old woman" exchanging a few whispered remarks before sinking into their speedy slumbers. Then she, too, after slipping off her shoes and loosening a few garments, lay down to watch the flickering embers which sparkled between her and solitude, — one of the sweetest and speediest modes of saying good-night to wakefulness and good-morrow to dreamland.

CHAPTER VII.

ANNE MEETS THE MEANEST MAN.

SUMMER night — unless fear distort the vision — is beautiful, but summer morning in malarial regions (to the experienced dweller) is positively ugly. All night the world is a lovely, half veiled Danaë; with break of day she becomes a squalid, unkempt, disorderly invalid. A blue, unwholesome-looking haze spreads over every flat space, and the rays of dawn silver its surface with a pale, sickly light. The dew which is refreshing at night-fall is dank at daybreak. Ague, like the ghost of a giant snake, crawls visible over the land: men shudder at the sight, and their flesh creeps at its very hideousness. Only the tree-tops, far up and out of reach, glorying in the early rays, are truly happy places; and the birds know it and make the most of it by then and there doing up most of their music, their laundrywork, their toilets, and their love-making for all day.

It seemed to Anne that she had scarcely got to sleep when a noise woke her which sounded in her dreams like the rumbling of an omnibus over Charles River bridge, but which was, in fact, only the passage of old Anstey across the warped and "teetering" boards which formed the floor of the garret. Then by the gray light that came peering and peeping in through various imperfectly closed apertures, especially the low wide chimney open to the sky, she saw his bare feet descend the ladder, followed by the rest of his person somewhat more clothed, but not much. First he raked up the embers into a blaze, then went out and got a pail of water, from which he filled a kettle, which he afterwards hung on the crane to boil. Then he looked over toward Anne, she having just time to close her eyes in pretended slumber.

People of Anstey's class have not the smallest appreciation of the delicate coyness of sleep. They think that the only things needful to secure sound slumber are two: first, a place to lie down in, and, second, leisure in the intervals of labor. Sleep they regard as at best a necessary evil, and even down to this age of the world they think that early rising is a virtue! Annoyance at being roused would be inconceivable to old Anstey, unless uprising and working were the purpose of the awakening. So when he saw, or thought he saw, that Anne was fast asleep, he simply called out: —

"O-H-H-H Miss Sparrer!"

"Well, Mr. Anstey?"

"I'm a-goin' aout t' milk naow, 'n' I thort I'd tell ye th' ain't no call fer ye t' git up fer a spell yet. Th' ole woman she 'll be daown 'n' git some breakf's'; 'n' ye kin jest sleep 's long ye wanter."

"Thank you."

So Anne turned her face to the wall with the intention of renewing the effort to restore exhausted nature. But what is this — this horrible bag of rustling corn-husks her head is resting on? These unspeakable "comforts" that are trying to do duty as sheet, blanket, and counterpane combined! This rudely lumpy surface whereon they are spread! Those closely adjacent logs which she knows must be swarming with insects! Is it imagination, or is she herself already infested? Ugh! She springs from the bed as from a viper's nest, and stands on the floor, hastily examines her shoes and puts them on and goes out into the air, where she is confronted with the ugly morning picture before mentioned, — disheveled Nature before she has her face washed, her hair combed, or her shoes and stockings on.

Near by stands a rude bench, made by thrusting four saplings through holes bored in a slab of wood, and on the bench sits an iron skillet, which, by the piece of soap near at hand and certain other indications, she knows to be the family lavatory. The skillet she fills at the well, and then making her simple toilet (aided by a very small allowance of pocket-handkerchief and a great deal of fresh air), she feels like a new woman. She even ventures on a short walk in the weedy garden-patch, but the dew makes this a disagreeable experience and she soon gets back to the house.

Anne thought she knew all about poverty. She had certainly seen it in her factory-town, clear down to the very door of the poor-house. But the poor-house folk themselves did not live like this: they would not have put up with it. And those naturalistic enthusiasts — how sublimely they talk about the charms of Nature! How sacred Nature's mysteries! How much more you adored her the nearer you got to her! How inalienable the rights of all her creatures, even the humblest and least attractive! Ugh! Did they know about bugs? Are malodorous parasites Nature's creatures with inalienable rights? Stuff! Mankind has been for twenty thousand years improving upon Nature, subduing her forces and killing her bugs — now the idea of going back!

So musing, she came back to the house-door, where the sound and smell of frying meat saluted her. There she met Mrs. Anstey for the first time. It is well that our story does not demand that she should be described, for she was really almost "unspeakable," with her bare head and feet, and her whole system ruined with the ceaseless drug-taking which prevailed at that day, so much more, even, than at this. The children were not quite so bad, because, being ungoverned whelps, they had rebelled, often with success, against the ever-recurring Christian duty to take medicine.

"Howdy marm! Yer a-lookin' peart. H'yer you cubs! Hike out o' h'yer fr'm raound that thar fire! Ain't ye got no manners? Bijah, why ain't ye aout a-helpin' yer father do the chores? You Silas! git daown offen that stule 'n' give the lady a chance t' set. Hike naow er I'll make ye! Go read yer book!"

But Silas, knowing that this last infliction was the penalty reserved for the gravest offenses, none of which had he yet committed that morning, merely gave up the stool and lounged over to the other side of the fire, whence he could stare at Anne continuously.

"You Eureky! Why don't ye turn that bread? Hain't ye got no eyes?"

This was obviously unjust, for Eureka, a tall girl, almost a woman, was just then to all appearance entirely composed of eyes glued upon the visitor. If she had possessed any other organ of sense — a nose, for instance — it would have informed her that the "sody" biscuits were burning on one side.

"You Silas! Mind naow ye don't git t' git no breakf's' not ontel ye 've washed up! Elviry yew stop yer whimperin'! Shell I hev t' git after ye with a chunk? Go read yer book!"

Now came Anstey with the milk, the straining whereof Anne did not see, which was fortunate for her breakfast appetite. She would have preferred that the milk should remain like "the quality of mercy" in Portia's speech. Breakfast was soon set — dumped rather — upon the table; where some "set by" on the old man's invitation, and some only helped themselves and haled away their respective portions to individual feeding-places. It was all rather dreadful even to Anne's unpampered taste, and she could not do much in the way of partaking.

"No meat? Why, I 'm a-feared ye won't make

nothin' of a meal! Jest tea 'n' bread 'n' milk don't go fur. Ain't ye got nothin' else, ole woman — store fixin's o' no kind?"

"Oh, I 'm doing finely! I have been quite out of the habit of eating meat at breakfast, and bread and milk are my favorite substitute."

This was true enough regarding meat, especially during her mother's illness, when they could scarcely afford it.

"Wal, ef I 'd a thought, I c'd a give her some o' the drops o' 'lixir vity to a give her an appetite."

"That 's so! My o' woman she 's paowerfle on docterin'. Ye kin tie t' *her* every time!"

This was said with undisguised admiration and marital pride.

"'Course we got eggs — ef ye like eggs."

Anne at once expressed devoted fondness for eggs.

"You Reeky! G' out 'n' git s'm eggs; 'n' mind ye don't disturb the settin' hens."

When Eureka returned with the eggs, Anne observed preparations for frying them in the meat gravy. She ventured the suggestion that they should be boiled.

"Biled eggs? Ye don't say! Wal, *we* don't think biled eggs fit fer shucks, on'y fer the chill'n t' take t' scule. Hows'ever, — Eureky, you fetch in that skillet. Mind ye wash it aout, tew."

Eggs boiled in the wash-basin rather staggered poor Anne, but so long as the shells were not cracked what difference could it make? The eggs were put in, and boiled some ten or fifteen minutes. Then when the water was poured off and the skillet set on the table, she (not without many misgivings) wiped each *very* dry, and peeled off the shell *very* carefully, and so secured a shiny ball of nourishing food pure as a snow-flake, which she munched with a good deal of satisfaction.

The old woman of course could not drop the fascinating subject of medicine yet a while.

"Oh, no, I ain't no great shakes compared to yer way-up city doctors. Tell yew! Can't they give physic? No matter what yer complaint is they 've got suth'n' other 't 'll knock it! 'N' that 's more 'n what the best of our country doctors kin say!"

"'Course that 's so," volunteered old Anstey. "Them big city doctors they don't 'llaow t' come away aout h'yer! I 've heern tell haow they hev their reg'lar 'zaminations o' candidates, same 's if it wuz preachers 'n' school-teachers: 'n' them 's kin tell what 'll knock all complaints, they station in the big cities; 'n' them 's kin tell what 'll knock half, say, why they send them t' mejum-sized places, like say Springville or Danfield; 'n' them 's can't tell what 'll knock hardly anythin' 'ceptin' agur, 'n' fits, 'n' roomatiz 'n' sech like, why the' send sech 's them t' Wayback 'n' sech like."

"'Course that 's so! Tell me! Don't I know it? 'N' that 's the reason why we country ladies we don't have no health! Its teetotally and intirely the doctors, altogether! 'N' partly the quality o' the physic th' sell h'yer, tew. Many 's the time I 've bought what was cracked up to be good strong med'cine t' Wayback; yes 'n' paid a good price fer it, tew, 'n' it did n't seem t' take no holt."

"I 've often wondered why them big town docters don't put up a mixter of all ther strong med'cines, 'n' put in what 's good fer everythin' — not leave aout a single complaint — 'n' send it aout inter the kedntry ter save the lives of their feller-creeters. It 'd have a big sale, I tell ye!"

"Wal, naow, ther wuz a man he come by with suth'n' o' thet kind — a pannersee he called it — thet 'd cure every mortial thing. An' he had another med'cine thet was cracked up t' be paowerfle good fer fits. Wal, I bought some o' both. To be sure we ain't had no fits yet, but *then*, ther ain't no tellin' haow soon we may. Then it kind o' struck me thet ef the pannersee would cure fits among the rest, what wuz the fit-med'cine good fer: so I as't him in case o' fits which I sh 'd give; 'n' he kinder laughed as he rid off, 'n' sung aout 'both.' I tuk the pannersee 'cordin' t' directions, but" (here she sighed) "I never see 's it done me much good." (This with an air of resigned melancholy at the well-recognized fact that her case formed an exception to the general experience of humanity.) "The fit-med'cine I guess I got sumwhers naow. I 'll gladly give ye a dose Miss Sparrer ef ye feel any ways poorly."

"Thank you very much, but I am quite well. I 'm almost always perfectly well."

"Wal, naow, ye ra'ly look it. Ollers lived in a city, I s'pose."

"Yes, almost always."

"Ah yah! There's whar it is! Wha' d' I tell ye? Ye hed them big city docters ollers clust by. 'N' the most paowerfle med'cines, no matter whut the' cost, nuther."

"I don't remember ever to have had a doctor in my life — to any sickness of my own."

"What! Doctered yerself 'n' bought yer own med'cines?"

"No, did n't need any medicines, and did n't take any."

"Haow? never sick?"

"Oh, yes, often ailing just a little."

"Then haow did ye knock the diseases?"

"Just let them alone, and they went away of themselves."

"What!" in chorus.

"Yes. I never had much faith in doctors or doctor-stuff."

"Wal! I swaow t' man!"

"Wal, I know 't if I hed n't a had things t' a-took in time, at the beginnin', we 'd a all a be'n dead long ago. Thar 's nothin' like meetin' a disease in time."

"I always found that letting it alone in time was better."

Here occurred an explosion of chuckles from Bijah's bench.

"Yew h'yer me? That settles it! No more physic fer me!"

"Me, too!" from Silas.

"Silas Anstey, you shet up! Go read yer book!

As fer you, Bijah, yew 've got cause t' be thankfle that ye 've got payrents thet 's able t' buy yer needfle med'cines, 'n' knows haow t' pr'scribe fer ye, — yes 'n' make ye take it tew, big 's ye be!"

"Not much!" says Bijah, and slides out of the door, followed by Silas.

The family now scattered to their several avocations: Eureka and her mother "doing up" the breakfast things in less than five minutes. Then Mrs. Anstey seated herself beside the fire-place with her knitting and a short pipe which she lighted with a coal held (greatly to Anne's astonishment) in her toil-hardened fingers.

"I don't expect ladies smoke whar yew come from."

"Well, I never knew of their doing so."

"No. Like 's not if I wuz fixed same 's they be I 'd be full 's praoud 's th' best on 'em. It 's all owin' t' haow ye 're fixed. We ladies aout h'yer in th' woods don't give a cent fer looks. My old dad use ter say 'blessin's on th' man 't invented eatin', 'coz ye kin smoke arter it.' He wuz a reg'lar old he-one fer terbacker."

"I should think so!"

To give herself light, she pulled the plug out of the "knitting hole," which let a tiny ray fall directly on her busy needles. Seeing Anne look at the arrangement with interest she explained its convenience.

"*He* fixed this string t' hang th' plug up by, 'coz the chil'n wuz ollers a-burnin' on it up: 'n' he made it long, ye see, so 's I c'd poke aout th' snow in winter 'n' not have t' spend my breath a-blowin' on it aout, ner yit wade aoutside t' clar it away. But, then, sometimes it drifts 'n' banks up right smart higher than the hoel: 'n' besides, when it's stormy it blows in so I can't stan' it, 'n' I jest hev t' put in th' plug n' light a candle."

"I should think you would run the risk of rheumatism."

"Wal, yes, that shoulder is ollers th' wust. Th' docters sez ye kin tell which side o' th' chimley th' knittin'-hoel is by seein' which o' the lady's arms is th' stiffest."

Eureka, emboldened by time and by a little encouragement from Anne, grew to be a trifle less shy, and studied with wondering admiration her simple traveling outfit,—the first city-made costume she had ever had the happiness to feast her wild eyes upon. She did not examine it for the sake of learning how to dress herself, but more in the spirit with which a Sioux Indian might observe a photographic apparatus,—"Big Medicine!" So wonderfully perfect in all appointments; so exquisitely neat in fabric, device, and construction; so beautiful in results! Simple girl! But perhaps she will attain, before we lose sight of her, to something more comparable to this ladylike-ness than she now thinks possible. We shall see.

Anne had early learned that it is not polite to "eat and run; like the beggars." So she devoted herself to the old woman for an hour or more: furnished her a listener; precious gift to the loquacious and lonely!

The talk turned quite naturally to Mr. Prouder.

"Zury he's wal fixed. His dad come aout a year ahead of my o' man 'n' located a section same as he did. 'N' no man 'n' woman never worked no harder ner we did. But then—we did n't hev no Zury; 'n' Ephr'm Praouder, he did n't have no babes a-comin' right along as we did. We 've buried three. Many's the day I've tromped barefooted, droppin' 'n' kiverin' corn, long arter I'd oughter ben layin' up, 'n' sewin' 'n' gittin ready." And she showed her misshapen hands and feet in needless confirmation of her words. Anne, trying to get at more agreeable themes, ventured:—

"Why, there must have been Indians here when you came."

"Injins? Oh yes, th' wuz some aout on the Vermilion."

"Hostile Indians?"

"Hoss-tile? Wal, no; they was all a-foot then. The'd sold their ponies fer whiskey, mostly. All on 'em did arter the Black Hawk War. But the' never troubled us none. The rale trouble with us wuz 't we could n't git ahead fur enough t' git no stawk onter the place t' eat up th' crap. It were ollers morgidged a-fore it wuz gethered; 'n' then it hed t' be sold in th' shock 'er in th' ear, instead o' feedin' on it 'n' sellin' the pork."

"The hog is a pretty respectable animal, after all, is n't he?"

"Yew better b'lieve it! Breeds like a housefly 'n' grows like a punkin! Takes care of himself s' long 's the' 's an acorn, er a snake, er a nubbin he kin git at; in th' woods, in th' cornfield, in th' barn, in th' garding — it 's all one t' him s' long 's he kin find a hole in the fence big enough t' git th' little end of his snaout intew — th' rest on him follers, soon er late."

"I 've read somewhere that without the hog navies could not be kept afloat, nor armies in the field."

"Wal, I s'pose it 's so, ef it 's in print. Anyhaow, yew kin tell 'em fr'm me, th't th' kedntry could n't bé settled not a half, no ner a quarter 's fast ef the' worn't no hawgs. The' eats everythin', 'n' everythin' the' eats turns right inter clear meat. 'N' when ye kill 'em th' ain't no waste t' speak of — it 's all thar, fr'm the nose t' the tail, sound 's a fresh-laid egg!"

"Yes, the same book I was speaking of before says there is nothing that flies the air or swims the sea or walks the earth that gives so much to use and so little to waste."

"Dew the' say thet naow? Wal, I give in, the' *dew* know a leetle suth'n' even in the big cities whar th' books is made up!"

"I should think beef would be better. You can work the poor ox all his life and eat him when he 's dead."

"Ah yah! Cattle 's tew slow fer Western farmers t' work. Beef ain't nowher's alongside o' pork. A caow don't usially have but one calf a year; 'n' it takes the calf four years t' come t' anythin'; 'n' every year it costs more t' keep ner it dooz t' keep a hawg all his life. Th' saow she hez tew er three litters a year, 'n' lots o' pigs every time; 'n' in tew years th' pigs is all hawgs ready t' kill. Tell me! I jest love t' see 'em 'raound! Th' squeal of a hawg 's the sweetest music th't kin be fer a farmer's ears!"

"But there 's the milk and butter."

"Oh ya-as. Beef 's th' rich man's luxury, 'n' pork 's the poor man's needcessity. When we can't git butter we kin eat lard, 'n' when we can't git milk we kin drink water; but when we can't git pork we must jes' starve tew death."

"Did the Prouders raise swine?"

"Wal, old Ephr'm he wuz lucky enough t' git a-holt on s'm hawgs fust thing, 'n' stick tew 'em like grim death tew a dead nigger."

"Why could n't you do so too?"

"Wal, ye see — we did n't hev no Zury, ner no luck. N' matter haow hard we 'd try t' winter over a few, the' wuz sure t' be all eat up, er sold off, er dead a-fore spring come. Wunst we did hev a-seemin' good show fer doin' it — it wuz jest arter we morgidged aour sec'n' quarter-section. We hed sixteen likely hawgs 'n' shoats, 'n' a poor, mis'able, — wal, pootty good straw-stack t' shelter 'em. It saounded jest *good* t' hear 'em squeal, a-craowdin' one another alongside th' straw t' keep warm! Th' o' man he 'd wake up in the night 'n' larf, 'n' say 'the'mometer must be daown below Nero! Hear 'em a-pullin' kiver?' Ye see he meant the' wuz like childern a-quar'lin' fer the bed-clo's. Wal, one orfle night the' crawled tew fur under, 'n' the wind it jest blowed 'n' canted th' hull stack right over ontew 'em; 'n' come mornin' th' wuz all dead — th' snow spread smooth 'n' white over 'em all — layin' thar smothered under th' straw 'n' snow!" What a spasm of pain, distress, disappointment, *despair*, wrinkled that old face at the recollection of this cruel blow!

"Oh, Mrs. Anstey! I could cry to think of it!"

"Could ye, naow? Ye 're a sweet-hearted gal! Wal, if cryin' tears o' heart's blood c'd a-brought 'em t' life agin, I 'd a shed 'em when I went aout 'n' looked at 'em, all a-layin' stiff 'n' dead in rows 'n' heaps! Not one left — 'n' th' morgidge a-comin' due! That quarter wuz sold, 'n' Zury he bid it in."

"I hate him!"

"O ye hain't any cause t' hate him fer a-biddin' on it in. Somebody hed t' hev it. We lost tew more, under morgidges; 'n' th' one we 've got left is morgidged — he hol's th' morgidge — 'n' it jest keeps aour noses t' the grin'-stone t' keep a-holt on it 'n' pay interest. So fur we 've done it — I dunno haow long we kin keep it up. When we can't, then we 've got t' turn renters, like many is — 'n' rentin' a farm is nex' door t' th' poorhaouse!"

"Oh, well — your boys are coming along — and Mr. Anstey is a good man I 'm sure; you 'll come out all right."

"Oh, yes; my o' man he 's all right. He ain't

s' smart 's most; 'n' th' ain't none s' smart 's Zury; but yit I dunno 's I 'd care t' swap."

She did well to stand up for Anstey. He was a good man and a good citizen, and a pillar of the church. He always put on shoes to go to meeting, even in summer (stockings, of course, were not required), and as one shoe squeaked and the other did not, his march up the bare aisle was quite impressive. "Squeak — clump — squeak — clump" they went, all the way from the door to the "amen corner," where his devoutness gave him a place.

"Now, Mrs. Anstey, it is growing late, and I must get to the tavern at Wayback in time for dinner. I am *wonderfully* thankful to you for your kindness!"

"Yew? Beholden tew us? Nary a mite! I guess ye dunno, chile, what a blessin' it is t' see sech a face 's yourn, 'n' talk with sech a gal 's yew be, aout in this neck o' woods! I 'm only scare't fer fear we can't git t' keep ye! Ef so be ye dew stop 'raound these parts ye wun't ferget t' come 'n' see th' Ansteys, naow, will ye?"

"Aha, my dear friend — if you knew me you would n't have any doubt about my remembering you and getting just as well acquainted as you 'll allow."

"Wal, I 'll wait 'n' see if ye keep yer word. God bless 'n' care fer ye!"

It would have amused and pleased poor Anne to hear (if she could have understood them) the comments on her when next the Ansteys met about the social (?) board.

"Ki! She 's right on it, ain't she!"

"Ya-as. She ain't no slaouch, back part o' th' spellin'-book er not."

"Talk aboaut splay-feet, knock-knees, caow-hocks, 'n' parrot-toes — did ye see her step aout daown th' road? She did n' seem hardly t' tech her feet t' the graoun'!" (Anne's experience behind the cotton-frames had made her a perfect Atalanta.)

"Gimme a brick-top, arter this." (This was young Silas' tribute to her charms.)

"Tell ye one thing — I 'm a-goin' t' see Zury, 'n' put him up t' a thing er tew! Them ornery whelps, Bromwell 'n' all! Deestrick Number Seven ain't a-goin' t' lose sech a gal 's *that*, not if I have my say-so."

Anne set off in fine spirits. Her walk was comparatively happy. Sometimes she whistled gayly and sweetly, finding that the tones she tried for in vain last night when they might have done some good were again at her service now when she needed them less — like the flattering accents of fair-weather friends. Every little while she would take out the dingy spelling-book and learn by heart a question and answer, and say it over aloud as she walked along.

Often she laughed at herself for her last evening's darkness-panic, and as often she resolved *never* to be so foolish again — and then remembered that her life had been dotted with just such panics, and just such recoveries, each followed by just such resolutions. In vain she told herself that she ought to be the same woman in the dark as in the light. She *was* the same — it was the rest of creation that was unstable, and changed its character every night from natural to unnatural and supernatural — and horrible!

In the confusion of the previous night she had forgotten to wind her watch, so she did not know how time was passing. Fearing to lose that civilized (or at least half-civilized) noon dinner, she quickened her steps, and soon came in sight of "Wayback," now a cluster of houses surrounding the gristmill and sawmill on the river-bank. The few buildings were new, middle-aged, and old, as indicated by the various degrees of fading which they had undergone — green lumber, seasoned lumber, and gray, weather-beaten boards reduced almost to the color of the air that has dessicated them. They glared under the pitiless sunshine, asking in vain for the shadows of trees which had been on the ground before any houses intruded, but which had been unwisely sacrificed, leaving only ugly stumps to show where they had stood.

The tavern was a two-storied frame structure of more exterior promise than interior excellence. It had a long broad piazza garnished with several massive chairs, made large enough in the frame to stand a great deal of whittling, but yet not large enough to escape being whittled down to emaciation in all their available limbs. It was kept by one Peleg Thum, its builder, who, not having enough money to finish and furnish it, had been forced to borrow. Zury was the lender: and thenceforth, as Tom Lackner, the storekeeper, said, "The difference between Peleg Thum and Zury Prouder's thumb was that Zury's thumb was on top."

When Anne reached the tavern she entered the public room (office, post-office, etc.) of the hotel, glanced up at the clock, and saw that it pointed to — half-past ten! Of course it must have stopped in the night. She passed into the darkened dining-room — no signs of dinner — could she be too late to get anything? She penetrated further (startling a myriad of flies which broke the silence of the room with a hum like that of a bee-hive in swarming time), and at last found her friend McVey — clerk-steward-porter-man-of-all-work, who glanced at the sun and said he guessed the clock was about right. "A leetle fahst if anything."

So it was. A farmer's day, beginning long before "sun-up," seems to the unaccustomed urban to be half done when it is only fairly begun. It takes time for a person accustomed to "civilized hours" to realize that five hours added to four A. M. brings nine A. M. just as surely as the same space added to eight A. M. brings one P. M.

John Endicott McVey was a real New Englander, but scarcely a typical one: he was too slender in body and mind — too soft in head and heart. He had "seen better days" even at that early age. If he had gone on seeing them, through the medium of an inherited fortune or even a good salaried position in Boston, he would have passed a highly creditable life, — perhaps (if the fortune had been a large one) have had children named for him, or even a street in a suburb! But a palm is out of place in a prairie. John's handsome face and tall, fine figure fitted him to lead the german, but not to lead boorish Americans.

"Will you sit down, Miss Sparrow? Well, how in the nation did you pass last evening?" (He said "Well" in two syllables — "Way-ell" — and continued: "Haow in the nat-i-o-n did you pahss lahst evenin'?" But we will not inflict another dialect on the long-suffering reader.)

"Oh, after the school-board meeting I went to Mr. Anstey's for bed and breakfast."

"I tried the school last year, but soon gave it up. I am here temporarily, waiting for some better opening."

It was quite refreshing to Anne to hear her native tongue again, but now she only said: —

"Can you give me a room, and have my trunk sent up — the one I brought here on the stage yesterday?"

"Why certainly! Right away?"

"Yes — and have me called in time for dinner?"

"Why certainly." And he proceeded to do all that was required, with an air that indicated that he found it only a pleasure to serve a person with whom he was so much disposed to be friendly as Miss Sparrow. He felt a certain possessory responsibility for her, though a stranger, from having been instrumental in bringing her out West.

Anne found her room bare and hideous, but a chamber of state compared with last night. After some comforting ceremonies which can be best appreciated by a woman who has passed two nights without undressing, she lay down with the spelling book in hand and read herself to sleep in less than four minutes by the sun.

Two hours later Anne entered the dining-hall, refreshed and radiant, with an excellent appetite for her dinner. There she was greeted by a good-looking man, neither young nor old; strong, bold, gay, and sharp. He set a place for her, and made himself so serviceable that she innocently took him for the host. They dined together, and he, being just in from a journey (though chiefly occupied in talking about himself), was willing and able to give to everybody the news of the world.

He called Anne by name, evidently knew a good deal about her, and as evidently wished to know more; but made his researches so naively and good-naturedly that she was rather amused than offended or annoyed at the easy task of baffling them. After the meal was over he voluntarily introduced himself as "Usury Praouder, the meeanest ma-an in Spring Caounty," and she recognized the mighty arbiter of her destiny in the matter of the pedagogism of School District Number Seven.

"So ye could n't quite hit it off with the school board, could n't ye?"

"Who told you that?"

"Oh, I know everythin'— don't need t' be told things like common folks!"

"Everything? Do you know the back part of the spelling-book?"

"No, but I know enough not t' have t' know it, 'n' that 's better 'n knowin' on it."

"Well, Mr. Prouder, I don't know so much as that; so I'll bid you good day and go and learn it."

"Oh, never ye mind that! I 'll tell ye haow t' git along 'thaout havin' t' know it."

"How is that?"

"Oh, you jest leave the whole thing t' me, 'n' I 'll fix ye aout."

"Well, I want to know the back part of the spelling-book, too! Good-bye!"

"Oh say! Miss Sparrer!"

But she was off and away up-stairs in a flash: and between naps that afternoon she mastered the ridiculous little shibboleth from beginning to end. She could have shut the book and made a very fair copy of it from memory.

At tea Mr. Prouder did not appear, which somewhat disconcerted her. And in the evening the school board failed to meet according to programme, or to send her any word, which further unwomaned her, whereupon she passed a rather miserable night — none the better for the many naps of the day preceding it — some few tears finding their way to her lonely pillow. But with the bright morning came renewed strength and courage as usual.

So when at breakfast Zury Prouder made his appearance, confident, gay, and egotistical as ever, she felt as if it was just what she had always expected.

"Wal, Miss Sparrer, I fixed that all right, as I said I would."

"Indeed? All right? How?"

"Well, you 're t' have the jawb — leastways if you 'll agree to our terms."

"Terms? I thought the pay was fixed and settled."

"Wal — yes — so 't is, — in a way. But bein' 's ye ain't quite prepared in yer examination, the board proposes t' give ye half wages fer the fust quarter. No more no less."

Here a hard look settled over Zury's strong face; a mask of straight, level brow, half-shut eyes, square jaws, and drawn lips, which every man who ever dealt with him learned to know, soon or late in their intercourse, to his cost.

"But I 'd rather stand another examination — with you on the board."

This little bit of flattery softened Zury's face, but not his heart.

"No school-board ain't no ways obleeged t' examine a candidate more 'n wunst, s' fur 's I 've read the law." (He had never looked at any law in the matter, nor she either.) "'N' then the trouble 's right h'yer. The board 's disposed, if I say th' word, t' put McVey right in, 'thaout any furder examination, he havin' already passed perfect, O. K. and A1."

The blood came to Anne's face as she fully took in this pitiful *shave*, but she choked down her indignation with the thought that the whole pay was so small that the loss of half of it for three months was scarcely worth thinking of.

"Oh, well! I'll take it. But I don't see how you can be the meanest man in Spring County. They must be all pretty mean!"

"Sho, sho! We're poor country folks aout here, 'n' not half ner a quarter up t' city ways o' makin' 'n' savin' money!"

This was said with a deprecatory smile, as if she had tried to flatter him and Spring County together. Now the fact was (though Anne did not find it out till long afterward) that Prouder had easily forced the board to agree to engage Miss Sparrow, to whom he had taken a liking, and this cut of a few dollars out of her wages was an after-thought purely his own.

After Anne came to know Zury Prouder better she would have been able to anticipate just such a dodge on his part. This was the kind of man our old friend had grown to be. Whatever difficult or baffling or puzzling task he set his strong hand to moved forward at once. Sometimes it seemed almost like harnessing a horse to a hand-cart. Only, when all was said and done, some bunch of gain, great or small, would always be found to have resulted either to the party for whom he was acting, or to himself as was oftenest the case, or to both. We shall note many a case wherein, in the years that followed, Anne had this experience: some word or act of his would clear her way of an obstruction apparently impregnable. Zury would always rather do a kind act than an unkind one, especially if he could make more profit by the former. But even if no profit was to accrue, he would do it for fun, provided that he suffered no loss. He was an accomplished cattle and horse breeder; that part of his large business he attended to personally. He loved to see his beasts enjoy themselves. Nothing pleased him better than to buy a poor, suffering "critter" out of its misery for fifty dollars, and then feed it well, use it well, work it well, and sell it well for a hundred dollars.

Everything he touched turned to gold. He never knew what weariness was, by day or night, by week, by month, or by year. (If ever disposed to try to remember what it meant to be tired, he would look back on that first corn-plowing.) He was school director, supervisor, assessor; to which offices, as before observed, people elected him because he did the work so openly and so well; not because he did not manage them so that his own taxes were less than they should be. His standing in his church was excellent for similar reasons among others. Without his wealth he could not have had these positions, and without the positions his riches would have been less.

"I jest make one hand wash th' other."

CHAPTER VIII.

HOW ANNE BOARDS 'ROUND, AND HOW SHE LIKES IT.

"Now, Mr. Proudor, this 'boarding around' — how is that managed?"

"Wal, ye see — the thing's divided up kinder this way. Th' d'rectors they make up a schedule o' haow many fam'lies the' is in th' deestrick taxable fer boardin' th' teacher, 'n' then the' put th' names in a hat 'n' then dror 'em aout; 'n' th' order the' happen t' come in, *they* take th' teacher turn 'n' turn abaout. 'Course it's pootty hard on a fam'ly th't only schools one child t' board th' teacher 's long 's a fam'ly hez ter thet 's got a half a dozen: but *then.* It 's all owin' t' haow ye look at it. Th' big little fam'lies is hard enough t' keep, anyhaow. 'N' th' wust luck is when ye hain't got none at all."

"But I suppose that in the families where there are six children the teacher only gets one sixth as much to eat as in the others, so that makes it square."

"Should n't wonder. Guess there 's some broods o' chickens I know in the deestrick whar a strange pullet like yew 'll hev t' scratch raoun' pootty lively t' grow fat enough t' kill very soon."

"Oh dear me!"

"Them 's kin afford it, kin commute the teacher's board by payin' a dollar a week instead o' takin' her. But then it 's only a few th't 's well-fixed enough t' spare so much cash."

"Oh, I see. The poor ones can board the teacher, and the rich ones can give her a dollar a week to stay away!"

"Eggzackly."

"So all who can feed her decently, she can keep away from; while the places where she 'll starve she must go to."

"Oh ye need n't be afeared 't anybody 'll want t' pay *yew* aout rather 'n' t' keep ye."

Anne began to smile gently, pluming herself on the implied compliment.

"Ye see y' ain't like a man. All *yew* 'll eat won't come to no dollar a week."

Her smile died away.

"So she must move, bag and baggage, from one place to another, between every two fortnights! Coming by chance that way it will sometimes be from one end of the district to the other!"

"Wal, they kind o' change raound with one another. Sometimes th' won't nobody want t' take ye', 'n' then agin there 'll be two 'r three to wunst."

"Oh, how dreadful! As if I were a pauper, shoved on from one parish to another!"

"Human natur 's human natur. Come fust frost when the' all want t' be a-killin', the' 'll all want t' git through boardin' teacher while th' pork's fresh. Tell yew! By the time ye've lighted on tew or three haouses jest at killin' time—tenderlines, sausages, spare-ribs, pigs-feet, tongues, 'n' head-cheese over 'n' over agin t' each haouse—ye'll be 's fat 's fat, 'n' most like feel 's tho' th' brustles wuz a-spraoutin' daown yer back."

"I can't *bear* fat pork, and I shall *starve*."

"The''s ben a good many folks jes' a-goin' t' starve on pork, 'n' very few's ever done it, I reckon."

"Oh, I can *not* stand this. How far is it to Springville, and what will it cost me to get there?"

"Springville's abaout ten thaousan' miles, 'n' th' fare'll be abaout a dollar a mile."

"Then I'll walk, and beg my way from door to door! I may as well beg from strangers on that road as be a pauper all over School District Number Seven!"

"Naow ye jest better hold yer hosses. Ye're a-borr'in' trouble. Hain't ye never learnt yit not t' cross a river ontel ye come tew it?"

"I've come to the river now, this minute—and there's neither bridge nor ford nor ferry!"

For a few minutes Zury watched her; the face flushed and lined with trouble; the eyes so round with apprehension that they looked almost perpendicularly oval; her foot nervously beating the floor; her right hand supporting her left elbow, while her left forefinger tapped on her teeth in a manner rather peculiar and characteristic.

(Her mother used to call it " Anne's puzzlementary gesture.") Zury 's pause was, consciously or otherwise, for dramatic effect, and to observe her tribulation before relieving it.

" Nary bridge, ford, ner ferry — then we must swim er wade. Zury's here yet — the me-anest ma-an in Spring Caounty t' be turned back on his tracks."

Anne called back her eyes from the far-away prospect they were studying on the office floor, and fixed them on his face.

" I b'lieve I 's good 's told the board 't I 'd take my boardin' turn fust off, bein' 's they kinder hung back." (The fact was that he had told the school-board that he had done his share already by boarding McVey during *his* short tenure of office, but something seemed to have changed his views of duty.)

" Oh! Are you married? Do your children come to the school?"

This time it was Zury's look that wandered far away from the present place and time for a space of silence about as long as the last. Then he spoke in the touching tone of an old grief.

" We hain't got no livin' children. The Lord gave and taketh, an' blessed be His name."

During the silence which followed, poor Anne rapidly constructed a scheme wherein she proposed to make herself so charming in the Prouder household that at the end of her allotted space they would beg her to stay on and on indefinitely.

" Who form your family, then?"

"Mary — that 's my o' woman ; 'n' S'manthy that 's her sister ; 'n' *her* child, little Alphy."

"Rather a small family."

"Smaller 'n I wish it wuz!" A sigh. "But then ther 's the hands 'baout th' place."

"Well, but after you get tired of me — what then?"

"Wal, after yer tew weeks is up, we 'll see."

("There," thought the hopeful girl, "he thinks the same that I was thinking.")

"When would you like to have me come?"

"I guess I 'll ride home, 'n' fetch a team over fer ye this arternoon ef that 'll suit ye, — 'n' friend McVey kin anyway spare ye." (This was a sly reference to the manifest interest poor John Endicott was beginning to take in his fair compatriot.)

"Oh, I think there need be no delay. But I feel as if I were being led blindfold into a path where I can see only two inches before my nose. Two weeks I mean."

The Prouder mansion was a fine example of the Early Vandal or Aboriginal Prairie architecture; large, high, square, white, and hideously ugly. The windows and doors were of the most distressing symmetry and regularity. The eaves projected only barely far enough to clear the walls and deliver into bright tin gutters shining in the sun. No opening had any perceptible cap projecting over it, so all looked like eyes devoid of eyebrows. It was set much too near the front gate, with which it was connected by a walk composed of two planks several feet apart. Outside the gate was a space evidently used in common by cows, horses, pigs, old plows, woodpiles, and stramonium weeds, which last were its only shade.

Behind the frame house was still standing the old log shanty, so speedily erected years before, and still connected with all the family associations — struggle, hardship, sickness, birth, and death. Not that Zury had any such foolish sentiment about it. He would have sold it for ten dollars any day but for two reasons: first; it was convenient as a summer kitchen and a winter wood-house, and, second, nobody would give ten dollars for it. It was a most distressed looking place now — so dirty, so ragged with decaying bark, the roof so sunken, and its old black clapboards so warped and wildly displaced. Inside, however, was the same old fire-place, with the knitting hole behind it, where the mother had so often sat plying her busy needles in the single ray.

Zury had often threatened to have the old eyesore pulled down and cut up for fire-wood, but its usefulness and the trouble of destroying it still saved its life.

Anne and Prouder on arrival were greeted with demonstrative affection by Shep and his tribe, or rather by his tribe and Shep, as the latter brought up the rear as became his age and infirmities.

"Thar! thar! Daown Shep! Don't ye let 'em spile yer clo's, Miss Sparrer. Daown ye ornery whelp! Th' ol' dorg 's a-gittin pretty scaly nowadays — 'd oughter ben dead 'n' buried long ago, but I don't seem t' have no time t' tend t' things abaout the haouse."

"Why, poor old Sheppy! Did his master want to kill him? No, no, Sheppy; you must n't be killed, and you must n't kiss me before folks! You are *very* nicely placed here, Mr. Prouder." Then she glanced around to see what there was she could possibly praise. "Oh, what lovely hollyhocks! It must be pleasant to live so near the grand old woods!"

"Yes — it 's handy t' have fire-wood clust by, 'n' not fur t' haul. I cal'late t' have the trees on that thar forty girdled naow, soon 's I kin git raound to it, so 's it 'll look a leetle more cleared up 'n' civilized back o' the haouse."

Anne was rather struck with the idea of forty acres of dead, girdled trees as a symbol of civilization, but she did not have time to make any remarks.

"Wal, Mary, here we be," said Prouder, as a plain, spare woman appeared at the door. "Miss Sparrer, lemme make ye 'quainted 'th my wife."

"Pleased t' know ye, Miss Sparrer."

Mrs. Prouder was faded, like her calico. She looked older than her husband, but it was probably because of her thinness, pallor, and sadness. Her face was not wrinkled, except about the lips, which were "all gone," as were her cheeks, too, because of the ruthless sacrifice of teeth which prevailed then (and does to this day) among both men and women of her class. Their enunciation of principles of dental policy are announced about as follows: —

"Ef one o' my teeth c'mences t' ache, why I go 'n' have it aout, fust 's last, n' matter ef it *dooz* hurt! I 'd a heap sight druther have the pain all in one big wrench th'n spread over day 'n' night fer a week!"

Forthwith the misguided and inexperienced Eastern girl began trying to make herself agreeable. She asked about everything and admired everything with an effusiveness that was embarrassing to the proud Westerners.

"Oh, what a picturesque old place that is back there! Can I go out and see it?"

"Wal, S'manthy she 's in thar cookin' supper naow, I 'xpeck; but t'-morrer, when it 's sort o' righted up, the' 'll be time enough."

"That thar 's the haouse me 'n' father put up when we fus' got here. Father 'n' mother 'n' me 'n' a little one that died; 'n' ol' Shep — we all lived in the covered wagin we come aout in ontel that thar shanty was done. All dead naow but me 'n' ole Shep here."

"And Shep is a little like the house — not much left except the bark."

"Wal — yes — in a way. Ol' Shep's hide it dew git pretty rusty: hair comes aout right smart. Right smart, on' it 's clean gone in spots. He ain't much 'count no more." Here the poor old dog looked up deprecatingly with his rheumy eyes, and went slowly out as if he had understood every word. Perhaps he had caught the sound of his name, and felt a dumb regret that it did not indicate affection and sympathy on their part, and usefulness on his, as of old.

"I should like to make a drawing of the old house, if you please."

"Why, sartin. Yew kin make a picter o' *this* haouse ef ye like. Make a heap poottier picter!"

"Oh, yes, more elegant and comfortable; but not so picturesque. Perhaps I can make a sketch that will take in both."

Anne's room, the "spăr-chămber," was comfortable — the furnishing evidently somewhat modeled after that of the guest-rooms of the tavern at Wayback: but there was one dreadful luxury which the tavern was free from, — a deep feather bed. A bit of rag carpet covered the middle of the floor; wretched prints of ringleted, red-and-white, large foreheaded "Mary" and "Eliza" graced the walls in company with a six-by-ten mirror, which broadened and shortened her face so much that it made her low-spirited to look in it, and glad that it hung so high that she could only do so by standing on tip-toe.

The rest of the mansion was like unto the "spăr-chămber." The "settin'-room" was a darkened corner apartment with vigorous cross-lights, a black horsehair sofa, rocker, and two other chairs; a patch of rag-carpet, a black Franklin stove now full of asparagus bushes, a wooden clock on a shelf; and, last and greatest, the most appalling caricature of Zury which could be conceived by the mind of man. It was a pastel half-length, life-size as to the bust, and as nearly so as to the head as the limits of the picture-frame would allow. The figure seemed to have been first drawn with great care, but a little too high up on the canvas; so that the head had to be squeezed in on top of it as might best be done under the circumstances — and the frame; and the observer felt a certain regret that the frame had not been a little shorter so as to shut it out altogether.

"A gentleman 't taught th' school three winters ago, he boarded with us nigh onter tew months over his boardin' time, an' he painted that picter o' Zury t' pay fer his board."

"It looks rather like."

"Wal, folks sez so; but I can't see no resemblance. Han's'm' picter, though!"

Anne glanced at her to see if this was sarcasm, but no: all was severe truth and directness in that grave, sad face. They stood still for a moment, each looking out from one of the windows. Then, with a feeling of surprise and almost alarm, Anne heard the other say, in a touching tone of weariness and despair — a falling cadence of mingled sigh and groan, —

"Oh Lordy, Lordy!"

She was too much startled to do anything but look and listen for more, but Mrs. Prouder only moved away toward the eating-room, where supper was soon served. As she looked out of the back window she observed Prouder and the three hired men using the wash-basin, towel, and comb in turn and cleaning their boots on the grass preparatory to supper. Then they all trooped in and sat down in their habit as they lived.

The table was spread with a vast and heterogeneous lot of food. Pork, beef, and mutton, all cooked alike, and all hot: potatoes hot from the same pot; hot soda biscuits in stacks; green tea, hot and strong; pickles, stewed wild grapes, wild-grape pies, cake in loaves, and all the other indicia of rude plenty.

"Come, Miss Sparrer," said Zury. "Set by, 'n' see ef ye can't make a meal. Good fer ye t' have t' live wunst in a while like poor folks has t' live all the time!"

"Now, Mr. Prouder, I'm sure you've no need to apologize. I can assure you that ninety-nine men out of a hundred all over the world would be glad to sit down to such a well-spread board as this." (She meant well!)

The meal went on almost in silence; Anne's efforts to keep up a cheerful flow of talk being spasmodic and fruitless. Even Zury, who could talk so well where talk was customary and appropriate, seemed preoccupied and attentive only to the business in hand. The "hired hands," elbows on the table and heads low over the food, shoveled it in without a pause or a word, except occasionally to rattle a spoon in the cup and say "tea!" when they desired to be served by Mrs. Prouder and her sister who carried around the pot. Then each, as he finished his meal, pushed back his chair and silently departed.

In spite of the best good-will in the world Anne made but a poor meal. The truth is, the cleaning of boots on the grass had not been a process resulting in absolute purification. Ammonia is the inevitable bane of all intercourse with horses and cattle. Oh, why can we not be led by Thoreau and Walt Whitman to glory in the breath of Nature — all the breaths of Nature? But we cannot.

After the meal, if Anne had had the wisdom of the serpent, which is in keeping with her dove-like harmlessness, she would simply have withdrawn to the sitting-room and let the women make their slovenly supper in peace, and then tidy themselves up to join her. But no: such supernatural shrewdness was not hers. She felt, and showed, an ill-timed cordiality to Semantha, younger sister of Mrs. Prouder (now a widow), as much too fat as the latter was too thin. She wanted to see Semantha's little daughter, who had quietly been confined in the back kitchen until she could be made presentable to the guest.

"Now you 've been waiting on us; you must let me wait on you while you eat. Sit down, do, and tell me what to pass to you!"

"No, thankye. We 'll jest cl'ar off a place h'yer on this side an' set all we want in reach."

Then Anne took the squalid, dirty, and malodorous child on her knee, to the poor mother's utter discomfiture.

"What 's your name, little one?"

The child said not one word, but went on munching a great piece of crumby, unwholesome cake.

"Can't you tell me your little name? And

how old you are? And whether you are a good girl or not?"

No answer.

"You Alphy! Tell the lady yer name!"

Dead silence.

"Oh, you 'm a bad child! Go read yer book! Ye must excuse her mom: she ain't got no manners, 'n' I ain't never ben able t' beat none inter her, whip her all I could. Ner keep her lookin' decent nuther."

Whereupon the child slipped down from Anne's lap and went and leaned against her mother, casting back looks of defiance at her enemy and would-be jailer.

"Tea!" said the child, jogging her mother and pointing to the cup, filled with a pale green decoction of such lye-like strength that Anne had felt compelled to leave her own modicum of it almost untasted. Semantha placed the cup at Alpha's lips and allowed her to drink all she wanted.

"I see you are not afraid to give your little girl tea."

"Tea? No, indeed! I ollers 'llauw 't what 's good enough fer me ain't none tew good fer Alphy."

Anne wished to stay and help the others clear the table and wash the dishes; but, finding that they absolutely would not begin as long as she was there, she brushed off the cake-crumbs and went out of doors, where she looked over the fence and watched the milking. Then she picked her way gingerly down to the "spring-house," where the milk was kept; a little frame structure built over a scanty fountain, down on the bank of the "branch" in the hollow. Later she went back to the sitting-room and found there the two women and the child, slightly "slicked up" and made presentable. From them she learned all she could about the school — neither of them had ever visited it. She tried, also, to talk a little about other things; but they seemed as devoid of curiosity as of ideas. And twice, during the short evening, was she startled by that "Oh Lordy, Lordy!" which one might naturally have looked for in the cancer-ward of a hospital for incurables, but scarcely in the sunny out-door world.

"I 've got a little room here I use fer a kind of an office, 'n' if ye 'll come in a minute we 'll fix up yer 'pintment-paper fer the school."

So Anne followed Zury to a wretched cubby-hole, with a more wretched desk and a most wretched pen and ink sneaking among a lot of dusty, grimy, blotted papers, scored with the wildly sprawling hieroglyphics of rough hands hardened by toil. Records are not necessary to such men as Zury Prouder, except to keep other people in mind of mutual undertakings. He and men of his kind remember words, facts, and figures to an extent that would appall a methodical business man accustomed to make a written record of all that occurs. Zury had "writin's" for everything which might be disputed by other men, for the purpose of settling differences; but for the mere purpose of keeping things in his own memory, no lapse of time could make any memorandum necessary.

"Naow, here's th' blank fer scheduling yer 'pintment." And he took out a long printed form with spaces for answers.

"First I'll put th' date — thar — we're fixed on that. Naow, name?"

"Anne Sparrow."

"Where born?"

"Massachusetts."

"Sex?"

"Unfortunately, female."

"Age at 'pintment?"

"Oh, what do they want to know that for? Do they expect a woman to tell her age?"

"Wal, they 'xpect her t' tell some age er other; 'n' one old enough to show she comes within the statit — over eighteen and under seventy."

"Oh, well, I'm old enough to vote if women had their rights."

"Put ye daown a hunderd, then; women 'd oughter to be voters; jest as they touch th' even hunderd, 'n' not a minute before."

"Well, I'm twenty-one, and if I don't know more than the average voters" —

"'Course ye do! That's th' reason we men want t' shet ye aout ontel ye 've fergot a lot."

"Just like you! Well, what next?"

"Married or single?"

Anne's color rose. Said she, —

"Now, Mr. Prouder, is all this necessary?"

"Not unless ye want t' dror money aout of th' deestrict fun's. Ef ye dew, why, then, I 've got t' fill all th' blanks in this h'yer paper."

"Let me take it, please." He handed it to her and she scanned it carefully, to gain time, while conscious that his eyes were fixed on her glowing face.

"Can I keep this a while?"

"Oh, yes. It don't make no diff'rence, 's I know on. I 've told ye fair and square about th' money part." So she folded the paper, and they returned to the "sett'n' rewm."

As early as possible Anne retired to her room. The bed problem was still to be settled. What should she do in that mushy cloud? Sleep in it? Scarcely, as she was not an angel *yet*. Still she could try; so when prepared for slumber she set the chair by the bedside, turned down the clothes, and stepped high and clear over the edge into the middle; then the other foot; then she stooped down, lay down, and felt as if she were sinking into the ocean.

Under these circumstances it was hard to get asleep and easy to awake. She rose betimes in the morning, and after making her bed, watched until the men-folks had breakfasted, and descended to eat with the others. But no; they would not sit down with her. When she had quite finished they took their meal in their usual higgledy-piggledy way. She was hurt, yet not disheartened, and resolved to persevere in her kind efforts until she should wear out their reserve. But to change women's natures is a hard task. They are the conservatives of the race. No such feeble and familiar force as the doings of one of their own sex can move them, — if a *man* gets to persuading them, — why, that is different.

In a day or two Anne made her sketch of the house, the log shanty, and old Shep. All were slightly flattered, of course; the ugliness of the new house modified, and that of the old house and dog intensified. The women were much impressed with the work, but not in unmixed gratification. The old log structure, Anne's favorite, on which she had bestowed much loving labor, was offensive to them.

"Wal, thar! Ef Zury don't have that old eyesore took daown *naow*, and a frame kitchen put up, then I'll give up!"

Zury's own comment was characteristic. (He had had more chance to observe engravings and prints.) "Gee Rusalem! Ain't that all-fired cute? Naow ef I wuz a-tryin' t' sell th' place, that 'd help right smart! A feller 'd like enough give a heap more fer the homestead ef he see sech a pootty picter on 't!" Then, for fear of encouraging any idea of owing Anne anything for her work, he added: "But then, 'course I ain't thinkin' o' sellin' it."

So her little effort won for her some applause and fame; but this power, among the rest, marked and accentuated the difference between her and her new friends, which she was trying to lessen.

Zury had told Anne so much about their early doings in the log shanty that she insisted, one day, on being admitted to its interior; and he, being less subject to false pride than his "women-folks," piloted her thither at once.

"Thar—ye kin see the split log floor I laid; see it through the cracks? We put them boards on it arterw'ds when mam wuz sick. Thar's whar th' bed stood—sis 'n' mam 'n' dad all died on that thar bed, 'n' wuz laid out ontew it. Thar, 'longside th' fire, 's mam's old knittin'-hoel. Them punkins is a-dryin' up thar on th' same ol' poles we useter dry 'em on. Same old fly-trap, tew." And he pointed to two boards, an inch or so apart, baited with honey on their inner faces, hanging overhead where the women could conveniently clap them together occasionally, whereby a myriad of flies had been sacrificed, and their unburied remains were left to tell the tale.

"And some of the old newspapering yet remains!"

"Ya-as. Right up in that corner is a story I read th' beginning of; — 'n' th' eend of it ain't nowhar!" And he sighed as with an ancient grievance.

"What, there—over the flour-barrel? I'd like to read it!"

"Wal, ye kin ef ye wanter. But I would n't ef I wuz yew! It'll jest hawnt ye!"

"Oh, I'll risk that!"

"Wal, so be it. H'yer, I'll set a cheer fer ye t' step up on."

"What — there? No chair for me, I thank you!" She stepped back a pace or two, gathered up her skirts, and skipped to the top of the flour-barrel like a bird.

"Great Scott! Look at her once! Ye 're a reg'lar deer 'n' no mistake."

"Of course I am — if you spell it right."

Then she read the thrilling tale, taking about four minutes to take in what had probably occupied all Zury's spare time for as many days. After she had finished it she pondered a moment and then said: —

"Oh, I know the end of that story — and I'll write it out for you."

"Sakes alive! If ye only would, I'd" —

"Well, I will."

CHAPTER IX.

UNIVERSALISM, AND "COMMON-LAW MARRIAGE."

By means of assiduous cultivation of little Alpha, Anne managed to make some small headway with her mother, and in a day or two contrived to have a quiet talk with her down at the "spring house." (School was not to begin — "take in" — till the following Monday.)

"Wal, I tell ye haow 't is, Miss Sparrer. Mary she warn't never no gre't of a talker, but still she held her own with th' rest on us ontel she got mar'rd; 'n' she had tew babes right along, 'n' then the' both upped 'n' died, e'enabaout together; 'n' then — wal, I dunno 's I 've saw her t' smile sence. 'N' so it goes."

"Dear, dear! Poor thing! And that is what makes her do so?"

"Do so? Haow?"

"Why, 'Oh Lordy, Lordy!' you know."

"Wal, I dunno 's I ever noticed her doin' that pertickler, 'n' yet naow ye say it, it dooz sound like her, tew!"

"Why, she does it nearly twenty times a day."

"Law suz! Is that so! Wal, I s'pose I got so used to it I 've clean forgot all abaout it."

"I suppose she says that whenever she thinks

of her children, and thinks of them every time she says that."

"Likely, likely. Same time she lost 'em she lost all hopes o' havin' more: 'n' Zury he never says nothin'; but he 's gettin' pootty well fixed, 'n' nat'rally would wish t' have somebody of his own blood t' leave all his truck tew: so Mary she jest wishes she c'd die so he could have a chance for another wife 'n' more chill'n; but she says she can't even die; 'n' so it goes!"

"And not even a Hagar she can offer to the patriarch!"

"Wal, no. Them was Bible times, ye know. We 're Christians now: though Zury ain't never experunced religion the' dew say!"

"Never experienced religion?"

"No. Never be'n convicted o' sin at any of the revivals, 'n' made a child o' grace by a change o' heart, ye know."

"Oh!" said Anne, who had almost forgotten there was such a thing, and that she was now in the very region where a public, spasmodic regeneration was looked upon as necessary to individual salvation. "But he is a good man, I suppose."

"Oh, Zury dooz 'ccordin' tew his lights, and he 's too good a friend t' th' church t' make 'em 's pertickler as they 'd be 'th yew 'n' me. He 's often be'n made the objeck of special prayers; to meetin' 'n' camp-meetin's 'n' sech; 'n' he 's ben led t' th' anxious seat more times 'n' ye c'd shake a stick at — but nary tear ner cry fer mercy could they ever git outer him! Not even when others, men, women, and childern wuz a-fallin' 'n' a-shoutin' all over the place. 'N' so it goes."

After a few moments' silence she went on in a mysterious whisper: —

"It come pootty nigh gittin' him in trouble wunst, tew!"

"Did he go astray?"

"Wal, 't wuz this way. Some o' the brothren they upped 'n' 'llaowed 's haow Zury wuz a Universalist!"

"A Universalist?"

"Nothin' shorter! 'Llaowed they 'd seed Universalist papers hid in th' barn!"

"Well, suppose he had been."

"Aha — I guess you dunno what a Universalist is!" (Then with a still more horrified whisper.) "It 's a person that believes 't all mankind 'll be saved!" (A pause to note the effect of this frightful thought.) "'Course no true Christian kin b'lieve no sech a doctrine 's that! Why, if I b'lieved I should n't be punished hereafter, I 'd jest go out an' be jest 's wicked 's ever I c'd be!"

"What did Mr. Prouder do?"

"Oh, he jes' upped 'n' proved it was all a m'licious lie, gotten up t' hurt him. He moved a c'mittee be 'pinted that very meetin' t' come up 'n' sarch the barn nex' day. Wal, they 'mended it so 't the c'mittee went right up same night; 'n' sure enough, they foun' a batch o' papers! 'N' then Zury showed haow he 'd bought a new fannin'-mill; 'n' the fans wuz packed in old papers, 'n' he never knowd what wuz printed onto 'em. 'N' they reported t' the conf'rence; 'n' the conf'rence they held a secret meetin' 'n' had a pootty lively time, but the' voted by a majority t' clear Zury 'n' censure the fannin'-mill comp'ny; 'n' that the brothren would n't buy no fannin'-mills o' that make 'thaout they 'd clear themselves o' the charge; 'n' the comp'ny they come out in all the papers in advertisements, sayin' 't ef it ever did happen 't wuz an accident 'n' should n't happen agin, 'n' advertised fer old Orthodox papers t' be furnished 'em fer packin' purposes, 'n' so many wuz sent 'em they hed t' hire a barn t' store 'em in; 'n' it wuz the best thing fer 'em ever happened in their business. 'N' so it goes."

"Well, suppose they *had* proved it on Mr. Prouder."

"Oh, 't would n't a-done at all! Zury he mought abaout 's well a hed a pack o' cards found onto th' place. A Universalist right into a Christian c'munity! He 'd a hed to a got aout o' Spring Caounty best way he could, I reck'n, 'n' lucky ef he car'r'd anythin' away with him, tew, barrin' a coat o' tar 'n' feathers mebby."

"Do they feel so about here now?" asked Anne, glad to have learned so much so early.

"Wal, I 'm 'fraid th' ain't such a strong feelin' naow. I fear we 're a-fallin' from grace, spite o' the prayers of the righteous which availeth much. The preachers 'n' class-leaders says we be. Preacher he gin us a paowerfle *dis*course a while back from Rev'lations third, fifteenth, '*So then that thaou art lewkwarm*, and *neither cold ner hot*

I will spew thee aout of my maouth.' When I got home I jest upped 'n' l'arnt that tex' by heart; 'n' I think 't anybody th't 'd let a Universalist live 'mongst God's people better larn that tex' 'n' tremble, that 's all! 'N' so it goes."

Of course the critical moment for Anne was when she began school. Her heart beat quick, her color came and went; but she set her lips together and (coached by Eureka Anstey) stepped to the door and rapped smartly on the frame with her ruler. The scholars came trooping in; disorderly yet not very noisy, because all the boys and most of the girls were barefoot.

They took seats as they had been accustomed, the girls on the right and the boys on the left, on benches standing in front of desks which backed against the wall on three sides of the bare room, the fourth side being given up to the teacher's desk and the two entrance doors. An inner line of hard, backless, and armless benches accommodated the children too small to use the desks. In the midst stood a long, rusty, rectangular stove.

A most unpromising lot of scholars they looked to her Eastern eyes. All degrees of coarseness, ignorance, suspicion, insubordination, seemed to be the rule; decent considerateness and conscience the exception. Always the young are cruel to their teachers: the lower the grade the greater the cruelty. These scholars were low in grade, and their appearance was even more repellant than their real nature because of their uncouth rusticity.

Anne had brought with her some blank books ruled and headed for scholars' names, ages, attendance, and so forth; the first of the kind ever seen in District Number Seven. This novelty, together with the interest excited by the new teacher's pretty appearance, kept a moderate degree of order during the preliminary roll-call, distribution of books, and other necessary proceedings.

"Now, scholars, we will begin by singing. What hymns do you know?" Dead silence. "Any one may speak." More silence. "Do you know 'When Thee I seek Protecting Power'?" No answer. "Let us try that."

Then she sang a verse all through alone, no one attempting to join.

"Eureka, my dear, come here, please." Eureka bashfully came forward amid the titters of the rest. A whispered conference revealed the fact that they knew "When I can read my title clear." So Anne gave it out, started it, and sang one verse — alone as before.

"Why don't you sing, scholars? Eureka, why do you not sing?"

"That ain't the right tune."

"What tune do you sing it to?" For some time nobody spoke; then some boy said, "The tune of when I kin read," at which sally they all laughed. Poor Anne was baffled and already half disheartened. Still, she put on a brave face and said: —

"Let us try Old Hundred. I 'm sure you all know that."

So she sang "From all that dwell below the skies" — again entirely alone.

"Is not that the tune you have heard?"

"Them ain't th' right words."

"What *are* the words, then?" No answer. "Eureka, dear, what words have you been used to sing Old Hundred to?"

"Be thaou O God."

"Then we will sing those words." And she sang the verse — once more as a solo.

"Do join me in singing! Why will you not?"

"This ain't no singin'-scule. We did n't come h'yer t' larn t' sing." This rude speech came from a hulking fellow whom she had noticed as sitting with his elbows on his knees and his head bent over them, seemingly the better to throw rebellious remarks right and left in semi-secrecy.

"You should trust your teacher. I will teach you everything you came to learn, and singing besides, if you will let me. I am going to try hard to make you all love me — if you can."

Then clasping her hands tightly together to give her fortitude to bear her trials she came forward, and said in gentle tones of touching appeal: —

"Have I no friends among you all? I hoped to have you all for my friends. I will, if you do not prevent it. I am a long way from home — all alone — you are my only hope."

"Better go back whar ye come from."

"I can't, now. I *must* keep on trying here. Now, if there are any of you who are willing to stand by me — like young ladies and gentlemen — please all sing with me this time."

Then she sang the verse again, and to her slight relief there were several girlish voices half audible with hers.

"There! I know I shall find some one to love! Now, once more!"

This time there was quite a fair volume of sound, and she tried to think the worst was past.

As soon as the verse was ended, the same dreadful boor called loudly, —

"Please 'm', m' I g' aout?"

"What did you say?"

"I want ou'doors."

"You want out-doors."

"Thet 's wut I said! I want aout."

At last she understood this Westernism, new to her. To "want out" is to desire to go out.

"You can go at ten o'clock intermission. Not before."

"Why not can't I?"

"You cannot go till then. It is only a few minutes now."

"I guess I kin!"

"If you go now, you can't come back any more."

"Yew bet I kin come back when I 'm a-min' ter."

"What 's your name?"

"Pudd'n' tame." General laughter.

"Will any scholar tell me that boy's name?" No answer. "I 'll call the roll to find it out." Then she read over her list, marking the answers — and found all the names marked, although the rebel had not spoken. Some one had answered for him.

"You can go, and not return." He did not stir.

By this time ten o'clock had arrived.

"Girls, please all rise and stand still in your places. Now all turn toward me and stand still. Now, while I sing, all march quietly out, keeping step to my singing." She sang "Hail Columbia," keeping time by clapping her hands, and the girls departed with a good deal of decorum; some even entering into her spirit sufficiently to clap their hands in time with hers, and to continue the singing and marching in the open air. When all were out she closed and locked their door, and went over to the boys' door.

"Boys, please go out quietly, one by one, as I call your names."

"No sirree, hoss-fly and buggee!" cried the rebel. "C'm on boys!" And he bolted through the open window.

"Silas Anstey! Please stand at that window and don't let any one else go out." Silas hesitated a moment, and the bully's voice came in.

"C'm on Sile!"

Anne looked at Silas with a sweet, confiding smile — and prevailed. He stood with his back to the window while the other boys filed out one by one as their names were called.

"I 'll lick yew, Sile Anstey, jest 's quick 's yew stick yer snoot aout h'yer!"

As he passed her Anne said, "John Felser?"

He nodded. She touched his hand and said, gently, "I have a friend, after all!"

"Yew bet!" Then when he got outside: "Whar 's th' ornery whelp 's a-goin' t' lick me?" But the whelp was nowhere to be seen. He had departed, followed by the jeers of all the rest.

When the school was again started, however, he returned, and began shouting, from a safe distance, a stream of ribald abuse.

"Please 'm,' m' I g' aout," said Silas.

"Not till next intermission, Silas. We must keep to our rules."

Then she put as good a face on the situation as she could, and allotted to all such lessons as they seemed to be fitted for, and set them to studying. As the horrid words kept on coming in, Anne said:—

"The boys may listen to such language if they like, but" (turning to the girls) "we ladies must do this way to protect ourselves." She bent over her desk with her hands covering her ears. Instantly, every girl was poring over her book, her ears closed to all sounds.

The turn things had taken was, on the whole, favorable to the cause of law and order, because every soul within was enlisted against the brute without. Still, the session was a failure. At the eleven o'clock intermission he had again disappeared, only to re-appear as soon as school was again called. Some laughed, some talked about the matter, all were upset.

At "noon-spell" Silas said, as he came out,

"Let's go fer him, boys!" And they went. All the long hour, while poor Anne was pretending to eat the huge "piece" — cold sausage, johnny-cake, pie, honey, et cetera, which she had brought from home (for which the events of the morning had left her no appetite), she heard the answering cries of the scouting parties searching all possible and impossible places within reach, — a fruitless search. The enemy had retired out of range, she fondly hoped, for good. But no — the affliction continued, at intervals, up to the three o'clock intermission, at the close of which, she observed that Silas did not come in with the rest.

"Alas! — my one ally has deserted me," she thought, and felt as if she must give up and burst out crying. It was with a mixture of horror and relief that she heard, soon after, Silas's voice: —

"Ye would, would ye! Ye ornery whelp!" followed by unmistakable indications of a battle royal. Instantly began a tendency of spectators to doors and windows, which she repressed with difficulty; using, as the most effectual expedient, a singing lesson. She made all join her in Old Hundred, and then, with more difficulty, induced them to sing, "When I can read," in the tune they were accustomed to: an air wherein five separate notes, bound together, are fitted to the monosyllable which ends the second line.

She joined them after hearing the air once through. Even while she sang she could not help thinking of her knight outside, fighting her battle in the woodland lists; and she tremblingly hoped for his success in the tourney.

"Ask me not what a maiden feels
　When left in that dread hour alone.
Perchance her reason stoops or reels.
　Perchance a courage not her own
　Braces her heart to desperate tone."

The singers had only reached the middle of the second verse of "When I can read," —

"When I've been there ten thousand years
　Bright shining as the su-ŭ-ŭ-ŭ-ŭn,"

when the music suddenly stopped, and all eyes were turned toward the boys' door. Silas had dragged up his adversary, and now had him pinned down on the door-stone, beaten, but still sullen and struggling.

"Want him in?"

"If he wants to come, and is willing to behave himself in a way fit for the company of a lady — and of proper boys and girls."

"Dew ye, John?" With a fresh shake.

"No, I don't! 'N' I'll kill yew, Sile Anstey, fust chance I git!"

"Yew 'll kill thunder!" And Silas freed his hold, and started him down the road with a rousing kick.

"Silas," said Anne with a smile that belied the reproof, "don't you know it is very wrong to fight?"

"No, I don't! Not when a feller 's spilin' fer a lickin' th' way he wuz!"

"Well, it is — quite wrong to fight — in most cases. Now come here and hold still while I sew your collar where it 's torn!" And she whipped out her needle and thread and repaired the battle-rents in her champion's armor, while he stood the observed of all observers and the hero of the hour.

Yes — it was, on the whole, a victory for law and order, but Anne had none of the joy of triumph. The day's experiences were dreadful: altogether abhorrent to her sensitive soul. Rebellion, insult, ridicule, defiance, brutal violence. Such sights, smells, and sounds; such barbarism in manners, dress, and person; such seeming badness of heart and ignorance of right views and standards, she had never met, nor dreamed of. How did she know but that Felser's friends had a right to force him upon the school, behave himself as he might? Was she mistress or slave? Who could tell?

A sudden sense of loathing for her new environments, and a passionate longing to return to her old ones, seized on her with overwhelming, stifling force. She restrained her feelings with difficulty till four o'clock came, barely managed to dismiss the young cubs with the pretense of a smile, and then hastened to lock herself in and be alone once more — alone with her homesick misery. Boston, dear Boston! Why could she not fly there, over hill and dale and lake and river, like a homing pigeon! At that moment she loved, in memory, the very smell of its wharves, the mud of its gutters! Better its poor-house — hospital — jail — anything — than all the wretched West!

She cried as if her heart would break. She rolled her bowed and aching head from side to side on her arms crossed on the desk, and asked herself in sobs, —

"Oh, what have I done — what have I done that I should be brought down to this? Do I deserve this fate? Dear Boston — civilization — decency — shall I ever see you again? Or any of you? Oh home — home — home — is there any home in the wide world for poor me!"

When her paroxysm of homesickness had somewhat spent itself, though her face was still all distorted with tears, shed and unshed, she heard a knock at the door. There flashed across her a wild wish that she had committed some heinous crime in Boston, and that this was a summons to return there and be tried for her life. Next followed the more rational thought that the knock probably came from some scholar returning to get a book or ask a question.

She opened the door: there stood Mr. Prouder! She was so glad to see his strong, friendly, smiling face that she almost forgot to care for her appearance; but it did not matter; helplessness was much more likely to appeal to Zury than good looks.

"Haowdy, haowdy, Miss Sparrer. Why, bless my soul 'n' body! Yer eyes looks like tew hoels burnt in a blankit! Ye be'n a-cryin'? The' hain't be'n a-lickin' *yew*, hev the'?"

"Worse, if anything!" (Her sobs broke out afresh at the bitter memory.) "They abused me, and disobeyed me, and la-la-la-*laughed* at me!"

"Oh laws a massy; don't ye let that faze ye,

not a mite! Larfed at ye, did the'? Wal, jest yew larf back at 'em! I'll bet the' wuz full as ludickerous ez yew be — mebbe more so — leastways in some things. 'Course some o' yer high-up scollops took daown offen th' top shelf way back — pronouncin' yer words so carefle, wearin' yer Sunday clo's a week days, 'n' so f'rth — dooz make most folks larf wunst in a while. But *then* — ye'll git all over them p'cool'arities arter a bit."

"Oh no-no-no!" said she, shuddering at the thought of ever growing to be like these *animals*.

"Oh yes ye will, tew! Don't ye be discouridged! I've saw it lots o' times! Ye'll be all right shortly. The' use' ter hev a verse o' po'try when I went t' scule: —

'Scoldin' don't hurt none,
Whippin' don't last long,
Kill me you daresent.'

Wal, naow, larfin don't hurt none, ner last long, ner kill nobody. Come along; git right in th' wagin 'n' I'll tote ye home; 'n' ye kin tell me all abaout it, a-goin'. Ye know ye got me t' back yer — th' meanest man in Spring Caounty t' try t' git ahead of! Ye'll fergit all these yer leetle teo-stubbin's in three shakes of a lamb's tail."

She felt better already, and after a few little touches of brightening up she jumped into the wagon, — putting her hand in his and her foot on the hub, the tire, the side, the seat, and in, — and they drove homeward. Zury listened with sympathetic gravity and silence as she poured out the story of her woeful experiences, encouraging her to go into all its details, driving slow so as to give her ample time, and making no sign to indicate whether he considered the day a catastrophe, defeat her achievement, disgrace and contumely her future lot in life, — or otherwise. His reserve puzzled and frightened her.

"Well, Mr. Prouder, why don't you say something?"

"Hev ye got threw?"

"Why — yes, I think so."

"Noth'n' furder?"

"Not a thing."

"Sure enough?"

"Yes-yes-yes! Don't ask me that again, please!"

Then he broke into laughter that made the tall woods ring.

"Why, I did n't think *you* would laugh at me, too!" And the ready kerchief sprang to her eyes again.

"Who, me? Why, I can't help a-larfin' when I see haow blind ye be! Don't ye see we 've got 'em? It 's all plain sailin' from this on! Ye 've beat 'em aouter the'r boots!"

"Why — how? I think they 've beaten me."

"Don't ye fool yerself, not a cent's wuth! Ye 're a reg'lar Salem witch! Ye 've took all Deestrick Number Seven right daown — greased it, pinned its ears back, and swallered it hull!"

"Why, of course John Felser's family and all their friends will be set against me! I shall think I see an enemy every time I meet man, woman, or child!"

"John Felser's fiddle-sticks! He hain't got no family. Lucky fer him, tew: ef he hed a decent father he 'd git laced with a hickory saplin' till he could n't wiggle. Ef Sile hed n't a g'in it tew him, I 'd a done it m'self! Him t' up 'n' try his tricks on yew! A limb 's he is!"

"Oh, if he would only stay away! But I suppose every one has equal rights in a public school."

"Not a bit of it! That 's th' big holt ye 've got on 'em: it 's a free gift, 'n' the scule board kin bar aout sech as can't behave. 'N' the' 'll dew it tew, naow the' see 't ye 've made th' thing work. Ye 've redeemed the deestrick. Yewr scule 's th' fust one as hez gi'n us a speck o' hope fer a coon's age. John Felser wuz th' wust, but he hed a heap o' follerin' till naow: 'n' here ye be, boss of 'em all!"

"Well, I 'm glad to hear such good news. If I had known all I was undertaking, I should not have ventured to make the experiment."

"'Course ye would n't. Thet 's why I kep' mum, 'n' told th' folks not t' let on abaout it, nuther!"

"Do you really think it is all right?"

"Surely! Like 's not ye 'll find some o' th' big gals thar by seven in th' morn'n'; cleanin' things up fer ye, 'n' puttin' flowers on th' stove, 'n' yer desk, 'n' one thing another. By this time it 's got all over th' deestrick haow ye tuck yer stan' 'n' stuck right up tew it — got the scholars all on yer side but one, 'n' got him licked like sixty, 'thaout ever a-raisin' yer han' t' strike, ner yer voice t' quar'l. Oh, yew 'll dew! I guessed 's much fust time I set eyes on ye."

"Well, I feel better! Do you know, Mr. Prouder, you 've saved me from failure again? I should have failed in getting the place if it had not been for you; and to-day, before I saw you, I was ready to resolve never, never, *never* to enter that school-house again!"

He looked at her with a pleased smile so long that she felt her face flushing and turned away. Then he hurried his horses and drove home.

Prouder's prophecy turned out, of course, correct, down to its minutest details — the public sentiment — the brooms — the flowers: blue gentians from the prairie and flaming tiger-lilies from the woods.

On the first Saturday holiday Anne went to Wayback "to look for letters." She had a charming ride over on a slow and comfortable horse, and found there Squire Brown, lawyer, postmaster, and justice of the peace.

"Haowdy, Miss Sparrer! Wun't ye 'light?"

"Yes, thank you. I 'll sit down and rest a while, and take a glass of water, please."

Then, after the usual commonplaces on weather, health, et cetera, she said, —

"You are one of the school board, I believe, Squire."

"Yes, Miss Sparrer: 'n' I 'm glad t' hear ye 're a-gittin' things in shape there. I expect ye hed it hot fer a while, by what I hear! But ye jest reached fer 'em 'n' gethered 'em in! Ye 've got yer papers all fixed I expect?"

"Well — no: to tell you the truth I was so taken aback at all those questions that I rebelled against answering them. Birthplace — age — I don't what all!"

"Name, birthplace, sex, age, married or single" —

"Yes! there now; the marriage laws of some States are so different from those of others that a man might call himself married when in fact according to the law of Illinois he is single!"

"Oh, as t' that, the laws here abaout marr'in' 's pootty simple."

"How do you mean simple?"

"Ye jest come t' me when ye wanter git marr'd 'n' I 'll tell ye all ye need t' know. 'N' I jedge it won't be long, nuther, he-he!"

"When I want to marry? Don't all women always want to marry? I want to marry now — only I don't know any man in the world I would have! Tell me now when there is n't anybody; because if there ever should be anybody — which I don't expect — I shall be too bashful!"

"Oh, ye want t' be forehanded, dew ye? Wal: any jestice o' th' peace, magistrate, or minister o' the gospel in charge of — any ministerial charge — can marry ye by any form of words th't gives evidence of present consent 'n' futur intention on both sides."

"Justice of the peace, magistrate, or clergyman! No one else?"

"No, nobody else. If anybody else pertends t' marry yer he kin be punished — though even then if ye live t'gether as man 'n' wife the marr'ge is good. The husband 'n' wife ain't punished — only so fur 's they torment one another, 's a matter of course."

"So that 's the only kind of marriage recognized in Illinois, is it?"

"No, I can't say exactly that. Thar 's what 's called a common-law marr'ge. If a man 'n' woman, of lawfle age, 'n' unmarried, says by present words that the' then 'n' there marry each other fer good 'n' all, — not future words th't they 're a-*goin'* t' be man 'n' wife, y' understand, — 'n' then the' afterwards live together publicly as sech, why, they 're married, hard and fast."

"Oh, I see. There must be the words of marriage, and the living together, *both* to make that kind of marriage, must there? Either without the other" —

"Ain't no arthly accaount."

"Well, I will never be married by anybody but a justice of the peace, Squire Brown; and if I have much influence in the matter, you shall be the man."

"Thankee, thankee, Miss Sparrer. *Which* man?"

"Well, I won't say which — certainly not till I 'm asked."

All this gay talk was of course duly detailed to Prouder, when he and Brown next met, as a new illustration of the brilliancy of the wonderful young stranger, who was, by the way, a universal and inexhaustible subject of talk. Prouder listened with much interest, made no remarks, but cogitated long about the matter.

As soon as Anne got back to the farm-house she filled out the rest of the unfinished document, and at the first opportunity handed it to Zury.

"Not married, hey? Well, at your age I should n't a thought ye 'd a ben afraid t' own it. Y' ain't hardly begun t' be an ol' maid yit!"

Anne's talk with Semantha gave her a new interest in Zury, and she studied him more than ever. Still keeping in mind her innocent scheme of making her home permanent with the Prouders instead of transitory with unknown Toms, Dicks, and Harrys, she took careful and constant heed against all possible tendency, on her own part or on his, to any intimacy other than such as might arise between them from her position as his wife's friend. This took more than a little care, for she was quite a novelty to Zury. Not even the young women whom he had seen in cities during his business wanderings had ever seemed to him so attractive, so interesting, so amusing. As to her good looks, they doubtless had their effect on him, though he was quite unconscious of it, having never in his life thought of womanly beauty except as "a snare."

She maintained her untrammeled relations with the family in another way, too. Thus: John Endicott McVey took occasion on two Sunday evenings to call on her, dressed in Boston clothes, and using pure Boston-i-a-n language, and she really made the most of him ; concealing the fact that he struck her as very light and useless timber — "dozy" or "brashy" as Zury would have characterized it. On the second evening he proposed marriage, and she was good enough to decline it, not as a glaringly absurd joke, but merely as a proposition, reasonable from his point of view, though quite out of the question from hers. He was, after all, the most presentable and available man in the neighborhood, and she grew to like him for his pronunciation of words, though the words were not worth pronouncing.

The school went on prosperously. The most unruly boys became suddenly the teacher's most loyal adherents. Silas was her "secular arm" to quell the last remnant of rebellion, after which consummation Anne had a fine chance to make peace and inculcate order. One boy, inherently vicious and dangerous to the delicacy of the girl-scholars, was scared nearly out of his wits by a word in his ear from the terrible Zury Prouder. (Teachers of mixed schools should always be women, so that the girls can have near them the friendly ear and voice of one of their own sex.)

The first two weeks at the Prouder domicile were about as Anne had expected, except that she did not get quite so intimate with Mrs. Prouder as she had hoped to be. Not quite the hoped-for cordiality in receiving as well as in rendering services was manifested by the poor, sighing woman. When Anne had proposed reading aloud as an attention which might alleviate the weariness of work in which she was not allowed to join, and a half-and-half consent was obtained, she found that it was "a chapter" that was both desired and expected. She knew, as well as she knew her existence, that her society and suggestive talk, in that dull, rich house, was worth more than any luxury their money had ever purchased them or ever could — let alone the imperceptible cost of her food and shelter.

So she listened with smiling confidence when Zury opened the subject.

"Wal, Miss Sparrer! Our tew weeks ends tomorrer!"

"Why, so it does! How the time has flown by! It seems only a day or two since I first darkened your hospitable doors."

"I 've ben a-thinkin' haow t' 'range things t' suit yer best."

Now it 's coming, thought she.

"'N' I guess I 've fixed it abaout right fer all hands."

She quietly composed her little speech of thanks for an invitation to stay on indefinitely, accepting on condition that she should be allowed to do her share of the work.

"To-morrer I 'll take ye over t' brother Bromwell's. Ye know him pus'nally a'ready, 'n' ye 'll find his folks all O. K. Right up-an'-a-comin' all the time."

Would that ringing in her ears go on growing

worse till she fell forward? There, now it was getting better: but now — would those tears persist and push clear out, or could she quell them by swallowing rapidly? No use! There they come. If they had not come, the other, the faintness, would have prevailed. So it was as well — the least of two evils.

After all her efforts — all her hopes! She had failed. She always failed. She always must fail. Nobody loved her. Nobody ever did or ever could. Of course not. She was a fool to think otherwise even for a moment.

"Why — Miss Sparrer — be ye sick? Don't ye like what I've be'n 'n' gone 'n' done? Ye don't bear no ill-will agin Bromwell, dew ye? He meant all fer th' best, 'n' 'll be a good friend t' ye when he knows ye 's well 's we dew. Best thing y' kin dew to git the whole deestrick on yer side is t' go 'n' board t' every haouse in it."

Well! That was balm! But if he thought so, why did he let her go? Why did not he say, "I've plenty of everything except what you've plenty of. Now just stay right on with my wife, and the obligation will be mutual?" But as he did not she must say something.

"Oh, don't mind my ways, Mr. Prouder; I get a little lonesome and homesick sometimes — and foolish — that's all. But I get over it at once." Whereupon her words were belied by a new flood of tears and sobs. The tide swelled afresh and ran over again and again, while Zury looked on in wondering, half-comprehending pity and sympathy. He never could have imagined that the love of such dull beings as Mary and Semantha could be longed for by the brilliant city girl. So little did he know of women's hearts! After a puzzled silence he broke out: —

"What an old dromedary I be! Mebbe ye'd like t' hev me go, 'n' them come 'n' talk t' ye a spell," and he started to bring the others.

"Oh, no — no! Do you think they could have heard my foolishness?"

"No — I reck'n not — they're both in the kitchen" — and he listened — "Semanthy she's a-singin', so likely they could n't hear."

Anne listened, too, and easily recognized the high, nasal treble of the minstrel, drawling her one ditty; the only poetry she knew except Watts's hymns.

As Prouder said to his wife when, later, he was relating the circumstance of Anne's outburst: —

"Doggone me ef I did n't think, one spell, 's haow she wuz sorry t' leave us!"

He privately dwelt on the subject a good deal. In fact, if he had been a self-observant man he would have noticed that his thoughts were very much in the habit of dwelling upon Anne Sparrow.

Here is the cheerful song Semantha sang as a lightener of toil; or a pious exercise; or as a tribute to poetry and music; or — anything else: —

A story I will now relate.
'T was of a gal named Polly Bates;

She 'd dress up fine and curl her hair,
When others was ingaged in prayer.

She 'd go to balls, she 'd dance and play
In spite of all her friends could say :
"I 'll turn to God when I grow old
And then he will receive my soul."

One Friday morning she fell sick.
Her stubborn heart begun to prick.
She now was sorry she done wrong,
But had put off the day too long.

She called her father to her bed.
Her eyes was rolling in her head.
"Oh father, father, fare you well
While wretched Polly groans in hell.

"Oh mother, mother, you I leave.
For wretched Polly do not grieve.
As I am now you soon shall be.
Prepare for death and follow me."

Her face grew black, her hands grew cold.
Her spirit left its earthly mould.
Now all young friends a warning take,
And quit your sins for Polly's sake.

CHAPTER X.

HOW FARES THE TRANSPLANTED MAYFLOWER?

NEXT day, when Prouder was driving over to Bromwell's with Anne and her trunk, she asked, —

"Where do I go next, after brother Bromwell's, Mr. Prouder?"

"Wal, brother Peddicomb, he 'llaows t' begin t' kill in abaout tew weeks — so thet 'll make a month, t'gether with Bromwell's; 'n' then brother Anstey, he thinks he 'll be 'baout ready t' kill — ef he ain't quite ready, brother Peddicomb he 'll lend him some of his meat."

"Oh, Mr. Prouder, I can't bear it!"

"What — pork?"

"Oh, no; but this dreadful boarding 'round."

"Sho! Dew tell! I wanter know! Why, most young sculemoms they likes it, 'n' sez it 's like a reg'lar raound o' visits — jest a reg'lar weddin' trip, only no husban'; 'n' 's *they* say all the better on that account, but you 'n' me knows 't sech talk 's that fr'm young gals 's t' be took by contrairies."

"Oh, I wish I could live at the school-house."

"Wal, it 's big enough, goodness knows. McVey he 'd like t' have ye come 'n' board 't th' tahv'rn, I guess."

Anne laughed.

"'N' go through a leetle ceremony fust off, t' simplify matters."

"That would be too long a contract on too short notice. But now you are the great fixer of things — you fix things so I can live at the school-house."

This compliment put Zury on his mettle, and he at once slowed up the team to give them more time to cogitate.

"Lessee-lessee — fust thing is room; nex' thing is furniture, nex' thing is food, 'n' nex' thing is company. I *am* a-needin' a new p'tition in th' barn."

"I don't see how your needing the same thing I do is going to help me, unless you get the partition and I come and steal it away some night."

"Ha-ha! yes, you'd be a dreffle burglar t' meet on a dark night! But my p'tition 'd make abaout three quarters of a scaow-load, 'n' your stuff 'd make th' other quarter, so we c'd git it pootty cheap from daown river." (There was a delinquent saw-miller there who owed him money.)

"How cheap?"

"Wal, the p'tition complete 'd cost abaout thirteen dollars, — all in."

"Oh, I could n't stand that!"

"Wal, naow, look h'yer; ortent the deestrick t' have a room thar anyhaow, t' keep records 'n' books 'n' papers in, 'n' t' hold board meetin's in, 'n' sech like?"

"But that would raise your school-tax."

"Never ye mind that. Ther's money in the

treasury, 'n' this 'd be construction, 'n' c'd come aouter th' fund made by the sale of th' scule-section of land." (Zury wanted to save that saw-mill debt.) "Naow, ye 're goin' t' stop with Bromwell 'n' Peddicomb; 'n' o' man Anstey 'll be on aour side anyhaow. Ef yew can't fetch them other tew galoots 'raound in a month, y' ain't the gal I take ye fer!"

"Oh, you flatter me! Now, how about furniture?"

"Wal, I 've got a leetle lot stored t' Wayback 't I took on a chattle mortgidge from a feller 't tried t' cl'ar aout with it. I 'll let ye have it at half what it 'd cost ye." (So he did; being twice what it had cost him.) "Only by bad luck there 's two beds."

"Bad luck? Good luck! I think of providing food and company at one blow. The big girls can come and visit me week and week about, and bring me food from their houses, the same as if I were boarding around with them."

"That 's business!"

"But how about fuel?"

"What, firewood? Oh, the' 's plenty of that daown in this h'yer wooden country. Several pays their school-tax in firewood."

"Then — Oh, dear me! is it all right? Have I a home?" And she proceeded to sing "'Mid pleasures and palaces" in her treble voice, and the "charm from the skies" seemed to soar away back to the skies it came from. When she had done one stanza she whistled it all through as an interlude before she sang the next. Could this be the same girl who had cried herself half sick the night before?

"Look aout, Miss Sparrer, —

> 'Whistlin' gals, 'n' crowin' hens,
> Ollers comes t' some bad ends.'"

"No, Mr. Prouder, you 've got it wrong, —

> 'Girls that whistle, 'n' hens that crow,
> Take their comfort as they go.'"

"He-he! I never heered *that* before! What I have heered is, —

> 'Whistlin' gals, 'n' good fat sheep
> Is the very best stock fer a farmer t' keep.'

An' I hev n't got none o' them nuther, 'xcep' the sheep."

"No! And it 's too bad!"

"I wish I had one — jest like yew!"

"I 'd be a trifle old for you — but still!"

"Not a mite tew old fer a darter. Ye 're younger 'n many a gal o' half yer age! Not tew old fer a darter, ner yit tew young fer — suth'n else, ef I wuz a single man!"

"Well, just please remember that you 're not," and she reddened under his gaze.

"Wal! H'yer we be to brother Bromwell's. Don't ferget ye 've got some 'lectioneerin' t' dew!"

"No danger."

We will skip Anne's stay with the Bromwells and the Peddicombs. At each place, for various reasons, she had more success than with the Prouders. One reason was this, she did not try so hard: she was more reserved; listened more, and talked less; in short, did not "slop over," as the expressive Western phrase is. Both these men were farmers of the same grade as Zury Prouder; not as rich, but quite as comfortable, and possessing a little more pretension to cultivation and enlightened comfort. They enjoyed showing Anne the difference between them and the Prouders.

Now behold her, singing and whistling "Home, Sweet Home," in her own little board palace, partitioned off within the walls of the school-house. This was a happy habitation, in spite of some disadvantages. She was compelled, of course, to leave it often alone; and not being an experienced hand at "kiverin' fire," she sometimes found the vestal flame on her home altar extinguished on her return to it. Then there was nothing to be done but run all the way to the Ansteys for a burning brand.

"Oh, Mr. Anstey! Please lend me a little fire."

"Surelye, if ye'll fetch it back when ye're done with it."

"Oh, I always pay my debts, with interest; but my creditors must come and ask for what they want. I don't follow them about to get square with them. You can come over and warm yourself by my fire sufficiently to pay for this whenever you like."

So the gay girl would trip away with her burning brand, waving and managing it to retain the fire, and yet not let it creep up so far as to burn her fingers, making a subject almost well worthy to be painted if there had only been some artist to observe it. But there was not.

Reekie Anstey was her first room-mate, as it was to the Ansteys she was to have gone next. And oh, such a wondering and adoring companion! The first of a long series of similar visitors. As long as Anne kept up this residence did she have one or other of the larger girls to sleep there, each enjoying the privilege for two weeks at a time, and vying with the others in the supplies brought to their lady-mistress. None so dull as not to appreciate the occasion. Then, for once in their lives, did they learn how a lady conducts herself at two important times in her day, — when she goes to bed, and when she gets up. Five occasions, perhaps, would be more accurate, for the three meals were almost equally instructive.

For a long time were these visits looked forward to by the eager lasses, and for a longer — lifelong — looked back upon. Teacher and scholar had much freedom in the day-time, each visiting and receiving visits at will. Only one thing was exacted as an invariable rule, — that Anne must never for an instant, at home or abroad, asleep or awake, be left alone between sunset and sunrise.

While the changed life was a novelty, Anne enjoyed it greatly. The freedom was so perfect: nature (under proper restrictions) so lovely! Above all, the children were so fond of her, and her sense of usefulness so gratifying! *Almost* soul-satisfying! The summer gave place to autumn, and she taught her great girls, —

"The melancholy days are come, the saddest of the year,
Of wailing winds and naked woods, and meadows brown and sere.

Heaped in the hollows of the grove the autumn leaves lie dead:
They rustle to the eddying gust and to the rabbit's tread."

Then, when (after the early frosts) fell the sweet, lingering "Indian Summer," she taught them, —

"And now when comes the calm mild day, as still such days will come,
To call the squirrel and the bee from out their winter home;
The south wind searches for the flowers whose fragrance late he bore,
And sighs to find them in the wood and by the stream no more."

Some of those children felt as if a window had opened in heaven and they had received a new revelation, where Poetry dawned upon them like a planet sailing into the field of a telescope.

Even winter did not daunt her. The roar of a black storm through the treetops was awful; but inside, the lamp burned bright. Zero sunshine was pale as death, but she kept warmth and cheer about her. The exhilarating quality of the thin air was a constant tonic. Let us peep in on a bitter cold morning scene.

"Why, Eureka!" (A yawn.) "You up already?" (Another.)

"Well, yes, Miss Sparrow. It must be considerable past sun-up, only you can't see much light owin' to frost on the winder — window I mean. An' the clock's froze up, an' — everythin'."

"Dear, dear! you'll freeze, too! What have you on?"

"Oh, I'm all right! I've slipped on my shoes, and got the comforter wropped 'raoun' me."

"You poor girl! Come into my bed and let me slip on my — things and make that fire. Did it keep? I covered it carefully!"

"Oh yes, it 's all right; leastways the' 's enough t' light up by, an' th' boys' whittlin's fer kindlin' come in awful handy! Thar, — hear it?" And as she closed the stove door the fire began sucking the pure oxygen with a roar like a steam-fan.

"How is the water?"

"Froze solid to the bottom of the pail! But I emptied all the pitchers an' things last night, so the' 's nothin' busted. Oh dear! I set the milk-jug on the hearth, but yet it 's froze too. But I don't see as it 's cracked. I 'll jest leave it on the hearth whar it 'll thor gradial. Thar!"

"Now come right into my warm nest and let me cuddle you!"

"Oh no, Miss Sparrow; I 'm too cold. I 'll go back to my own bed. I 'd freeze you to death."

"Do as I tell you, my child! Come here this minute! There — snuggle up — oh you are *icy!*" And then the stove (if it had n't been talking to itself too loud to hear anything else) might have listened to cooings and kissings between the loving young women (clasped and interlaced into a long, indistinguishable mass) that would have warmed its glowing iron heart still further, if anything could do so.

"Oh — what 's that?"

"Massyful man alive — it 's the milk! It must have be'n cracked after all!"

"Well, tea is pretty good without milk."

"But let me git up and wipe it up."

"No, you shan't go till it gets warm."

"But the burnt milk 'll smell the house up fer all day!"

"Well, let it. It 's a clean smell, any way." More inarticulate endearments.

"Now, Miss Sparrow — jest look at that stove! Red hot on the top, and side, and back, and a spot in the pipe! Lemme jest git up 'n' shet the damper, 'n' set on the kittle!"

The strong and perfect girl sprang from the bed into the frosty air without a shudder: slipped her ill-shaped shoes on her well-shaped feet, and in her single airy garment, white, long, straight, and clinging like the robes of Fra Angelico's angels, flew hither and yon on her well-known tasks. Those feet would do for a sculptor's model. Going barefoot, as a child, if not too long continued, and on too severe tasks, gives to the foot a fine set of curves, strong and lithe. Each toe grows to maturity perfect and separate from its neighbors, having, at will, a life and motion of its own. It is almost as different from more civilized toes as a fresh grape is from a packed raisin.

The lost milk was soon dried up, and the enthusiastic stove, when its supply of air was cut off, squealed and complained like a pig driven from its dinner.

Unhappily, the best part of isolation is the beginning of it. Anne's grew tiresome, more and more so, as the weeks and months dragged slowly by. She made her own clothes; she washed, starched, and ironed for herself; she did fancy work; she read and re-read every scrap of printed matter she could get at; she drew and sketched a great number of scenes, which covered the walls of her private domain, and even spread out into the great school-room. She wrote a good deal: in fact, it may be said in strict confidence that this book would never have been written but for the nucleus of material created by her that winter.

She saved a little money (almost all she earned), which Prouder kept for her, paying her ten per cent. interest, while he lent it out at twenty.

She did not have as many visits as she would have liked from the mothers of her scholars. It is such a task to get through work, to get "slicked up," to get away from home three or four miles, and to get back and into working garb in time for the quickly returning household cares, that country wives are usually steady stay-at-homes. Besides, among her friends' homes two were in some confusion. Peddicomb had died, leaving his affairs "kinder mixed." When his daughter Semantha had married, her father had "set off" her portion to her (one of his three quarter sections); her "shiftless" husband had induced her to mortgage it (to Prouder), and then departed to look for a favorable investment for the proceeds. He probably found it, for he never came back, and the quarter section fell in to swell Prouder's holdings; very nicely, too, as it "jined on" to the one set off to Mary, his own wife. As the reader has learned, Semantha and her child now lived at the Prouders'; the third sister, Flora, still stayed at home in the farm-house on the remaining "quarter," managing it as well as she could.

Mary Prouder, Zury's wife, had departed early in autumn on a visit to the Peddicomb ancestral halls in Ohio in search of health and strength, her portion of which blessings had dwindled to a minimum. When Anne bade her good-by she seemed, with her hollow cheeks, her prematurely aged face, and her "Oh Lordy, Lordy!" like the rearguard of death or the vanguard of the resurrection. The few letters which came, at first from her own hand and later from the hands of others, gave Zury but poor encouragement to hope for her recovery. Already people (in the meeting-house horse-shed, or while walking and riding home, and on other gossipy occasions) had begun to say, —

"Would n't wonder ef Zury had a good sight t' git a-holt on t' other quarter of th' Peddicomb place, 'thaout it a-costin' him a cent, barrin' th' jestice fee."

It was customary to have on February 22d a school "Exhibition" with speeches, dialogues, and so forth; and Anne conceived the daring novelty of "A Scene from New England History." The scene was to be the marriage of Priscilla and John Alden — she to be the fair Puritan, and John Endicott McVey to be the other chief performer. Her deft fingers easily arranged the costume for herself; and John (who had seen it enacted "at home"). by the aid of an old artillery short-sword (a relic of 1812), and some long, woolen stockings, managed a costume sufficiently *unlike* anything the West had ever seen (or the East, North, or South either, for that matter) to bear a possible resemblance to the actual original. If he was not like John Alden, what was he like?

When all was arranged Anne was startled by a serious obstacle, which her discreet old friend Mrs. Anstey revealed to her.

"Ye dunno, I don't mistrust, thet foolish folks is a-passin' the'r remarks abaout yer a-bein' a-goin' t' stan' up with Johnny McVey in a mock-mar-r'ge, as ye might say."

"Oh pshaw! McVey, indeed! Marriages are often displayed in theatres, and nobody in his senses ever takes them to mean anything!"

"Ya-as — but then ye know th' school-haouse ain't no theayter; 'n' ef it wuz, perfessin' Christians, in course, would n't never go inter it, ner nigh tew it, nuther. It 's a meetin'-haouse, — a haouse of God; 'n' marriages a many hez be'n performed thar a'ready. 'N' ef yew 'n' Johnny wuz a-goin t' marry, thar 's whar ye 'd naytrally be, 'n' sayin' th' same words, tew."

Anne with difficulty repressed her disgust at such childish folly.

"'N' then the' 's another thing: both on ye bein' single 'n' marriageable the' 's them as sez ye mought find yerself marr'd t' Johnny, 'thaout never mistrustin' sech a thing!"

"Heavens and earth! Have I got to attend to" — but here anger was reinforced by discretion, and both conspired to reduce her to silence. She bade Mrs. Anstey good-by with flaming cheeks, brow, and temples; not saying whether she would be warned by these hints or not.

Mrs. Anstey, who loved and respected the lonely and heedless young stranger, was in a good deal of perturbation lest she got herself in trouble by her consciousness of rectitude and her obstinacy. So she communicated her fears to Zury when next he passed her way.

Soon Anne saw Zury fastening his horse to one of the "hitchin' trees" in front of the schoolhouse, and she knew at a glance, by some kind of instinct, that he had come on the subject of the proposed "play-acting" scene, and hurried on her armor, offensive and defensive, accordingly.

"Howdy, Miss Sparrer. So ye 've tuk up with Johnny's proposial, after all."

"I taken up John's proposal? Well! I have heard that those most interested in a piece of news were always the last to learn it; now I know the saying is true."

"Sho, sho! No need t' git wrathy abaout it! Johnny he 's a pootty good feller, whut th' is of him, 'n' plenty of him sech as 't is."

"Much or little, he 's too much for me; I thank you all the same — and the rest of my kind friends in the community, likewise!"

"Thanks seems t' be plenty with yew this arternoon."

"I have enough to pay all the debts I owe in the world, — but that is not saying much." Then conscious that the sharp eyes of her that-week's-companion were doubtless scanning her, closely, from some coign of vantage, she insisted on Zury's coming in, where there would be a safe party of three instead of the notoriously perilous party of two. Once inside, she and her girl friend took pains to show Zury the little platform built by the hands of her loyal boy-scholars in preparation for the "Exhibition."

"Wha' d' ye 'llaow t' show up?"

"Oh, speeches and dialogues, and some singing."

"That all?"

"Yes, I guess so."

Then her companion made bold to add a word.

"Mr. Prouder, they 've about talked Miss Sparrer out of the best part of our show!" And she proceeded to expatiate upon the rare delight the world was to lose in missing that representation of the "Puritan wedding;" even going so far as to bring out the prim dress, which deft-fingered Anne had devised with a high pointed hood, a white muslin waist, a neckerchief and an apron.

"Hard lines, I dew say! All that nice work got t' be throw'd away! But then, it 'd be better t' throw away tew frocks like that than t' throw away yer standin' in a God-fearin' community — naow would n't it?"

"Depends a little on whether the community 's right and I wrong, or vice versa."

"Not a mite! Not a blamed mite! More of a loss ef ye 're right th'n ef ye 're wrong; jest 's it 's more loss t' lose a good shillin' th'n a bad one."

"A woman ought n't to care for the esteem of a community of perfect" —

"Idgits, wuz ye goin' t' say? Mebbe ye 're right abaout th' esteem o' fools; but I pity yew ef y' ever have t' live amongst 'em after ye 've lost it!"

She knew he had in his mind the "Universalist" episode in his own past, and she began to appreciate more than ever the despotic tyranny of a lawless and unbridled "freedom" of opinion. It was this same "freedom" that had doomed her Quaker compatriots of only a few generations ago to be "whipped from parish to parish at the cart's tail."

"Oh, well, if they can stand it, I can." And she tossed her head in contemptuous scorn.

"If you 'n' Johnny wuz married, er even if either of ye was in th' married state a'ready, nobody 'd say a word; but two single folks, of course" —

"Oh, bother! Let us change the subject. When did you hear from Mrs. Prouder?"

"Quite a while."

"How was she?"

"'Baout th' same. Downcy — dunno 's the' said whether she wuz bedfast er not. By the way, ef I don't misremember she sent word I wuz t' tell ye haowdy fer her."

"Did she really? I'm glad she was so kind as to think of me! Will you give her my love when you write?"

"Sartin, sartin; 'n' I'll be a-writin' agin 'n a week er tew. Naow I must be a-joggin'. Wish ye good day! Good day, Loviny." And he went out; but Lovina followed him for some private words, and soon Anne heard herself called out to where Zury sat on his horse ready to ride away.

"Miss Sparrow, Mr. Prouder says it would be all right if you was to do the scene with him instead of Mr. McVey."

"Oh, no; I'm off the notion altogether. I've begun to pick my dress to pieces already."

Zury's face darkened.

"O. K. Only ye better not speak of it, Loviny, t' nobody. Th' might think it cur'us th't Miss Sparrer was hot fer it when it wuz a young feller wuz in question, 'n' cooled off 's soon 's th' idee wuz started t' dew it with an old married man, old enough t' be her — uncle."

His evident mortification was "nuts" to Anne, and she laughed one of her merry laughs.

"Oh, you're none too old for the part. John Alden was no chicken when he married Priscilla. But I hate to give in to such foolish notions."

"Oh, *do*, Miss Sparrow! There, I got it all fixed, and now *you* are the one to spoil it all!" And poor Lovina began to cry. Anne went out and kissed her, and dried her eyes, saying, —

"Well, well; there, there, my dear. Fix it any way you like. What difference can it make to me, or anybody else, who is gifted with common sense!"

So it was all arranged. John Endicott McVey unwillingly "took the bag t' hold," as the boys said, when it was announced that he was ousted from his place as bridegroom and assigned the subordinate one of Parson.

The great day approached. The programme was arranged: songs by the school, songs by Miss Sparrow, recitations by scholars, and three scenes of "A Puritan Wedding." A list of these, written in "large hand," on a foolscap sheet, was the copy set by Miss Sparrow to the "first class in writing" for some days prior to the momentous one; and by effort, emulation, and comparison a large number of available sheets were ready to scatter about the seats on the exhibition evening. Never was such a congress of merry sleighs, steaming horses, and jingling bells, laughing youths and maidens, and gossiping men and women; and never such a crowd in the school-house as filled it to the very window-spaces long before the time for beginning the performance.

The curtain drawn aside, behold a really charming bevy of healthy, smiling scholars, standing in ranks ready to begin "The Star-spangled Banner."

To Anne's surprise and chagrin not a sound of applause greeted the scene!

But she gave the signal and led off, —

"Oh say can you see by the dawn's early light
What so proudly we hailed at the twilight's last gleaming,"

and the verses followed each other in due order,

in a fine volume of youthful voice. *Still not a sign of approval.* And yet some signs of satisfaction seemed to shine in the faces of the audience.

Anne still hoped for better things, and stepped out — looking like a red-haired angel, as a scholar mistakenly said — to give them "The Mellow Horn" in her finest style, with "Araby's Daughter" reserved for an encore.

Encore! Not a note of recognition for her, or of approval of her song! She bowed herself out in some confusion, a degree of dismay approaching dangerously near to tears. She almost threw herself into Zury's arms, crying, —

"What does it mean?"

"What dooz what mean?"

"Why, don't you see? They don't like it!"

"Don't like it! Bless yer heart, ye 're away off ef ye think so! Like it! Why the' don't know whether the' 're a-standin' on the'r heads er the'r heels, the' 're so tickled!"

"Then why don't they applaud?"

"Oh, clap 'n' stomp d' ye mean? The' ain't a one on 'em as knows enough, I don't expect!"

"Oh, I can't go on this way! I shall die if everything falls flat like this!"

"Wal, I 'll fix *that* all O. K."

He slipped out and had a short colloquy with Peleg Thum, explaining to him that when the folks liked anything they must "encore," that is to say, clap and stamp. So Peleg got into a group of congenial spirits, and after the curtain fell on the next piece they "encored;" whereupon the whole silent audience turned toward the group of innovators, wondering what *that* meant! Was it part of the show? Peleg explained:—

"That 's *applause.* That 's what the' call 'encorin'' — clappin' 'n' stompin' is."

The boys nearest to Peleg were the first to catch the idea, and from them it spread like wildfire. The novel joy of making a licensed noise in public became so popular that it was soon difficult to obtain silence in time for the next thing on the programme. Again Peleg's aid was invoked, and it was understood that when he raised his stick and shouted, "Thar, thar, boys!" quiet must be restored — by the strong hand if needful.

When Anne came on and sang "The Mistletoe Bough" in her sweetest tones and clearest English, the delight was so overwhelming that Peleg himself forgot to stop "encoring" or to check anybody else, and *then* she gave "Araby's Daughter" as an encore.

The excitement flagged a little during the recitation of "Fitz James and Roderick Dhu" by Silas Anstey, — gestures like those of a lay-figure, and voice like the sounds in a whispering gallery, — but expectation was strained to the utmost as the finale, "The Puritan Marriage," fell due.

"Priscilla on her way to meeting" was a shawled, hooded, and mittened embodiment of Puritanism. True, her kerchief was figured and her apron cross-barred, but what of that? Her Bible wrapped in a handkerchief was *very* puritanical. Her soliloquy pointed to the cruel sea at the east of her, the more cruel savages on the west, the dark woods all about her. And home, dear England, so far, far away! (Handkerchief.) But had not the Christian his home wherever he could set up faith's altar, as *here* at the meeting-house, toward which her steps were tending? And were seas or savages frightful to any one who was compassed about by the legions of heaven? She passed on to meeting, and the scene closed.

"Priscilla returning from meeting" was met by John Alden (dreadfully like Zury Prouder), who in honest, hearty words and manner (unfortunately reminding you of Zury Prouder's words and manners) urged the claims of Captain Miles Standish to the hand and heart of the fair Priscilla. She temporized — she turned away — she frowned — she smiled archly and suggestively upon the impenetrable Alden. As to her heart, it was otherwise engaged. As to her hand — she pulled off her mitten and gave it to the opaque messenger, and desired that he give it to Captain Standish, telling him, with her respectful duty, that *that* was as near to the hand that it fitted as he would ever come!

Then when the swain was slowly and regretfully departing she called after him, "Why dost thou not ask for thyself, John?" with a demureness that ought to have brought down the house.

He approaches, he kneels and kisses her hand, and the curtain falls amid thunders of applause.

"The marriage" was solemnized in due form. McVey, with a quarter of a pound of flour in his long hair, with an immensely long gown (fashioned by Anne out of black muslin), and long bands of white paper, was solemn and stately; a little audience of favored scholars was appropriately bashful and giggling, and Anne, her hood and shawl and mittens laid aside, was — Priscilla herself — a curly, blushing, smiling bride.

No one knew any just cause or impediment. John Alden (in a Zury-esque manner) said to all the minister's inquisitive queries "I will," and Priscilla in modest treble made the same reply to similar questions.

After McVey had pronounced them man and wife they turned to the little audience of four, seated on the stage, and Priscilla in audible voice asked them to wait there until she should return with the bride cake. She disappeared, and came back promptly with a huge tray piled high with bits of cake, each wrapped in a bit of paper. She paused and asked them if that would be enough: whereat the outside audience laughed. The instructed scholar answered loudly "No!" which awakened more merriment. Then she sent out the minister, who presently came back with a great pile of similar packages, and Priscilla sweetly asked a second girl if *that* would satisfy their feeble appetites. Again she was answered "No!" amid louder roars. So she sent out John himself, who brought in a bushel-basket full of little bundles, saying that that was all they could have. After the scholars had taken the three receptacles in charge, Anne stepped to the front and said that for fear her bridesmaids might make themselves sick, she would suggest that the audience should share in the feast; and each person as he or she accepted a package must accept with it her thanks for their kind attention.

The cake-bearers stepped forth, and the curtain fell for the last time. The stamping and clapping rose to a roar, only quieted as each individual received his little package, which occupied his hands and his mind and stopped his "encoring."

Anne could not complain of the quality of the thanks she received from such of her audience as she had a chance to speak with — that is, the old folks. The young men, now as always, seemed to consider her a person of a different sphere from theirs. Little she cared, however, so long as she could get the disorder cleared away and rest her tired body in bed. The comments on the homeward drive were many, and generally enthusiastic.

"Tell ye what, fellers, Pele Thum 'llaows 't he 's be'n t' shows in Springville whar the' charged tew shillin' a head t' come in, th't warn't no better 'n that wuz! Way aout h'yer, t' th' Wayback meetin'-haouse!" This was perhaps the most wildly extravagant praise that was uttered, and everybody who heard it repeated it to everybody else as the acme of eulogy. At the same time, some consistent old "hard-heads" either kept silence or whispered to each other comments wherein the ominous word "play-actin'" bore a large part. All the programmes were carried away, and probably some of them exist as "momentums" to this day in farm-houses in Spring County.

And next day came the news that Zury's wife had died a week before.

. . . .

Now the air is full of buzzing gossip. "Never c'd be a clearer case of a jedgement on play-actin'. Th' Lord's hand 's in it, sure enough!"

"I felt kind o' wicked a-settin' there 'n' jest a-lookin' on! Should n' wonder a mite if the cuss wuz t' fall on th' c'munity; leastways on all th't did n't bear the'r testimony agin it fr'm the word go!"

"Ye 're mighty right tew! Mark my words; the' 'll be more die th'n jest poor Mary, innercent 's she wuz, 'n' s'lected 's th' instrument of th' Lord's vengeance!"

"Yes sirree! 'N' it 's pootty hard t' think of a perfessing Christian hurried into the Presence, 'n' all fer the doin's o' them as ain't no perfessers as nobody knows on! 'D oughter to be a warnin' t' all on us, specially the Prepared. We dunno when we 'll be took, ner yet fer whose misdoin's!"

"Guess th' won't be nobody bold enough t' try it on agin, in th' face o' Providence."

"Yew bet the' don't sech doin's git t' be had h'yer agin, not in *one* while!" (And there was no one so bold. There was no more effort in the direction of that guilty and giddy gayety for many a year.)

"Zury 's in a pootty fix! If sculemom only

knowed it, she c'd jest take her grip-sack and march up t' his place, 'n' open th' door, 'n' go in 'n' squat right daown, then 'n' thar, fer keeps!"

The men came to corresponding (though slightly divergent) views: —

"Zury he's be'n 'n' gone 'n' played smart Aleck fer wunst! 'N' sculemom tew! He's got jest 's good a right t' go in 'n' out of her door 's she hez, t'day."

"Yes, sir! 'N' ef it's bolted, t' kick it in; 'n' holler 'come along Anne Proauder, 'n' git t' work.'"

To say that Anne was not much agitated would be untrue. Of course she heard but little of the row: and that little was sifted through the loving heart of Mrs. Anstey, so it was robbed of much of its bitterness. But cruel thoughts haunted her pillow and shortened her rest. This was a new State. In Massachusetts she felt sure that no advantage could be taken of her accidental predicament; but who could tell what might be the law and custom in Illinois? The idea was horrible! She, Anne Sparrow, in any way bound to that rustic, with his sordid views, his ignorance, his grizzling temples, and — ammonia! Oh no; it could not be! But that any one could think of it for a moment!

It is harder to say what Zury thought and felt, but it was much in the same line, until he had time to get some trustworthy knowledge of the law. There was Flora Peddicomb, with one hundred and sixty acres, well-fenced and well-built on, and well-stocked, and well-placed as to three hundred and twenty acres already his, and joining it on two sides. And there was Anne Sparrow, without a cent, and without the power to make or save a cent on a farm — and so smart and knowing that he was afraid of her!

So the two characters in the ill-starred "show" were trembling with mutual terrors; each afraid the other would claim the right to make of the twain one flesh. No more absurd situation has been seen since the warlike Dowler and the chivalrous Winkle both fled from Bath to Bristol, each bent on saving his life from the other.

Zury was the first to recover his equanimity. He easily got competent legal advice (gratis) which informed him that neither party could make that farce into a marriage without the co-operation of the other. So after a season of reserved gravity which repelled gossip, and which might be attributed to a decent respect for poor Mary's memory, he fell into his usual business-like manner — afraid of nothing on earth.

He would have liked to impart his self-confidence to poor Anne, but she avoided him as if he were an enemy. A few constrained words of common civility, always in company with some third person, and always concerning his dead wife, were all she vouchsafed him; she misinterpreted his renewed friendliness as a claim for closer intimacy; he misinterpreted her hauteur as offended feminine vanity.

She observed a coldness in the greetings of her female acquaintances which hurt her greatly; and her school showed, for a time, diminished attendance, diminished interest, and diminished personal respect, which hurt her more. During the daylight she managed to throw off much of this uneasiness, but with the darkness came the horror, as of old.

Time is balm: gossip, even gossip, the immortal fiend, grows first wild with hunger, then torpid with starvation when it is left absolutely without food. Things settled back into much of their old routine. For Zury, everlasting money-making. For Anne, ceaseless shedding of light from her little lamp of intelligence. For McVey, continual renewals of his hopeless passion — if so strong a word can be applied to his feeble emotions, alternately growing faint with absence and beaming in their full tepid warmth when a sight of Anne again blessed his eyes. For the rest of our friends, the ordinary dull current of life.

CHAPTER XI.

ANNE'S MONOTONY AT AN END — AND HER PEACE ALSO.

"OH Miss Sparrow! My mother said Boston must be pootty much of a place ef it turns out such gals as yew be!"

"Did she? Well, I'm glad — for dear old Boston! But you should say 'as you are,' not 'as you be.' What else did they say that was so pleasant?"

"Oh, gran'dad he 'llaowed Deestrick Number Seven wuz a differ'nt guess sort of a place sence you come."

"That's nice; I'm glad he likes my work. But D I S T R I C T does n't spell deeestrict. What did anybody else say that would comfort me?"

"Oh, the' warn't nobody else thar — but Bob 'n' Jim, 'n' my cousin Bill Evans from 'cross river."

"What did they say?"

"The' never spoke a word."

Straws show which way the wind blows, unconscious that they are doing so. The particular straw that indicated the direction of this particular breeze had some perception of his task, for after a moment he added: —

"You know the young fellers hain't be'n edicated in the Sparrow Deestrick school. *Districk* I would say." A general laugh ran through the group at this sally.

"No, indeed! Poor fellows, they don't know what they 've missed by growing up too soon. But then, if I have *your* love and your parents' appreciation, I don't care the least bit for the opinion of anybody else on earth!"

This might be called a fib — perhaps even a whopper. For where lives the woman who, looking about for evidences of her value in the world, is not pained by a lack of vigorous masculinity in them?

Why should she be so different from other women? Why should nobody in the world love her except her poor scholars and poorer John McVey? No one but herself knew that she had any beauty — such as it was. If she had been pale instead of rosy, spare instead of plump, blackhaired instead of blonde, eleven inches across the shoulders instead of fourteen, helpless and maudlin instead of strong and self-reliant, the dolts about her would have called her a "ha-an's'm lady."

But as it was, if the poor girl sent out any of those womanly glances we know of, that say "does he think me pretty?" they simply recoiled upon the sender — returned like Noah's dove from the waste, and without even an olive-branch.

Suppose they had admired her, she could hardly have endured them. The young men of her age seemed so much younger than she felt, with her more varied experience and broader knowledge of the world. However, they did not admire her. The girls who stayed with her were enthusiastic in her praise, but the accounts they took home of her and her ways displeased the others.

"Her 'n' Johnny McVey is both tarred with th' same stick. Stuck up? Stuck up ain't no name fer them city ducks! Nawth'n aout h'yer ain't good enough fer 'em — 'n' them 's poor 's jimpson-weed, tew!"

This community presented the extraordinary spectacle of a society without holidays and almost without amusements. The old "husking-bees" are unknown in the West, where corn is "shucked" as it stands in the field, and only the bare ears thrown into the wagon to be carried home. Sociable christenings, of course, there are none. A marriage is often merely a visit to the preacher or to the justice. An afternoon call on a week-day finds the house empty, save one or two busy women and a few unattractive, unkempt, ill-mannered children; and on Sunday social visiting is sacrilegious. A "quilting" which Anne attended was ghastly in its dullness. The younger women were proud and bashful, and talked together in whispers. She fairly talked herself out for the benefit of the elders, with some success, too; but after that even a photograph-album would have been a relief! Tea, when it came, softened things a little, but it was too late.

Anne was more of a bohemian than what the polite world would call a well-bred, well ordered damsel. She only seemed "a perfect woman nobly planned" by comparison with the very imperfect women (however nobly planned, however dutiful and devoted) about her. The desire for some girlish or womanly joy became almost a mania with her. She was tempted to encourage McVey — only he was too insignificant and already inconveniently in love with her. She burned for conquest! Could she not devise some innocent gratification of her vanity to ruffle her sordid existence?

Once in a certain week when her most tried and trustworthy scholar was her companion she devoted a whole evening to loading herself with all her few simple adornments, — a dotted muslin with lace undersleeves, a little silver diadem that had been her mother's, a gay belt, a pair of silk mitts, long silk stockings that only needed a little bit of darning, and dancing-shoes with narrow strings crossing each other on the instep as was the pretty fashion of those days. The whole outfit was worth only an absurdly small sum, yet when she got it on she looked radiant. By combining her own little mirror with one the friend had surreptitiously brought with her from home, and lighting *three* tallow dips all at once, she could see herself all over in about four chapters, a scene at a time and continued in our next. She liked it.

The humble companion was gratifyingly explosive, but the Spring County clodhoppers, if they could have peeped in upon the strange scene, would have only jeered: —

"Haow's that fer a brick-top? Geeswax! if

sculemom had any more freckles 'n what she 's got, whar on arth 'd she put 'em? Have t' carry raound a sheet o' paper in her hand, the hull page jam full o' left over freckles!"

Late in the spring there was to occur some kind of respectable picnic — a temperance celebration — at a point not far from Wayback, on the other side of the river. In Anne's rebellious state of mind she was tempted to intimate to McVey that he might have the honor of escorting her thither; whereupon he began scheming for the necessary leave of absence from the tavern. In vain he planned and twisted. As the tavern people wished to go, the drudge must stay and mind shop. In this dilemma he mentioned the matter to Prouder; and was met with one of those moral aphorisms which served Zury in such good stead on many occasions where a refusal was to be the answer to a request.

"Young man! Yew keep yer business, an' yer business 'll keep yew!"

"My business don't much more than keep me, anyhow. About all I get 's my board and lodging and clothes."

"Well, sonny, that 's all I git outer mine, ef ye come t' that."

"Expect *she* 'll be pretty considerable disappointed."

"Who?"

"Why, Miss Sparrow. (This rather sheepishly.) Did n't I mention she wanted to go?"

"Sho tew man! Ye don't say! Wal, we 'll see abaout it."

The quick mind of Zury was glad of the chance this seemed to present for reëstablishing his old safe, yet interesting and amusing, intimacy with Anne; so she was soon surprised by a message from him, brought by McVey, to the effect that they three would make the trip to the picnic. Anne refused promptly and decidedly, and was in a manner compelled to explain to John that since the *contretemps* about the "Puritan Wedding," she had thought best to keep clear of the widower — because folks *would* talk so!

Crestfallen John could only go again to the *Deus ex machina* with this discouraging report, and Zury seized the opportunity to have an explanation with the school-ma'am.

One day, after school hours, there came his well-known "rap-rap-rap-rap" on the school-house door — the one more blow than the three customary ones, being an unconscious mark of the more insistent and persistent nature of the rapper.

Anne was alone, and with a quickened pulse debated what she should do in view of this long-feared renewal of Zury's visits. She thought that he might conclude that she was absent, and go off without the dreaded interview; but, unluckily, Zury had seen her through the window and had no idea of being balked in his plans.

"Rap-rap-rap-rap-*RAP*."

Then Anne laughed down her tremors (it being broad daylight), and appeared at the door —

all in her pretty working *déshabillé*, with inky finger, and hair tucked behind her ears.

"Good day, Mr. Prouder. I 'm sorry I can't ask you in, but I am all alone. Eurcka Anstey is staying with me, but she has run home on an errand."

"Oh, wal" — stammered Zury, rather taken aback. He had never encountered just this development of female prudery before. "I — jest called tew — kinder pass the time o' day."

"Well, please to call and pass the time of some other day." And she was going to shut the door.

"Oh, say — Miss Sparrer! Ye ain't no call t' be afeared o' *me* — ole Zury Praouder! 'Course it wuz a leetle orkard fer a while arter th' kind o' play-actin' comin' accidental how it did 'n' when it did."

"I 'm not afraid of any man! I 'm only afraid of women and children — afraid the women may do me harm so that I can't do the children any more good."

"Wal, thet 's right — thet 's right, 'n' like ye tew. Th' women did talk fer a while, but I soon stopped it. I tol' 'em what 's the fact; th't that thar form o' words don't vally no more 'n th' wind, 'thaout yew 'n' me choose t' make it so."

He paused. Anne paled slightly in fear of what he might say next, and she hastened to "put her foot down for good and all" on any such idea.

"Then that settles it! You can set their minds

at rest. Tell them that if you were the last man left on earth I would n't marry you!" Then, ashamed of her rudeness, she added, with a slight smile, "Nor you me if I were the last woman."

"Jesso, jesso," said he; and as she noted his crestfallen aspect she was glad she had been so decided; although the fact was that his look did not mean blasted hope, but only the mortification the natural man must feel at being spurned by a fair feminine foot, even though he had no thought of kneeling thereat. A gay laugh would have been his proper rejoinder, but he was too simple, where women were concerned, to hide anything.

"I only went fer t' say th't *ef* th' wust come tew th' wust, we hed th' remedy in aour own hands."

"Well, we have n't. The remedy would be worse than the disease."

"Wal, then — thar we be! Naow things bein' as the' be, th' best way t' stop idle tongues a-waggin' is t' go on 's though no sech a thing ever got inter aour heads. Ain't it?"

She stood a while in her old attitude, and he could observe her oval nails tapping her teeth, all gleaming in the sunshine. (They were pretty nails, save the one on the thumb, marred by the "nibbing" of numberless quill pens.) The longer she waited the more eager Zury grew for her consent.

"Come right along. Ef the' strike at yew, the' strike at me, tew. We 'll be in th' same box, yew 'n' me. I 'm a man o' my word, 'n' I tell ye I 'll stan' by ye!"

Still she hesitated, while he, unaccustomed to sue in vain, was almost driven beyond his patience by her charms and her coyness. He even ventured to come nearer, while she edged gently away. She was not at all disposed to marry him, or any man; nevertheless, the suggestion was pleasant, and tended toward healing wounded pride and vanity. "Am I afraid of him?" she asked herself. "No, indeed! Shall I stay at home like a born coward? If I do I shall despise myself forever after." Then she said aloud: —

"I 'll go!"

Zury rode off homeward in great good humor with himself and the world. He just realized how much he had been unconsciously missing the brilliant Anne during the past weeks.

"Laws, haow I wish *she* owned the Peddicomb Place! Gee Rusalem! I would n't care ef she never milked a caow in her life. Jule kin dew th' milkin'." And his mind dwelt on her strange ways and her flattering concession in yielding to his persuasion. "But then — that thar question she faound it so hard t' answer! Marr'd er single. Marr'd er single." And he rode on with darkened brow. In fact, he rode on past his own place, clear over to the Peddicomb farm, and feasted his eyes on the handsome property. He did not see Flora Peddicomb, which was fortunate — for Flora.

Before the picnic day arrived the Wayback world heard, without surprise or alarm, that Zury Prouder wanted a team to take him across the river on the very afternoon set for that festivity and a man to fetch it back in case he should conclude to stay longer; also, that John McVey was to be the man, and that Miss Sparrow was to accompany John to the picnic.

"Ye see, a feller 's be'n a-off'rin' me t' pay my carr'ge-hire ef I 'd come over 'n' look at s'm parster he 's got t' lease 'n' s'm medder t' cut er t' sell in th' field, 'n' I kin go a Saturday er never."

Now behold the trio in the carryall being ferried over the river — McVey paying the ferriage — early on the eventful Saturday afternoon. Anne was in her dotted muslin and all, and her eyes and cheeks were beaming. She thought of the coming triumph, and in her thorough contentment kindly resolved that she would be most considerate to her crushed rivals, and not keep their lovers from them longer than a very little while. Then she took her slippers from her pocket and crossed the strings over the back of her fair, freckly hand to show Zury how they went. He opined "sech things is vanity an' a poor preparation fer the Lord's day tomorry" — but he kept looking all the same.

Zury left his young friends near the picnic, and drove on to see the leasable pasture and salable meadow.

The picnic was held in a pretty grove, cleared of underbrush, the platform for speakers and the seats for hearers being in a leafy bower, built of boughs and saplings suspended and strung from tree to tree. All was gay and pretty, and Anne prepared herself for happiness and a little innocent triumph.

But, alas! She was a swan among goslings. She never put on her little low shoes at all, nor her silver crescent. The other girls were not Spring County girls from her side the river, but all strangers to her. McVey knew nobody to introduce to her, even if he had had the pluck to do it. Most of the women were in silks or solid stuffs, — red, green, and blue, and ugly, — so that her cherished dotted muslin looked — well — ridiculous. She was the amusement of the whole rude crowd. They would pass by where she and McVey sat silent and abashed, and, before they had got fairly away, burst out laughing. "The freckles could n't find no more room on her face 'n' han's 'n' so the' broke out on her frock!" This went on until, taking the cue from each other, the friends formed a regular procession of couples past where our unhappy pair were seated; then when in desperation Anne seized John's arm and joined in the walk they all sat down and left the "show" to walk alone!

Oh the agony of anger, mortification, disappointment compressed into that one afternoon! As a confessed felon in a prisoner's dock before a gaping world, she could not have suffered more.

"John, do you want to marry me?"

"I do, Miss Sparrow; same as ever!"

"Well, you shall!"

When Prouder the powerful came upon the scene it was like a flash of light to her. Everybody knew him, and either liked or feared him — usually both. He saw at a glance what had taken place, and neglecting everybody else made straight for her with an air of delighted surprise, and she hailed him as a deliverer from torment.

"Wal, Miss Sparrer! Yew here? Wal, I wanter know!"

"What there is left of me, Mr. Prouder."

Then he sought out the managing committee and leading men of the occasion.

"Wal! T' other side o' th' river 's a-gittin' clean overslaughed by this side! Here, brother Fordham, brother Lowe, ye must a managed yer frolic pootty well t' dror in sech high-up comp'ny! 'Llaow a Spring Caounty citizen t' present tew a Posey Caounty C'mitty Miss Sparrer, from Bosting, in th' State o' Massychusetts, at present a-stayin' temperary in Illinois. But remember he don't present her fer keeps. Spring Caounty claims her. She 's only a loan t' Posey. She hain't be'n a denizen o' Spring long enough fer me t' call her Sister Sparrer yit, but mebbe we 'll be praoud t' call her so some day, when some Spring Caounty man calls her by *his* name before Squire Braown h'yer!

"H'yer, brother Stokes, — Miss Sparrer, from Bosting, in th' State o' Massychusetts: brother Stokes, the Presidin' Elder o' the Feet-washing Baptis' d'nom'nation. Brother Stokes, yew make Miss Sparrer acquainted 'raound a leetle whilst we seek a snack of that nourishment fer th' body, 'thaout which th' soul don't nourish wuth a cent."

The tide was turned, and Anne was anything but neglected for the rest of the day. Her face, her voice, her good English, and her Boston pronunciation of it, seemed to make an impression wherever she went. Still, it was the act of a friend, forcing her into a kind of success entirely among people much older than herself. It was not a personal conquest with her own bow and spear. It still remained a problem whether she was or was not a woman to be sought for and longed for like other girls.

She had one little bit of honey-sweet revenge. She saw speaking to Elder Stokes's wife one of the youths who had joined in the conspiracy to torment her. Said she to the Elder (who had remained near her, extremely attentive and conspicuously impressed), —

"How are the manners of young people in Posey County?"

"It is regrettable to observe, Miss Sparrow, that the manners of the young in the frontier caounties are not what they are in older settled c'munities further east. When I was to Bozry Theological College, deportment was tort abaout as strict as any other one branch. Consequently I am the more competent of judging."

"That young man, speaking to Mrs. Stokes, for instance; what educational institution has had the care of him?"

"That, mom, is my son Joab, and as yet he is without the benefit of collegiate education. Joab, my son! Step here a momint. I want to make you acquainted with Miss Sparrer, from Bosting, in the State of Massychusetts. One of the centres of Learning and the Arts of our country. I may say *the* centre."

Anne in the mean time looked very gravely and sweetly at the blushing Joab, who advanced holding out his fat, red hand. Then she turned to Mr. Stokes without accepting or returning Joab's salutation, and said, "Thank you. I did not wish to be introduced;" and walking the astonished Elder in the opposite direction, she added, "What a pity it is that all young men cannot go to Bozra College!" Then she gayly changed the subject to something quite different. McVey told her afterward that Joab never got over it as long as he lived, though he was never tired of protesting, "I warn't no wuss ner any o' the rest!"

As for Anne, she almost loved Prouder for his strength and kindness.

When it was getting dusk and time to go home Anne and McVey found Prouder, as usual, the centre of a circle of interested men. He was discoursing freely, and at the same time carving his initials and the date on an iron-wood stick which he had cut from the underbrush near by, and laid on his lap, protected by his well-known bandanna handkerchief. His was such an active nature that he always liked to be doing two things at once. Talking did not alone fill his attention.

"Yes, mom. I'm a-goin' home same way 's yew be, and 'll be glad of good comp'ny. Thar!

That stick 'll be a momentum, 's they say, of this h'yer picnic; fer which I, fer one, thank my brethern and sistern of Posey, and shall remember 'em in my prayers to the Throne."

When they got out on the road it was quite dark.

"What 's that?"

It was Anne's old foolish fear, that kept her always on the *qui vive* at night, which now was attracted by a long line of wavering flame on a hillside away inland from their road.

"'Pears like th' grass is afire over there. Guess we 're all right. Let 'em aout a leetle, my son."

McVey hurried on his horses, but still the fire seemed to be heading them off from the ferry, their objective point. Every little while there would be quite a large surge of blaze when the flame caught the longer grass of a marsh, or came across a brush heap or a dead tree-top in its path.

At length they met a fast-driven team that came near running into theirs in its mad career, making Anne cling to Zury in a sudden terror she could not control.

"Ye can't git through! Fences all afire! We had t' drive fer our lives."

"Haow 's th' river bank?"

"Oh, that 's all right afoot. Only ye can't drive a waggin that a-way."

With this the other team resumed its hurried course to the rear.

"Sho tew man, but them fellers is *good* 'n' scare't! I don't believe a word of it! Still, 's I might be held responsible fer th' team, yew tew better drive back 'n' stay over night, 'n' I 'll push through afoot by th' river bank ef I git druv offen th' road."

"How far is it to the ferry?"

"Oh, not more 'n a mild in a bee-line; but th' river makes a bend away from us h'yer, 'n' I may have t' go right smart of a ways raound."

"Oh, I cannot go back with Mr. McVey! Let me walk on with you!"

"Wal, ef ye wanter walk I can't pervent ye. Th' highway 's free tew all. But ef ye take my advice ye 'll go back. Make up yer mind pootty suddent, though, fer I 'm off." And he jumped from the vehicle.

"Oh, I cannot go back. I 'll go with you!"

So she sprang lightly to his side and prepared for starting. He only paused to give some last directions to McVey, and then joined her. They walked on at too rapid a pace to do much talking, and it was evident that Prouder was getting anxious as to the outcome.

At last the blazing fences made the road positively impassable, and they left it, still keeping as near it as the diagonal line of fire would permit. The sparks fell in showers; poor Anne's light muslin was ruined, and was a source of danger beside. The smoke was sweet, pungent, stifling. Prouder made her take hold of one end of his stick, while he kept hold of the other and piloted the way. Soon he felt her drop the stick, and, looking back, saw her fighting a fire in the skirt of her dress. He stepped back and smothered it.

"We'll head straight fer th' river 'n' git aout o' this, hit er miss."

So they turned their backs directly to the fire, and soon got into a more tenable place where they could see each other, as the fire's progress was slow, there being no wind; but the ground was terribly rough, and the underbrush and tree-tops' "down" almost impenetrable. They arrived at a little stream, and were forced to travel down its very bed. Anne hesitated at this.

"Hist up yer petticoats! Don't mind me!"

"Oh dear! Well, you go right on and don't—don't mind me. Just let me look out for myself." Then, managing her skirts as well as she could, she waded and stumbled forward.

"This h'yer branch'll take us right daown t' th' coal-mine on th' pint."

"Then how about the ferry?"

"Oh, that's past prayin' fer, ontel th' fire's reached th' river 'n' burnt itself aout so's ye kin pass over th' burnt deestrick."

"But where will we be when the fire reaches the river? Oh, dear!"

"We'll be in th' mouth o' th' coal-mine—ef so be Providence concludes t' spare us; 'n' I sh' think he could 's well 's not. Leastways yew'll be in th' coal-mine."

"I'll be—in the—? Where you are I'll be!"

"Wal, kin ye swim? I think some o' swimmin' th' river 'n' makin' fer hum. Folks 'll be scare't, smellin' th' fire 'n' not seein' on us back; 'n' if I go on over, I kin tell 'em we 're all O. K."

"No, I can't swim, but I can drown! And I will, too, before I 'll stay alone in any coal-mine. Oh! oh! oh! oh!" (These were sobs that seemed to wrench her heart out with their tumultuous violence.)

"Wal, thar! thar! thar! We 'll see! Doan't 'ee cry naow, there 's a good daughty!"

He turned and walked back to where she stood, helpless with sobbing, her dropped skirts swaying in the stream, and made her pick them up again, and then put his strong arm around her and helped and guided her as if she had been a baby, as she in her heart felt that she was. Strange beasts and reptiles seemed to be darting past her, fleeing from the fire. She does not know to this day whether they were real or imaginary.

"How much trouble I make you," she whispered.

At last they reached the coal-mine mouth, — a level drift in the river bluff. As they felt their way in something rushed past them outward: no doubt about it this time. Anne screamed and clasped Zury around the neck.

"Fox, I *guess*," said he, coolly, so as to avoid alarming her.

"Naow don't ye stir 'raound much, whilst I go fer a light."

She scarcely dared to breathe, or to put out her hand for steadiness, while he was gone. "Oh, dear," she thought, "I 'm going to be frightened!" and her skin began to erect itself in points, her ears to ring, and her hair to bristle audibly against the straw of her hat. The solid earth was threatening to heave and roll, and nausea was not far off, when Zury reappeared with a blazing brand he had snatched from the woods-fire. To her surprise she perceived that she was standing erect and firm, instead of waving and tottering as she had supposed. What a vision of life and comfort he appeared to her staring eyes!

He took his brand and explored the floor and sides of the drift for prior occupants. Nothing serious came to view: either there was nothing there, or whatever there was fled farther into the tunnel. The little flame shed a flaring, fitful light along the black, jagged walls of coal, some six feet apart, which stretched away into the solid hill, losing themselves in inky darkness, where the light could penetrate no farther. Anne trembled as her eyes strove in vain to fathom the mysterious void, and she turned again to the friendly form near by.

At one side of the passage there was a broad shelf cut into the solid coal, whereon the mule-drivers were wont to store their hay and grain. (Their rough feeding-stable was by this time blazing outside.) On the shelf there was some hay and a lot of empty bags.

"Thar! I swaow tew man! Ef that ain't th' blamedest providentialest thing I ever come acrost! I 'm jest a-goin' t' be able t' make ye as comf'table as Queen Victorey tew hum tew th'

Taower o' London, in three shakes of a lamb's tail! Thar! I 'll spread this hay daown, *so!* 'N' stuff some on 't inter a bag fer a piller, *so;* 'n' spread my hank'cher on it, *so;* 'n' then ye 'll lay daown, *so;* 'n' I 'll pull off yer wet shoes 'n' stockin's *so*, and *so;* 'n' wrap yer limbs up in my coat, *so;* so 's t' keep yer wet petticoats offen ye! Oh, law sakes alive. I 've got t' git hum somehaow!"

"Sure as you leave me I 'll follow you into that river and drown myself before your eyes! I 'd rather drown than go crazy! You don't know me! I should be a lunatic in an hour after I was left alone in this place! A raving madwoman for life!" And she prepared to put into execution her threat of following him to the river.

"Wal, wal! We 'll see, we 'll see. I 've got t' git s'm stuff fer this h'yer fire, anyhaow."

As he went out she divined, with the acuteness of the insane, that he was not coming back. She cast one frightened glance into the black mine, then took the poor little slippers from her pocket, slipped them on, scrambled off her shelf, and followed him, even stepping over the line of fire which he was building to bar ingress to the mine by any beast or creeping thing. She found him at his task, and never let him get a yard away from her in his search for fuel; following him as a cat does a mouse, while her wet skirts flapped about her stockingless ankles.

"Recklect I 've got lots o' things t' think of 'n' look aout fer."

"And I am alone in the world — quite alone — all alone!"

She felt and knew that he was watching his chance to run off to the river. If he did, she would go, too! She would never be alone in that black darkness — never — she would keep close to him until the kind water should close over her head like a coverlet and shut out the sight of it all. In the days that followed she often wished that such had been the outcome.

Perhaps when he saw her drowning he would turn back, and she could clasp him so tightly that she would not drown alone! She remembered how he had been her strong and constant friend and protector at every difficult step of her life here. Why had she repelled his suggestion of marriage? He, so cheerful, so fearless, so powerful in mind, body, estate, and position — why should he not be her husband — her sword and shield forever? What was that other kind of marriage Squire Brown told her of? Common law?

In her piteous plight she was suddenly seized with the boldness, the cunning, and the recklessness of desperation. "Mr. Prouder," she began, with a forced and sickly laugh, "if our mock-wedding had been a real one, you would n't offer to leave me here — to die — now would you?" Her wide-eyed, pretended smile, that was more like a grimace of terror, would have melted a harder heart than Zury's, but he was looking carefully away.

"Ye don't 'llaow t' let me go along hum, 'n' come back fer ye bright 'n' early in th' mornin'?"

"I WILL NOT."

She was Anne Sparrow, and dark night was all around above, and below, at right and left, before and behind her — Zury was the only object whereon her eyes could rest without a shudder. Insanity gibed and gibbered at her from all else. She took hold of his coat with both her hands, bowed her head upon them, and again sobbed aloud.

He took her in his arms and carried her over the fire to her rude couch, and did not try again to leave her. One of her slippers dropped from the white foot, now stained and splashed, and long afterward the mule-drivers cherished the misshapen little foot-covering that fitted so many strange prints in the soil near by.

CHAPTER XII.

ANNE COMPROMISED AND PERSECUTED.

In the first gray dawn Anne saw Prouder's figure outlined against the light of day at the mine-mouth. He put on his coat (which he had again wrapped about her poor feet and ankles), and threw fresh fuel on the fire, by which he proceeded to pull out and restore to usefulness her dried and stiffened shoes and stockings. She sat up in her low niche, vainly trying to reduce her clothes to some kind of order. Day had dawned, and she no longer cared what became of him — or of herself.

There he was, in all his undisguised vulgarity. Coarse and shabby, base and ignorant, egotistical and boorish, glorying in qualities he ought to be ashamed of; possessed by sordid greed, and — ammonia!

He brought her her shoes and stockings and silently gave them to her to put on.

"Miss Sparrer," he began, awkwardly; "it must be past four o'clock — I guess I 'll swim th' river naow 'n' make fer hum."

He paused to see if she had any objection. She made none, so he continued, —

"Th' woods-fire 's burnt itself plum aout, so 's

ye kin git t' th' road at th' ferry — er wherever ye like — 'n' McVey he 'll pick ye up as he comes by. 'Course ye 'll tell him I swum th' river."

"Yes."

"'N' ye hain't no call t' tell him jest when I swum it."

"No."

Then he walked a little way down the bank, turned, and came back and picked up his carved iron-wood stick.

"Bid ye good-day, Miss Sparrer."

He walked rapidly toward the river, and, finding a hollow log, thrust the cane into it out of sight, and walked on without it. He reached the river and began to cross, wading most of the way over before he came to the channel, where it was too deep to reach bottom. She remembered with languid wonder that he had not even shaken hands with her at parting. Then she saw him begin to swim, and could see only his head as he drifted down-stream. She asked herself if she should care if it disappeared under the surface, and felt doubtful of the answer. She even remembered to wonder if the saving of the ferriage was not an equivalent to him for the discomfort of his cold swim, and concluded that it probably was. The head did not disappear; she saw him emerge on the opposite shore, take off his coat, wring out the water, and put it on, then turn and wave his hand to her, to which cool greeting she made no response.

The way back to the wagon-road, over the black

ashes of last night's fire, though it had seemed so long in the smoky darkness, seemed absurdly short now. When she reached the track (the fences being all burned) she could scarcely believe it to be the road she was looking for, and even pushed across it and further away, but was recalled by seeing McVey approach with the team. He evidently hardly knew her. She was not young enough to look well in *déshabillé*, and now her bedraggled condition, her pale face and swelled eyelids, and her changed expression, all combined to make her look fully ten years older than she looked yesterday.

"Why — Miss Sparrow! The nation! That can never be you! Where in the world did you pass the night?"

"In the mouth of the coal-mine."

"Heavens and earth! Is that so? And where 's — where 's Mr. Prouder?"

"He swam the river and went home."

"Just fancy? And left you all alone?"

"Yes — left me all alone."

"If that ain't like him, I'll give up. And your gown is as good as gone up. You *do* look like the last of pea-time!"

He jumped down and helped her in, but it was with a twinkle in his eye that reminded her of the ridicule she had suffered from the picnic fiends of yesterday; and her unspoken thought was, "Idiot! if it rids me of *you*, I don't care how I look." The little feminine rage did her good. She shrouded herself in the horse-blankets as well as she could, and they crossed the ferry unnoticed.

"Could you drive back to the school-house without going through Wayback?"

"Sure-ly! The woods-road's the shortest, if you don't mind being shaken up some."

She did n't mind, and they soon arrived at the school-house without meeting any one, much to McVey's relief, in the present state of Anne's personal appearance. Not that his inclination for her was crushed, but then he was afraid somebody would laugh at her and him. Thus he lost his one precious chance of being lover-like and chivalrous, a chance he might have improved by treating her as the dearest girl in the world just when she felt as if she were the very — cheapest.

So as they drew up to the school-house, he ventured, baldly and stupidly: —

"When shall it be?"

"When shall what be?"

"Why, our — marriage."

"Never!"

"Are n't we engaged?"

"No! Go away! I never want to see you again — or anybody!" And she went in and slammed the door. Soon, however, she opened it again, and seeing him still there, looking almost idiotically downcast, she said: —

"Oh, Mr. McVey" —

He looked up.

"I thank you for your polite attention!" She essayed a smile — rather a rueful effort.

He brightened up at once.

"The pleasure 's mutual, Miss Sparrow," and he drove off quite rehabilitated.

Oh, the relief of home — even such a home as that — and of Sunday — even such a Sunday as that! She took off her dreadfully mussed garments; ran her hands into the silk stockings, noticing the little mended places she had darned so long ago — was it possible that it was only yesterday? — and after removing some of the traces of disaster, she walked over to the kind Ansteys' for a cup of hot tea and some of the boiled eggs which were now known to be her great staple of food. The Ansteys had both seen and smelt the smoke of the woods-fire, and Anstey had gone betimes to the tavern for news.

"I faound Zury Praouder in th' office t' the tahvern; he 'd clum in through th' winder arter all the folks hed gone t' bed, 'n' slep' all night in a cheer. He told me all abaout the fire, 'n' him a leavin' yew in the maouth o' the drift; 'n' I sez t' him, sez I, 'Zury, ye 'd oughter stayed with her if it cost yer a leg; she 's so *dog-goned* skeery in th' dark;' 'n' s's he, 'Wal, she 'llaowed she wuz willin' fer t' hev me, go 'n' so I come.' "

"Yes; I told him to come away."

"Wal, haow 'd ye git along all night?"

"Oh! Dreadfully!" and she shuddered from head to foot.

"Ah, yah! Wha' 'd I tell ye? Ye warn't so strong 's ye thort ye wuz!"

"No — I was horribly weak! What else did he tell you?"

"Wal, that 's the heft on it. He got some breakfast, 'n' lit aout fer hum. Said McVey 'd fetch ye over all right this mornin'. 'N' here ye be! All 's well 't ends well! But he 'd orter a stud by yer."

"Yes, he should have stood by me — and he would if I had insisted on it, I suppose."

"Don't ye wish ye hed?"

"Oh, I 'm too tired an' sick to care much about anything, except to go to bed and sleep — forever!"

"Sick, be ye? Wal, naow, thar 's that thar fits med'cine never ben used yit" —

"No, thank you, Mrs. Anstey, I have n't got fits *yet.* I 'll just go home and get to bed. Good-bye!" And she departed.

She threw herself on her bed and hid her face in her pillow. How long she cried she knew not, but blessed sleep came at last. "Oh, if sleep could only last forever!" was her first waking thought.

Late in the afternoon she was aroused by a knock at her door. She asked who was there, and recognized Prouder's voice in reply. She told him to wait a moment: then first smoothed her hair at her little mirror, and afterward took down the school-bell rope from the nail where it usually hung out of reach, and drew her chair near to it, and at last let Zury come in.

She saw at once that he was very much disturbed in spirit.

"I jest ben acrost the river."

She saw that he had — also that he had swum his horse and saved the ferriage.

"Yes: I 'llaowed I 'd jest go over 'n' see haow things wuz. Cur'us enough — I could n't find my stick I left."

"Gone! Could anybody passing have seen it?"

"No, not possible. Could n't a-found it 'thout the' 'd seen me put it thar."

"And if anybody did see you" —

A long pause followed this suggestion.

"*Yew* see me put it thar."

"Yes, I saw you."

Zury looked at her keenly, She suddenly perceived that he was thinking of the possibility of her using that mute witness as an ally to prove a "common law marriage" against his will! The blood rushed to her face and the fire to her eyes.

"*What* do you mean?" She sprang to her feet and glared as if she would have flown at him — as she would if her strength had been equal to her anger. *He* to fear a marriage with *her*, and to suspect her of plotting to force him into it.

"Sho, sho! Thar, naow! I did n't mean noth'n'. Did n' know but what ye mought a took it t' walk with, 'n' throwed it away some'ers."

She was slightly appeased, but still flushed and panting. Then she sat down again, and said, slowly, almost inaudibly:—

"Well but, Mr. Prouder — suppose anybody *did* see you put it there — perhaps" —

"Jesso, jesso. If the' did!"

Another anxious silence followed this suggestion; she torn with conflicting emotions.

"Wha' 'd ye 'llaow t' dew?"

"Nothing."

"Noth'n' no time?"

"No; go back East, perhaps."

"Wal, naow!" A great sigh of relief accompanied this explanation, which showed the disgusted girl that he hoped to escape his share of the responsibility.

"Of course I have your promise to help me all through."

"Oh — of course, of course!" And he rubbed his eyes and frowning brow in perplexed discomfort. "Ye know scule 's aout nex' month."

"Yes, I know. Perhaps you may as well pay me what money you owe me."

"Money!" A gasp.

"Yes, the money I lent you, with the interest."

"Oh! *Tew* be sure! Might 's well settle it up right naow, if it wa' n't Sunday."

"I guess its being Sunday won't hurt."

"Wal — ef ye 'd come a leetle furder from the winder — in case anybody sh'd see."

"Oh, I 'll stay here. You can go to the desk, if you like. I can do the interest in my head."

"No! Sho! Kin ye, though?" (This with a smile of returning comfort and admiration.) "Wal, naow, sposin' I wuz t' pay ye fer this quarter 's well 's the rest."

"Very well."

"Mebby I 'll not git it in fer six weeks er more.

So that 'll make us abaout squar on the int'rest matter, wun't it?"

"No."

"Why? 'Course ef ye dror money afore it 's due — 'n' I pay it aout afore I git it" —

"Have you any school money on hand?"

"Wal — I hain't figgered up. I mought have a leetle, 'n' then agin I mought n't. But if I hev, I 've a right t' keep it 'n' use it."

"Well, give me the other, and let this quarter go for the present; till I get back from the East."

"Oh, if ye 're set on goin' East sure enough" (this with a long breath of relief and hope), "I would n't trouble ye t' come away back h'yer jest t' git a little money."

"Just as you like." She saw that he was afraid of her still.

He calculated the interest, and after some discussion they agreed upon the amount, and he paid her.

"Naow would ye mind a-givin' me a receipt for all debts, dues 'n' demands, claims 'n' accaounts of every name and natur?"

"Oh, I have n't the slightest objection."

She went to her desk and wrote a quittance that even he could find no fault with.

"Naow we 're good friends, ain't we?"

"Same as ever."

"Ye don't think hard o' me fer — nothin'?"

"I don't blame you for anything! Not the least little bit in the world!"

And the tears sprang to her eyes, and began racing down her cheeks like mad before she could even wipe them away. It was for herself that she was heart-broken — that she should have nobody to blame.

The strong man was also quite moved. He tried to dry her tears; but this recalled her to her self-restraint, and she froze toward him at once. Finding that he had his arm on the back of her chair, and observing indications of aggressive interest, she rose and grasped the bell-rope. The bell gave a low warning clang at the touch.

"Wha — what ye doin'?"

"Oh, I sometimes ring this, and Uncle Anstey comes right over."

"Hum — ha! Wal, ye *are* — as I said before! Wal; I mus' be a-goin! Fare ye well, Miss Sparrer, ef so be 's I 'm not t' see ye agin; an' it 's likely I wun't. I wish ye well!"

And so without a hand-shake they parted, she wishing she were dead.

Zury grew very downcast on his way home.

"Sakes alive! What could n't she dew if she had a mind ter? Kin it be th't she 's a reg'lar schemer? That 's th' idee I hed a-comin' over — th't she'd ben a-layin' fer me all this time — mock marr'ge 'n' all — 'n' we all fooled by her fr'm the word go. But she ain't — I know that if I know anythin'. I 'd bet my life on her, even arter all 's said 'n' done! She 's honest, square, open, 'n' above-board, so fur as her present intentions goes — but *then!* S'posen she sh'd change her mind!"

He fairly groaned and perspired as he thought

of the possibilities. He felt as if the Peddicomb farm belonged to him already, and some one was trying to rob him of it! To be sure, she proposed to go away soon, and to hold her tongue meanwhile. But suppose she did not do so! He had lied as to the time when he crossed the river — appearances were all against him.

"Jes gimme a week, 'n' I'll fix that marr'ge question fer keeps! I'll marry Flory aout o' hand! But mebbe she wun't gimme no week! Ner no twenty-four hours, nuther! 'T would n't take but an afferdavy t' fix me fer life! Mebbe she's half way up t' the squire's a'ready! Oh Lordy, Lordy! Why did n't I offer her money — a hundred dollars, er say fifty!"

He even went so far as to turn his horse back toward the school-house, but before he had gone ten steps he bethought himself of the reason why he had not offered her money: it was because she was Anne Sparrow, and because of her look and voice when she said, "*What* do you mean?" Away from her he had forgotten these things, but now he once more saw her as in his secret heart he felt that she was — a woman above sordid schemes.

"Mebbe I kin help her along East 'thaout its costin' me nothin'. Lessee, lessee — haow kin that be worked?" And his mind ran off on this less disquieting train of thought.

Next day John McVey came to see Anne. (Tuesday was his regular day.) He observed her melancholy with much sorrow and sympathy, and did all he could to — increase it. His was too weak a nature to lead hers, just weak enough to follow it like a spaniel. Instead of attacking the enemy in blue, as Zury would have done, he at once took sides with sadness, that being the stronger of the combatants; and in his visits during the trying days now ensuing he was such a monument of woe that Anne felt almost gay by comparison. She might have laughed at him if she could have laughed at anything. John did not again broach the subject of marriage. Still, his silent constancy was far from being a discomfort to the poor, feeble girl, whose weakness and wretchedness only increased as the slow days wore on. On Thursday Anne learned that Zury and Flora Peddicomb were married. Zury had effected his second nuptials in the same business-like fashion which had marked his first. Her heart sank still lower in her breast as she listened to the news.

By Sunday, Anne knew that she was again in the hands of the Philistines. Somebody had seen Zury leave the mine, had stolen his carved stick, had told the story. Fully half the women in the little congregation had no words and no eyes for her; while some, the Ansteys and a few others, tried to make up by marked cordiality for the insulting distance of the rest. Vain effort! Put a sensitive woman in a community with even one hearty enemy, and the world is spoiled for her. It 's an omelet with one doubtful egg!

Fast and furious through all this week raged the factional warfare about the half-conscious, half-ignorant school-teacher. Her friends urged that nothing was proven against her; her enemies truly said that nothing was proven in her favor. That this latter charge was fatal, in a majority of minds, is emblematic of the state of feeling in such communities.

"Let alone this last job; what d' we know abaout her afore she come h'yer? Wha' 'd she come fer? Who 's she told whar she wuz 'n' what she wuz abaout afore she started? Sh' hain't told me — hez she told yew? If not, who in thunder hez she said a word tew?"

To this damning assault of raging, unsatisfied curiosity, Zury on one occasion stoutly urged: —

"Dunno 's she 'd any cause t' talk t' me, ner yew, ner any on us, abaout her own affairs. She 's arn't her pay honest, if ever a gal did; 'n' sh' ain't m'lested nobody."

No answer was then and there given to this plea, but glances were exchanged which said plainly, though mutely, what was spoken out in words as soon as the redoubtable Zury was absent: "Least said by Zury Prouder jist naow, th' better!"

"Ya-as!" "Yew bet." "Ye better b'lieve that's so!" came from grinning and nodding enemies. "'N' besides," added another, "*mebbe she 's a Universalist!*"

"True fer yew, Gabe! Sh' hain't made no perfesh'n 's nobody knows on. Did n't fetch no dismissal papers fr'm no constituted minister o' th' gospil, that she 's ever hed the civility t' 'xhibit in *this* neck o' woods!"

This capped the climax. This cast a pall of "odium theologicum" over both Anne and Zury, enfolding them *together*, and therefore adding a double, triple zest to the joy of striking at both.

"What business 's she in aour scule-haouse outer school hours I wonder! Who 's let it t' her fer a lodgin'; 'n' who gits th' rent; 'n' haow dooz he c'lect it?"

"Jesso, jesso, Gabe! I 'llaow aour money paid fer thet scule-haouse, 'n' I 'llaow th' ain't no one man 's ben auth'rized t' rent it aout — not as nobody knows on s' far 's heerd fr'm, up t' last accaounts."

"Action o' forcible entry 'n' detainer 'd lie, I reckon," suggested another man, who had himself been ousted by Zury from a rented farm, under the summary provisions of "the statute in that case made and provided."

"No 'casion fer no action, I reck'n. Leastways no action at law."

"I fer one 'd vote fer jest a rippin' aout all them boards — not techin' no property o' hern nuther!"

The shrewd Zury, though he never knew anything but vague rumors concerning this confab, saw plainly that his personal interests were almost identical with Anne's in the whole matter, and he had no difficulty in influencing his bride in the same direction. She had all a bride's confidence in her new husband. Probably she did not think deeply enough to see that her own married happiness depended on Anne's good name; all she thought or cared was that Zury said it was all right, and that Anne had always been good to her, and was now helpless and forlorn.

One afternoon Anne was startled at seeing Flora at her door, on foot and alone. She opened it and stood silent.

"Haowdy, haowdy, Miss Sparrer!"

"Good afternoon, Mrs. Prouder. Will you — will you come in?"

"Wal, yes, I guess I 'll stop a bit. Zury he 's druv on t' Wayback on s'm business, 'n' 'llaows t' call fer me a-goin' hum."

So she stepped in and sat down. A large, stout, "humbly" creature: the flat figure of a man, the face of an overgrown child, and the heart of a woman — a newly married woman, just called into unhoped-for happiness.

"Be ye peart? Ye don't look it. Look like ye hed a fit o' sickness sence I sor ye."

"No, I am far from well."

"What 's ailin' ye? Ye dew look *good* 'n' sick!"

"Oh, I don't know at all! I can neither eat nor sleep; and I 'm tired day and night." The blood, which had all left her face at the first sight of her visitor, now came back in a flood.

"Dew tell! I wanter know!" said the other, in a sympathetic voice. "Hain't ye tuk no physic fer it? The' 's a good doctor t' Wayback naow, I 've hearn tell."

"Oh, no. I never have a doctor, nor take medicine, you know."

"Jesso, jesso! It 's a wonder ye 've got along

's well 's ye hev! I hope ye hev n't let these yer foolish talkers hev no 'ffect on yer!"

The poor sufferer could stand it no longer; the interview was so different from what she had feared, the relief was so timely and so grateful, that she burst into tears once more, and sobbed as if her heart would break. The good-hearted Flora brought her chair up close, and against Anne's shuddering protests put her stout arms about her and drew her head down on her shoulder; patting and comforting her like a baby.

But few words passed between them, and those of little consequence. When Zury called for his wife, the women parted with mutual expressions of good-will.

"Remember," said Flora, as she climbed awkwardly into the wagon by means of the chair Anne held for her, "ye promised t' consult thet thar new doctor, fust chance ye git!"

"Oh, yes—I 'll consult him, to please you, whether I take his physic or not."

"Well—I bid ye good-day, 'n' God bless 'n' keep ye!"

"Thank you, thank you. Good-bye!" And they drove off.

"Goin' t' consult the doctor, is she?" said Zury.

"Yes, she is; 'n' it 's a God's marcy ef it ain't tew late, tew! Them ornery tattle-tales' lies hez brought her t' death's door, 'n' I dunno but whut it 's goin' t' be th' last on her, poor thing!" Then, after a long pause, during which Zury kept an unwonted silence, "She can't seem t' git no gal t' stop with her naow — tho' 't ain't a month sense the' wuz all a-waitin' fer their turn! Th' ornery cowards! Th' ain't let t' come no more, so th' ain't!"

"B' ain't they?"

"No, th' ain't! She 's a-stayin' t' th' Ansteys'!"

"Is, is she?"

"Yes. 'N' I jest begged 'n' begged her t' come right up t' our 'us, but she wuz stubborner 'n a muel. She jest *would n't.*"

"Would n't, would n't she? What reason 'd she give?"

"None at all. She just put her foot daown 't she would n't."

"Hmm!"

Anne set her little domicile in order and prepared to go over to the Ansteys'. Being afraid either to leave her purse in the lonely schoolhouse, or to carry it with her through the lonely woods, she had devised a hiding-place for it in a hole, excavated by some kindly woodpecker of a past season, in the tall stump of a dead tree at a little distance from the door; a nook wherein she would pop it, as she passed, so deftly that even if one had been walking by her side he would hardly have observed that she moved her hand. And there she always found it safe next morning. Having done this, among her other accustomed little ways, she walked on to the Ansteys', cogitating, with some restful relief, the visit she had had from Flora.

At tea she was more talkative than she had been of late, and even managed to "pick a bit," as Anstey expressed it. She detailed Mrs. Prouder's visit with the warm gratification it deserved, and added the information, which she knew would please Mrs. Anstey, that she had promised to consult the doctor.

"Ah, yah! I sh' think it wuz time! Ef it 's *in* time! Yew jest mark my words: ef he 'll give ye a sleepin' paowder 'n' a eatin' paowder — good strong ones, no odds what the' cost — ye 'll sleep fer tew days, 'n' eat all the' is aout, fust chance ye git! See ef ye don't. 'N' don't ye ferget t' mention th' fits med'cine, tew. Mebbe he 'll tell ye t' take that tew. It 's good med'cine, I don't misdoubt. Mus' be! Th' dose ain't but three drops!"

Anne promised. Then she confessed to a sleepiness that had been, alas, unusual of late in her experience, and got to bed and to sleep "as early as other folks."

A little later, when the old man was himself ready to retire, he was startled by a bright light over toward the school-house, that cast a red glow on that part of the sky.

"Heavens 'n' arth! Be they a-doin' on it? Kin the' be sech ornery heathens in this c'munity? The' be — sure 's yer born!"

"Wal, what next? Shall I call her? No! Do no good. It 's tew late t' dew anythin'. Oh Lord! Lord! Hev mercy on us all — on all but them 's hez done this thing — let them feel thy wrath 'n' thy burnin' — 's they will in thy good time! Amen!"

Meantime he was hurrying down the road in the dim hope of snatching some shred or patch of poor Anne's belongings from the hungry flames. But before he had gone far he saw advancing a straggling band of masked men on horseback, who at the same time perceived him and drew hastily together for consultation. Then one of them called out in a voice obviously disguised: —

"Halt there! O' man Anstey, ye jest git fer home, quick 's God 'll let ye. Ye can't dew no good, 'n' ye 'll come t' harm ef ye stir a step furder."

"I don't halt fer no murderin', burnin' thieves; not 's long 's I 'm on my way t' save the prop'ty of a poor, friendless gal! Yew kin jest add murder tew yer arson, soon 's ye like."

"We don't want t' harm ye, ef ye *be* th' friend o' that thar scarlet woman o' Babylon" —

"Ye 're a liar, Gabe Funk, 'n' I know yer, 'n' I kin prove it on yer! Ye ornery whelp! Burn the taown scule-haouse, would ye, ye ornery blaggard!"

The first speaker was now cowed and silent, and even turned and galloped off in the contrary direction, amid the jeering laughter of his companions. But another spoke in his stead: —

"We hain't burnt no scule-haouse, ner no prop'rty b'longin' t' th' gal. We jest smashed aout s'm boards th't did n't never hev no business in the scule-haouse; 'n' we fixed 'em so th' could n't be put back nuther, 'thaout ye kin build a p'tition aouter ashes. 'N' it 's all done, 'n' th' fire 's aout, near abaout; 's ye kin see fer yerself, ef ye only use yer old eyes!"

"Wal—ef it 's all over, wha' 'd ye want ter keep me away fr'm it fer? The cuss as shets o' man Anstey offen the public highway, a road as he 's put in his road-tax on same 's the rest why, he 's got ter kill him fust, that 's all!" And he resumed his walk as though they were not there. They silently divided their rank and let him pass.

At the school-house Anstey found things as the rioters had said. They had carried the lumber to a safe distance from the house before burning it, and had even taken some care to shut and barricade the door to defend Anne's belongings—all safe inside, so far as the old man could judge. So he went home to bed.

Next morning he broke the news to the family, but waited till after breakfast to say anything about it to Anne.

"The' 's ben a misdoin' with aour scule-haouse, Miss Sparrer, last night."

"What do you mean?"

"Wal—folks thought same 's we dew: 't ye better stay t' ol' Anstey's. So th' went 'n' busted up the new p'tition all t' flinders, so the' did, 'n' burnt the stuff."

Anne sat white, rigid, silent.

"The' did n't tech a hand t' noth'n' o' yourn. I see th' light, arter ye wuz in bed 'n' asleep, 'n' I went over, 'n' thar it wuz; the p'tition all carr'd aout 'n' burnt, 'n' yer things all set aside fer ye, 'n' the door closed up agin same 's the' faound it."

Well — what difference did it make to her? What could it make?

But oh! It did make a difference! To think that a lot of people hated her and her ways, and despised her well-meant efforts to be good to them and make them like and respect her! After all, it did not add much to her knowledge of how some of the community felt toward her.

"I see'd 'em — th' ornery whelps! — 'n' the' wuz n't but six on 'em all told — seven includin' one pup th't run away 's quick 's I tol' him I knowed him."

"Naow, Miss Sparrer," said Mrs. Anstey, "ye mus' n't go fer t' 'llaow we 'm all heathens h'yer abaouts. 'T ain't so; 'n' I would n' wonder if these h'yer ornery limbs o' Satan wuz t' find aout the diff'runce afore th' week 's aout."

"Doan't ye be a mite set back," added the old man. "Ef ye take my 'dvice, ye 'll go right over t' the scule-haouse, n' act so 's nobody would n't never guess the' 'd ever ben a p'tition thar. Keep shady 'n' see what turns up."

"Well, I will try," said the poor girl, and started over toward her wrecked kingdom and desecrated throne.

On approaching the spot she observed a few neighbors, brought over by sympathy or curiosity. The former class remained, while the latter silently withdrew as she approached.

Her heart swelled and rose to her throat, but she kept her eyes fixed on the ground until she came near the door, then cast one glance around and — fell forward on the ground, insensible.

All hurried up, and lifted her to the doorstep, where in a minute she revived and opened her eyes — piteously wandering at first, then gradually focusing themselves on the faces about her. She leaned forward as soon as she was able, and separated the by-standers so she could look at the heap of ashes and embers; then sank back, covered her eyes with her hands, and whispered faintly: —

"My money! It was hidden in that tree!"

The marauders had piled their fire around the dead stump, and that had burned with the rest.

CHAPTER XIII.

PANDORA'S BOX, WITH HOPE AT THE VERY BOTTOM.

THE first drop of balm came for poor Anne's wounds when there arose a reactionary storm of public indignation against the perpetrators of the school-house outrage. Those zealots of the stake and fagot had confidently expected to be greeted by God-fearing citizens with approval, evidenced by unusual nods and hand-grasps, accompanied with winks and smiles. This is the frontier substitute for trial and acquittal of "vigilance committees," — otherwise jocularly known as "necktie sociables," — where public enemies are by "lynch law" quietly put out of the way "between two days." But here, man after man, family after family, made haste to disclaim part or lot in the mean, sneaking deed which had robbed a poor girl of her all. In vain the amazed conspirators said to each other, "We did n' never *go fer* t' dew *that!*" They were even debarred the pleasure of saying this to anybody except each other, for it would have "give away" the fact that the burning was their doing.

Already, as Anne wandered about her former home, the signs of a revulsion of popular feeling began to make themselves manifest. She had forgotten that school was to "keep" that day, as usual, until she saw an unaccustomed concourse of scholars about her, such as reminded her of the palmy days before her troubles began. She at first thought that they were impelled by morbid curiosity to look at a rare and exciting scene; but she soon observed indications of other and better motives. Some of the mothers arrived with their daughters, and one brought a basket of provisions, with the simple explanation that she believed it was her daughter's turn to stay the week; ignoring the fact that it had been her turn some weeks ago, and she had been one of the bitterest critics. But Anne was too much disturbed to care for an apology, and also not a little solaced by the concession, ungracious and imperfect as it was.

"Well," she said, "you see how things are. The partition is gone" —

"Hain't ye got no spare beddin' t' hang up jes' raoun' yer tew beds, set clust t'gether?" She had seen this expedient for privacy so often tried that it seemed to her the simplest thing in the world.

"Why, yes — if I had any lines to hang up some quilts."

"Oh, grape-vines is better 'n lines, n' matter haow many ye hed! Oh, brother Anstey! Hi, yew, boy! Go tell Mr. Anstey t' come h'yer a minute."

So Anstey was called away from his bootless (and shoeless) quest among the embers for the ashes of Anne's little store of bank-notes; and between them arrangements were soon made for stretching the necessary grape-vines across where the partition had been. Anne and her friends were to occupy the place again in spite of of the black scheme to drive her from it.

Oh, if she could feel a little of her old strength and courage! Every mole-hill was now a mountain to her, every cobweb a thrall. As soon as school was dismissed she really surrendered all her old principles of skepticism and started for the village to see the doctor; accepting a "lift" from the first wagon that came along.

To her suprise Anne found the new physician to be a person of education, principle, and dignity: one of the class of men who have now so largely taken the place of the old style quacks, pretenders, self-promoted farriers, and such trash who had the fields and the grave-yards to a large extent under their grimy thumbs in the "early days."

He knew her by reputation, and knew the cruel loss she had sustained only the night before, so he quietly put aside the question of a fee when she raised that matter, and begged her to go on with her case.

Their conference was long, and, it may be supposed, painful. When it was over he looked very grave, and she — deathly. There is no milder term to do justice to her appearance.

The same wagon that had brought her to Wayback carried her home again. She had herself set down at the Ansteys, to get a little bit of love — without it she thought she should die at once.

These were her most faithful friends and adherents. Eureka had grown to be a quite presentable girl under Anne's effortless influence; tall, graceful, large-eyed, and large-hearted. And such devotion! Her heart's blood was ready for her dear teacher. The old man was devoted too, in his rough way.

"'Pears like that thar temp'runce barbecue 'd be the death on ye, arter all! No wonder, crazy 's yew be in the dark, t' be alone in a coal-mine all night, 'mongst the snakes 'n' lizards, *an'* the world a-burnin' up aoutside! Thut thar ornery Zury Praouder *he* 's got right smart t' answer fer. But yew keep a stiff upper lip 'n' yer nose full o' wind, 'n' ye 'll weather it yit. See 'f ye don't!"

"Oh, yes! I 'll get over it — some day and somehow."

Anne told of her having visited the new doctor, and that he had *not* prescribed for her.

"Did n' give ye no physic?" almost screamed Mrs. Anstey. "Wal, I don't think no gre't shakes o' him!"

The old woman's estimation of Anne had always been much interfered with by the latter's unchristian "viws" on physic. Medical heresy is so very like to blasphemy. And now the new doctor was turning out a heretic, too!

"Ye see what yer no-docterin' comes tew. Ef ye 'd a let me docter ye up a bit! Naow the' 's right smart o' that fits med'cine left — more 'n tew dozen doses, I reckon. I give some on it, 'baout a teaspoonfle, t' a hawg th't wuz a-ailin', but I could n't save her. She wuz dead in less 'n a minute. Mebbe I gin her tew much — mebbe not enough. Mos' likely it wuz tew late t' dew her any good. 'D orter tried it in time. Naow would n't ye like t' jest *try* it? Ye can't tell whether er no it 'll knock yer complaint till ye jest *try* it."

"No, thank you. I should be afraid to try it. Or — not exactly afraid" — a sigh. "I 've nothing to fear now, except living" — Then with a sudden fire: "Yes, you may give it to me. Perhaps I 'll take it. Perhaps it 'll cure all my troubles."

"Thar naow. It dooz me good t' h'yer ye talk like a Christian arter all. Thar 't is: ye 'll find the d'rections on the lay-bill — three drops in a spoonfle o' water. Ye 're right welcome tew it, tew."

So Anne said good-by all round, kissing often and long the weeping Eureka, and telling her, in the hearing of them all, that if there was anything left at the school-house when she was gone it was to be Eureka's. No, she could n't say just what day she should go, after school closed, nor when they would see her again. But some day — yes, of course in ample time to begin school again in the fall — if the directors wanted her. The chorus of indignant protests at this doubt brought only a wan smile to her wasted features.

"By the way, Mr. Anstey, have you seen Mr. Prouder lately?"

"Seen him yest'd'y; hain't sor him to-day."

"Well, it does n't matter. Good-bye! Good-bye!" and she dragged her slow steps toward the school-house, only to find that her proposed companion had got tired of being alone and had gone home. So she was left to herself. She sat down to think over the situation. What should she do? What could she do? She held her hideous little vial in her hand, studying the dirty label, thinking — thinking. Then she took the remains of her poor dotted muslin and the one slipper, and made of them a funeral pyre, on which she burned up certain old letters — not her mother's — and a package wherein she had many newspaper-clippings; all the book-notices and other things of hers which had ever met the dubious honor of print. She cried softly as they burned.

After this and a very few other lingering preparations for departure, she sat down out-of-doors on a rude seat the boys had made for her by her little flower-bed, and poured the whole contents of the vial into her one tablespoon.

How grim appear the portals of death unless approached through the long, dim antechamber of hopeless and wasting disease, of vitiating dissipation, or of kindly, disengaging old age! Let those answer who have faced it in the prime and flush of manhood.

She smelled of the dreadful dose — incredibly odious! She touched it with the tip of her tongue; and that settled at least one question, for such a shudder ran down her back and out through her limbs to the very tips of her fingers and toes, that the nauseous drug all spilled out of the spoon on the grass.

Anne rose and "took herself in hand." She looked at the house, at the trees, at the sky, compressing her thin lips and clenching her slender hands strenuously together.

"I am no suicide! I am no murderess! I am a New England woman! I owe life to the world and the world owes life to me. Both debts shall be paid!"

She went into the school-house, packed a few things in a satchel, locked the door, and walked all the way to Wayback, where McVey had the satisfaction of accommodating her with a room. Seeing that he lingered pensively about the door while she laid aside her bonnet and shawl, she asked him to come in and be seated.

"Did you wish to see me?"

"Well — Miss Sparrow, you can guess all I 've got to say. I 've been tellin' you the story ever since I met you, and suppose I shall keep on tellin' it right along."

"I should think you would have got over that foolish feeling, now that I am such a wreck in every way."

"Get over it! Never!"

"You do not know all." She hid her tired eyes in her handkerchief, and shed a few more of the hot tears to which they had grown so sadly accustomed. "I may be a widow for all you know. Or a divorced woman — or a deceived, betrayed, deserted girl. You know, I am sure, that I could not have been deliberately and intentionally — *bad.* I don't see how any woman of common sense could be *that*, let alone common principle."

"I don't ask any questions. I'm so downhearted at the idea of you East and me left here" — and he actually cried.

"A sickly, useless invalid would be enough to discourage even a rich man — and you are not rich, I suppose."

"Well, no; not to be called wealthy at present. The trouble I have found to be the want of capitle. If I only had capitle, I should no doubt progress. When I started out, I had a little capitle, from an aunt, but it was n't enough, and when it was gone I could n't get any more; and there it was, you see! Since then I've cast about in vain — all for the want of capitle."

"Nor any income either, I presume?"

"In point of fact, none to speak of. I find that parties who might be willin' to furnish capitle are invariably those who have none of their own, while those who hold capitle to any great extent are without exception unwillin' to part with it even in cases where it is most needed, indispensable, I may say — like my case for instance."

"To whom have you applied out here for assistance?"

"Well, I did approach Mr. Prouder on the subject of capitle."

"Did he offer you any large sum?"

"I can't say he did. He did n't seem to grasp the subject. In fact I was somewhat disappointed, for when he first began to reply he put his hand in his pocket; and said he, 'Young man, I'll give you'— and then keepin' his hand in his pocket he went on, 'a piece of advice. If you want capitle you slave for it and shave for it and save for it, same as I did.' Now this discouraged me a good deal, seein' his disinclination to entertain a broad comprehension of my situation."

"You did not mention — anything else?"

"Well, no. Seein' he did n't seem to grasp the subject, I did n't get round to it; though when I commenced, my intention was to mention that we were, so to speak, engaged to marry."

"Well, we are not. I am not well and you are not rich, so that settles it. Now, I would like to see Mr. Prouder whenever he happens to pass this way."

It was not long before she learned that Zury had been at the tavern and gone away again; when told that she wanted to see him, he had said that he had not time to stay that day, and did not know just when he should pass that way again.

Her courage still rose to the occasion. She wrote Zury a polite note to the effect that she would call at his house, if it would be out of the way for him to come to Wayback; or could he conveniently be at the school-house on Saturday afternoon? If she did not find him there she could walk on to the farm as well as not.

The days passed, Saturday came, and she walked slowly to the school-house. Nearing the door, she found Zury sitting in a quiet place near by. Instead of feeling stronger at the sight of his strength she felt weaker; a longing for his aid to her fainting steps seized upon her with irresistible force. She *must* have it!

"Howdy, Miss Sparrer? Glad t' see yer a lookin' so — wha — what's all this? Where 'n the nation 's the rest on ye gone tew?"

She unlocked the door, and dragged herself languidly to her old seat by the bell-rope, motioning him to a chair near by. He did not sit: he clutched his hands tightly together behind him and gazed at her with flushed face and wide-open eyes. When the silence grew insupportable she said in a piteous tone: —

"I give up! I 've given up forever!"

"Sho, sho, naow! That wun't never dew! Never in the world!"

"A lonely girl, hated and hunted by people I never harmed; homeless, penniless, pointed at; almost ashamed to show my face; and sick — sick — sick to death's door! Which way can I turn?"

Zury would have liked to say, "Turn which way ye min'ter, fer all me." He had been able to say so in times past, firmly; and to hold to it, too. But here he was amazed to find that he *could not.* The words stuck in his throat. He almost wanted, already, to talk the other way!

"The next question is, being homeless and penniless, am I friendless, too?"

"The' 's o' man Anstey."

"A pauper."

"The' 's Johnny McVey."

"A helpless fool." A long pause.

"Then the' 's Zury Prouder"—

"No pauper and no fool—but may be no friend either—after all his promises—and all that 's past!" The last words sadly reproachful.

Another silence followed, embarrassing to both, but agonizing to Zury.

"I tell you one thing, and swear it, too—if I must die, it will be in a way that will startle this community!"

"Die, Miss Sparrer!"

"I said so."

"Oh, Lord! what kin I dew? Ye know folks is couplin' my name an' yourn t'gether a'ready—'n' the' 'll dew it more."

"Yes, we are both talked about, I hear. Now, am I to die in despair, and you to live on as happy and prosperous as ever? Why don't they burn *you* out and leave *me* alone? Why do they attack the defenseless?"

"Way o' the world, I s'pose. *I* can't change it."

"You can't stir hand or foot for justice or—mercy?" A minute of silence. "Did you ever promise to stand by me? Are you a man or a cowardly dog?"

Zury repeated the question aloud; not as retorting upon her, but as setting a problem before himself. "Be I a man er a cowardly dog? Is Zury Praouder a man er a dog?" Another pause. "Miss Sparrer, I 've ollers jedged myself a man; naow we 'll see—we 'll see—we 'll see," and he sat long, staring at her and conning the problem.

"Wha' d' ye 'llaow t' dew?"

"I don't know."

"Wha' 'd' ye 'llaow t' say?"

"The truth. Whether I live or die, the truth."

"Ye 's good 's tol' me wunst, a-settin' in that very cheer, that ye worn't a-goin' t' say noth'n'."

"I never gave my word — and if I had I would n't keep it now — since things have so changed."

"Ye 'llaowed ye did n't blame me nary mite."

"I did n't and I don't blame you. Now whom do you blame for all that 's happened? Me?"

Silence.

"Maybe you *are* the meanest man that lives in Spring County, or in the whole world, or ever did live! And yet — somehow — I can *hardly* believe it."

"I be, I guess. But I ain't mean enough fer that. Not quite mean enough fer that!"

"Then, if I am no more to blame than you are, must I bear all the trouble and say nothing? I, a helpless girl? I guess not! And what 's more, I *know* not!"

"Haow 'll ye prove anythin'?"

"How will I prove what I say? I will just ask Zury Prouder if Anne Sparrow is a liar! What will he answer?"

After a pause she added, pleadingly, with something nearer a smile than she had yet ventured to try: "I shan't have to prove anything — nor charge anything. It won't come to that. You will stand by me, whatever happens!" Still his silence left her in doubt — despairing doubt. She repeated, very gently: "You 'll stand by me!" and slid softly to her knees and covered her face with her hands.

"Miss Sparrer! Ef ye think I won't stand by ye, ye 're wuss fooled than ye ever was afore in yer life! Er ever will be! Yew hear me!" (Taking her hands and raising her to her seat again.) "Yew hear me! Zury Praouder, the me-anest man in Spring Caounty; he 's the man 'll dew that thing ef it takes th' last critter he 's got onter th' place!"

As he said this, he listened to his own voice in wonder — almost in dismay. What was coming over him? But he did not retract, nor even for an instant regret.

At last the sufferer could smile a little. A real smile; not one of those pretended ones of the past weeks, which were sadder than tears to look at. She gave him her hand — so thin and white that the light seemed to shine through everywhere save where the blue veins obstructed it; and he took it gently and held it a moment. He would have kissed it, only he did not know how.

As he walked homeward, on his solitary way, his heart felt warmer and softer than it had since his children died. He wondered if he was the same man or somebody else, and concluded that a change had come over him of which he was glad — but might be sorry to-morrow.

If he was changed it was not very radically,

for he soon began planning and plotting how to keep his word and do his manly duty without its costing him anything; a scheme in which he of course succeeded, as we shall see hereafter.

And Anne? Let her speak (to herself) for herself: —

"*Now* — may he perform his promise: and *then* may I never see his face again!"

The new preacher, Elder Masten, — a fresh graduate from a theological seminary, but a "Son of Thunder," and a man of large natural power, — on the Sunday following the burning, "improved the occasion" in a stinging sermon from the text: "He that taketh the sword shall perish by the sword."

Anne was not able to drag herself to church, but it would have done her good to hear the sermon, and still more to hear the public comments during the dispersion of the congregation. The cruel murder of Lovejoy at Alton, by a pro-slavery mob, was fresh in the minds of both pastor and people. It barbed his shafts and prepared their hearts.

The sword — that is to say any violence, whether with arms or with fire or any other element of destruction — is excusable, justifiable, praiseworthy, necessary; — provided it is the All-wise who wields it. And when it is the Providentially ordained system of human government which wields it, it is still God who destroys; He using the system as His agent to do His work.

But when it is poor, weak, erring men who appeal to it, cloaking themselves with darkness, and shielding themselves with silence and disguise, then are they playing they are God! The crawling worm lifts his blind and slimy head, and says, "Vengeance is mine; I will repay!"

Beginning thus, Masten inveighed for a full hour, while women wept and men's eyes shone with indignation, their hearts beating hard and fast in the heat of the preacher's unstudied eloquence.

After the sermon Masten announced that he hoped for a full attendance at Wednesday evening prayer meeting, when steps would be taken looking toward making good to sister Sparrow the loss she had suffered.

The people crowded around the preacher as he came out, shaking hands most cordially, and giving their adhesion to his views. Then they separated by ones, twos, and threes, talking together as they went.

"Gee Whillikins! Did n't preacher give it tew 'em right!"

"Yew bet! I wish 't he had a-dwelt a leetle on th' 'perish by the sword' part of th' tex!"

"As haow?"

"Why, he *mought* a come t' th' conclusion th't 't was abaout time fer th' perishin' t' begin! 'T would n' take but a whisper fr'm preacher t' wipe aout them fellers offen th' face o' th' arth—leastways aouter th' baound'ries o' Spring Caounty!"

This suggestion had a great run of popularity until it reached Masten's ears, when he promptly nipped it — just in time.

"What! Preach against unlawful violence in one breath and blow an avenging fire with the next? Set up myself for the Deity — I who am the poorest worm in the clod?"

This killed the inchoate movement, and somewhat abashed its leader, but he said: —

"All th' same, ef I wuz Gabe Funk I 'd insure my barn."

"Yes, 'n' ef I wuz th' insurance comp'ny I would n't issue no policy ontew it!"

Then the conversation turned on the projected relief-meeting.

"I hain't got no money, but I 'll give a good hawg."

"So 'll I."

"Me 'n' my two sons 'll throw in a yearlin' calf."

"That 's talkin'! Let 's dew it up right. It 'll kinder take the cuss offen the taownship."

"Wonder haow much Zury Proauder 'll give!"

"He 'd orter throw in a good jag o' ready money. But he wun't."

"Yew bet he wun't! Bet ye he don't come t' th' meetin' at all!"

They were wrong. Zury was there, with his wife — and Squire Brown. They found the movement going on swimmingly. The most threatening trouble was an embarrassment of riches: for how was Anne to drive away a drove of hogs, a herd of calves, a flock of chickens, ducks, and geese, and a load of "truck," with hardly enough ready cash to feed them for a week?

As soon as the meeting came to order, Mr. Masten in the chair and Mr. McVey secretary, Zury moved that a committee of three be appointed by the chair to consider the matter which had called them together, and report at the next Wednesday evening meeting.

Murmurs of dissent arose on all sides. "Told ye Zury he 'd squirm aouter it somehaow."

"Blame me ef that ain't jest like Zury! It 's him t' find a patent plan fer not a-givin' nothin'."

Old Anstey got up first.

"I move that that motion don't pass. All 's in favior of it 's not a-passin' — " here the Chair called him to order, and reminded him that as brother Prouder's motion was not yet seconded it was not open for discussion.

"In order to open the subject for discussion," said the politic Squire Brown, "and for no other purpose, I second it."

"Then we 'll hear from brother Prouder in support of his motion," said the chairman.

So Zury said: —

"Mr. Chairman. If the' 's any man h'yer or elsewhar th't 's more opposed t' vi'lence th'n I be, I dunno th' man. 'N' ef ther 's a man h'yer er elsewhar th't 's more disposed t' stand by, and see through, a pilgrim, 'n' a stranger, 'n' a sojourner, th'n I be, I dunno thet man nuther. Ef Miss Sparrer wuz h'yer, I sh'd call on her freely t' say ef I 've shown myself her friend sence she come in these h'yer parts — er otherwise."

Some pious smiles passed between the gossipers at this unwary burst of confidence.

"But let 's see who owes her all this money. I 'll pay my sheer, every time. Who 's li'ble t' Miss Sparrer fer what wuz destroyed o' hers last week?"

Here more indignant murmurs burst forth, and even found a mouthpiece. Brother Bromwell put in his oar — he who always felt so sore under Prouder's dictation.

"Who owes it? Why seven men 't yew know 's well 's I dew, Zury Praouder! 'N' then tew yew know 's well 's I dew th't the' can't nothin' be proved agin 'em! 'N' yew know 's well 's I dew th't if ye c'd prove fortyleven hunderd dollars agin 'em ye could n' c'leck not forty cents aouter th' hull bilin' on 'em, so ye could n't!"

Bromwell's last words were lost in a storm of foot-stamping applause. (The Wayback public had learned to applaud.) Encouraged by it he went on.

"I move th't this h'yer meetin' don't want nobody t' help it aout th't wants t' try t' help it by a-henderin' on it."

Here the chairman again made peace by reminding the brother that there was one motion before the meeting, and it would be soon enough to consider another when that one should have been voted on. Zury meanwhile kept his feet, setting his face in the hard level lines that marked the "bed-rock" of his brave nature.

"Who said those seven men owed this money? Not me! Them ornery whelps they ain't capable of owin' ner payin' no more 'n any other haoun's pup. Naow ef brother Omri Bromwell ain't satisfied with my 'thority, I'll call on brother Braown."

So the Squire arose and said that at brother Prouder's request he had looked into the questions of law involved in "this h'yer burnin'," and finding that three or more persons had unlawfully conspired together; and together with force and arms had violently assaulted and injured the property of a person in the peace of the county; the offence amounted to a riot, and the county was pecuniarily responsible to the injured party.

This was a staggerer. But brother Bromwell came again to the rescue.

"S'posin' the' *be* a action agin the caounty fer damages; what 's the good of sech a scheme fer t' help Miss Sparrer? It 's jest a dodge t' put her off 'thaout her a-gittin' nothin', ner any call fer *some* folks t' putt the'r han's in the'r hard-hearted pockets." And he looked daggers at Prouder.

This brought Zury up again.

"Be I a man o' my word?"

No answer.

"Be I a man 't keeps his promises?"

Then a voice came from a back seat, —

"Oh yes — on'y ye don't never make none, not afore witnesses." A burst of laughter greeted this sally.

"I guess my promises 'll fetch 's much in open markit as his'n th't spoke last." He paused for a laugh, but none came. "Wal, I hev t' propose th't I'll advance th' amount of Miss Sparrer's claim, 'n' look t' Spring Caounty fer my pay!" And he sat down.

A moment's pause was required to take in the full sense of this; then there came a round of stamping in which all joined — everybody, of all shades and tones of feeling. Anne was to get her money — they were to save theirs — in short, Zury the Great had triumphed once more. He was made the committee to attend to it all.

This was the closing week of the school; so the relief would come in good time. What joy it was to the Ansteys to communicate the good news to poor Anne!

"Dunno what 's come over Zury! S'pose he knows which side his bread 's buttered ontew; but *then* — t' pay out good money 'n' buy in a lawsuit — thet ain't like Zury, not a mite." Anne reddened in silence. "Naow, Miss Sparrer, I look t' see ye gain a paound a day, at th' very least. Want ye fat enough t' kill, 'n' then not kill ye — that 's th' way t' treat prize live-stock like yew be!"

"I wish it could be so, Mrs. Anstey — but it cannot; not in this climate. I must get away, or die on your hands."

"Wal, God speed ye ef so it must be! Any-haow, ye 're fixed naow so ye *kin* go; 'n' thet 's a massy if ye got t' go er die. Most on us in sech a case 'd a hed ter dew th' other thing. Oh, ef thet thar pertend docter 'd only a guv ye some good strong physic! Of all things I dew dispise, it's a docter th't's afear'd t' give his own physic! What's he fer, dooz he s'pose! Ah yah!"

School had closed, and Anne's regular abiding place now was at the tavern. The independence and leisure suited her very well indeed. She could go on with her recuperation very nicely, barring two disquieting circumstances. The first was the perpetual propinquity of John Endicott McVey and Hopeless Passion, his Siamese twin. This was not a severe trial; he was constantly serviceable and never intrusive. In fact, she grew gradually to have quite a sisterly feeling of comfortable reliance on his quiet devotion; it was only that her troublesome Puritan conscience revolted at accepting so much and returning so little, either in the way of present regard or future intention.

The other matter was more serious, being nothing less than the prosaic consideration of a growing tavern-bill. Even this was soon relieved by the strong aid of her usual ally, Zury Prouder.

Zury was not a visitor of hers, but one day on coming down to dinner she saw him at the desk in deep conversation with the innkeeper, the subject being evidently a very anxious one for the latter. The talk, now loud, now low, finally settled down to an apparently amicable tenor, and at this point she was called in.

"Miss Sparrer, one moment ef *yew* please.

Brother Thum h'yer, he 's unlucky enough t' a-give a mortgidge on this prop'ty, 'n' I 'm lucky enough t' hold th' said mortgidge. I be'n a-askin' him fer a consid'able back int'rust — wal, so t' speak, right smart o' money — 'n' he 'llaows he can't pay it not jest naow, ner can't tell when he will be able so t' dew."

Thum rubbed his anxious brow and nodded assent.

"Wal, t' help him aout, it jest struck me th't I 'm some beholden t' yew, 'n' yew some t' him, 'n' goin' t' be more so, we hope: fer th' longer ye stay raound, th' better this c'munity 'll be suited, be it weeks, months, er years" —

Again Thum nodded — this time with a smile.

"Wal — t' make a long story short — he kin charge your accaount t' me, 'n' yew 'n' me kin fix it up, if so be yew 'gree t' aour plan."

Anne, in her "puzzlementary attitude," made a rapid mental calculation how long her little store of cash (when made good from county assets) would pay the modest weekly demands of Mr. Thum. This consideration was cut short by Zury.

"I don't 'llaow th't I 've got any right t' pledge th' caounty money fer sich a purpose, brother Thum. That must be a trust, t' be handed over in — tire."

"Wal — then — brother Prouder — what dooz that leave me? Ef th' other funds dew and owin' by yew t' Miss Sparrer give aout" —

"Wal, brother Thum, that 's my lookaout.

Th' caounty fun's ain't th' only thing I 'm a-owin' t' Miss Sparrer, by right smart. When I tell yew time 's up 'n' cash gi'n aout, why then yew kin aoust Miss Sparrer by any legle remedy th' law gives ye. But till I notify ye, in writin', ye kin go on a-entertainin' her, pervidin' of course ye 're still a owin' me, er my credit 's good with ye for th' overplus."

"Oh wal, that 'll last over t' kingdom come, I guess."

"Then it rests with you, Miss Sparrer!"

"I consent."

As Zury hurried off to mount his horse he glanced back, but he did not meet any answering look from Anne Sparrow.

CHAPTER XIV.

PASTORAL CARE FOR AN INTRACTABLE EWE-LAMB.

To Anne, at the tavern, a visitor is announced.

"Miss Sparrow, I believe."

"Yes sir. Are you Mr. Masten?"

"The same unworthy champion of a worthy cause. How did you know me, may I inquire? You have not attended any of the services I have held."

"I might retort, how do you know I have not?"

"Well, of course I look from my new pulpit on a sea, or at least a lake, of unknown faces: still, I should not have forgotten yours."

"Oh indeed!" (A little pause, a little blush, a little smile, a little of that vain movement of the head called "bridling.") "Well, I too could guess you were Mr. Masten without any miracle. And I am glad to see you."

"I thank you. I hear you have been sick."

"Yes. Nothing short of that would have kept me from your meetings; especially since I learned how much I am indebted to you for the movement which promises to relieve me from my worst trouble — almost my worst."

"Oh, you do not owe me any thanks. I was endeavoring to aid justice, which is the Lord's cause, not yours."

"To be sure. I did not suppose" —

"Of course I should have been glad to serve you personally; am glad now to find who it is that I have been made the humble instrument in setting right."

"Oh, I know well enough it would have made no difference with you."

"God is no respecter of persons: how could His professed servant be influenced by preference, even when it was so natural as it is in this case?" And he looked at her with a directness that startled her a little, awakening a forgotten feeling; a mixture of gratification and reserve that kept her silent.

"I have of course heard much about you."

"Yes, I'm afraid so."

Tears started from her heart, but before they reached her eyes he went on.

"Oh, you need not fear! Quite the contrary. As the conversation has reached me, it was such as made me think of you with thanks to God that He should have bestowed such a gift on this people."

At this the tears made their way, but with much of the bitterness filtered out on the road.

"And, since I have met you, I must try to be glad that I spoke on your side before making your acquaintance; so that I need not suspect myself of being moved to zeal by other than godly impulses, — by things of the earth, earthy."

Now she *must* rally him out of this sentimental

vein. So she dried her eyes, and dragged up a light smile from its long-used hiding-place.

"Oh, don't be alarmed as to that! A little better acquaintance will quite free your conscience from any suspicion of favoritism in my direction. You 've probably been talking to the Ansteys."

"Yes — and the Prouders, and others."

"Well, that may have misled you; but now that you come to headquarters, all the false glory will soon depart."

Not quite ready to keep up with her woman-wit he reddened in silence, and she changed the subject to things less personal.

"I hope you have learned to value the Ansteys as I do."

"They seem to be — the Lord's people: treasures hidden in measures of meal, not at once to be known for the value they possess. We must be cautious, I have learned, to avoid judging by exteriors. Do you not find it so?"

"Well, I had seen so many false jewels in fine settings in my life, before I met the Ansteys, that I was quite prepared to find specimens of the reverse. I have almost forgotten that they are not the pink of elegance. Don't you think Eureka very handsome?"

"Since you mention it, I do recall that she is well-favored for a — for a native. She may grow into a good-looking lady."

"Oh, I 'm sure you have not observed her eyes! They would be remarked anywhere! Don't fail to look at them."

"I will make a memoranda, and surely do as you sudgest."

"And as to cultivation — little things, of no great importance but yet sure of a certain appreciation in *your* eyes on account of your own superior education," — she looked for a self-satisfied smirk, and did not look in vain, — "I wish you would observe how much she has learned, even in the few months I have been aiding her in my poor way."

"I must allow, sister, that I had already found my attention called to a general improvement manifest in the lambs a kind Shepherd has given into your holy keeping, especially in their verbiage, which almost approaches your own."

Anne winced at "verbiage," but kept her face straight, and went on.

"So much result, from so small a cause, shows a capacity for cultivation which will lead her to perfect ladylikeness — under proper guidance. Of course Mrs. Anstey has prescribed for you?"

"Yes, truly! I am armed against all known diseases, and have only to await the assaults."

"But I hope that though nine old women can prescribe for a clergyman, one cannot make him take the dose."

"Well! To be frank with you, the only fear I now cherish of any ailment is the uncertainty how to parry Mrs. Anstey's good offices."

"Oh, do as I do. A laugh and a shake of the head is a good shield — if one could only always have the laugh at command!"

"Perhaps the good lady would not forgive me for my rebellious views as readily as she has forgiven you for yours."

"More readily! I have prepared the path for you!"

"Most true. You have been a pioneer of common sense regarding medical experiments—the voice of one crying in the wilderness, if I may quote holy writ without irreverence. Brother Prouder says you regard doctors, even graduated practitioners, as toll-gate keepers to the graveyard."

"Aha! That is his flowery garb for my simple expressions. He is a good deal of a poet."

This was a staggerer for the simple-hearted theological collegiate. The stony hardness of a pioneer endowed with the graces of a poet! The discussion that followed as to what poetry is; the novel thought that rhyme and metre are mere adjuncts and accessories; these suggestions were to him like the opening of a window toward sunrise. He listened spellbound; and, in his lumbering way, laid himself out to do his part and appear well before the fair Bostonian.

His success was not all that might have been desired. In the first place, besides his errors in the misuse and overuse of language, the Boston ă was beyond his grasp. His ă in "can't" was just the same as his ă in "can." Now McVey could say, in the same breath, "căn" and "cahn't," without a moment's preparation, or any caution to avoid the confusion of tongues which haunts some aspirants to this envied accomplishment. As when they fall into the mongrel "hăf-pahst."

Then, too, his habit of thought and his notion of reverent duty impelled the dragging in of frequent casual allusions to Deity, which were, to Anne, whimsical absurdities — a mixture of cant and blasphemy.

But most of all she was held aloof from sympathy with his effort to cultivate their acquaintance into intimacy, by the fact that her troubles and her illness seemed to have made her absolutely indifferent to the whole race of men. Her thin features had taken on that touching *hunted* look one sometimes sees in delicate animals. All she cared for was to know how to keep the other sex at a distance and how to get along without them. It was still a problem — a horrid puzzle, especially in the dark night when she ought to have been asleep instead of sobbing and shuddering on her lonely pillow. Oh if she could only fly to a heaven peopled entirely with female angels!

As to this new friend, whom a few weeks before she might have hailed with enthusiasm and counted among the most promising brightenings in her dull lot, she now only wished to be well rid of him. But this thought did not seriously disquiet her, for she said to herself, —

"He is *so* religious — I can cure him in short order of any troublesome penchant he may entertain for me. All I shall have to do is to let him know what a heathen I am! So that is off my mind."

Therefore she gave her fancy full play, and really enjoyed his call as the first intellectual privilege worthy the name which she had met with since she had left "home."

But Masten was not so safe. This delightful conversation was not to him a recalling of any old and long-forgotten pleasure. It was a new experience, the realization of dreams of what social intercourse might be, which dreams had hitherto never assumed more than a dim semblance of actuality in his acquaintance with a humble home, and the women and girls of a Western academy town; and the unlovely specimens he had met in his new field of labor, — simply, in his eyes, a drove of lambs to be coaxed and driven into the fold of the Good Shepherd; not lovely and charming human souls, like his new friend.

Toward the latter part of his call Anne noticed a growing seriousness in his mood and a more constant gravitation toward holy writ. He evidently had something on *his* mind. At last it came out.

"Sister Sparrow, will you accompany me to the Throne of Grace?"

She thought to herself, "Now is my time to put up the bars," and after a moment's pause answered, rather stiffly, —

"You must pray when and where you please, Mr. Masten, and permit me to do the same."

"Are not all times and places fitted for praying?"

"Well, no; not praying out aloud."

"Prayer is the food of the soul."

"My soul never eats between meals."

"Prayer is the Christian's breath of life."

"Well, perhaps so; but the healthiest breathing is inaudible."

Finding that his allegorical shafts recoiled upon him, he cast about for some more direct appeal; but she headed him off.

"I suppose a woman can speak confidentially to a minister — the priest never betrays the secrets of the confessional" —

"You mean to ask if I will keep what you say to myself? Most unquestionably!"

"Well, then, between ourselves, I 'm a heretic!'

"A — heretic?" He gazed at her with amused incredulity as if she had said, "I 'm a burglar."

"Yes — a despicable heretic! You know Boston is deeply tainted with false doctrine, heresy, and schism."

"I had surely heard that New England had, to some extent, harbored unchristian views, rejecting the plain teachings of the Bible and setting up the folly of man against the wisdom of God. But! Do we gather grapes of thorns or figs of thistles? Can such influences as I have observed among your scholars come from a Uni —" he checked himself as if it were a word not to be ventured in a lady's presence.

"A Unitarian? Oh, no, I don't call myself a Unitarian — I 'm afraid dear good Doctor Channing would n't own me! But at any rate I do not, can not, and will not join, except passively, in the customary forms of orthodox worship."

"Well, I'm glad you're not a Unitarian at least! But oh, my dear young Christian friend, how I must wrestle in prayer, for you if not with you! Yours I perceive to be a logical mind; I must prepare for your use some of the considerations which cannot fail to bring any reasoning being to the true faith! Promise me to attend divine service on Sabbath!"

"I'm afraid you'll preach at me, and the people will find it out somehow!"

"I will preach at Satan and all his works; I hope you're not Satan, in one of his most dangerous disguises; and I'm sure you are not, for your works are those of an angel of light."

"Well, now remember—those works of mine you make so much of will all be rubbed out like a picture off a slate, if you in any way, by words, looks, or actions, in the pulpit or out of it, let the Wayback world know as much about me as I have told you about myself. Or any inkling of it!"

"Yes, indeed, my—Miss Sparrow! We learn some cunning, even in a theological school,—some worldly wisdom, not going to the extent of 'pious fraud,'—though you did call me a priest a while ago!"

"Did I? Well, I take it back. Be as wise as a serpent, as well as harmless as a dove, won't you?"

"Surely, surely, Miss Sparrow! Anything you

give me Bible warrant for, you may command me to do. New Testament warrant, I *would* say."

They parted with expressions of good-will, pious on his side and hearty on both, although Anne had grown a little tired of him.

The enthusiastic young shepherd, as he walked rapidly away, kept saying to himself, "Oh, what a brand to snatch from the burning!" over and over again; and when he had got clear of the town and into the silent woods, he dropped on his knees and put up an earnest prayer for aid in this sweet heaven-appointed task that had just opened before him.

When he rose, brushed off his trousers, and walked on, he grew voluble and eloquent in scathing denunciations of the errors of heterodoxy. He cut and trimmed a stout hickory sapling to enable him to gesticulate without appearing to himself absurd. With it he swished off the heads of many mullein-stalks, each personifying some monstrous fallacy of heresy. "Salvation by works!" (swisht!) "Unity of the Godhead!" (swisht!) "Denial of verbal inspiration!" (swisht!) "Subordination of the Son!" (swisht!) "Universal salvation!" (swisht!)

Here his stick encountered a hidden obstacle, and broke at the point; but he cut off the splintered end and went forward with shorter strokes, not noticing the omen.

His next Sunday's sermon was half prepared before he had traveled the first two miles; and when polemics became wearisome his thoughts strayed to pleasanter themes; and pictures arose of a fair and shining penitent, brought (by Divine help) to glorious usefulness in a life rounding out and completing his own.

Before he dismissed this alluring vision, it had flown on so fast and so far as to portray Anne the observed of all observers at Conference, and insuring (even to a husband who was sure of it already) the most rapid advance to the very top of his profession.

On Sunday morning he gave out as his text for the morning sermon, "My Father is greater than I," and for the afternoon, "I and my Father are one." He demonstrated with irrefutable reasoning that the first had been said by the Earthly Nature speaking of the Heavenly Nature: and then he supplemented the argumentative by the denunciatory; shaking the most gory terrors over the heads of such unnamed and almost unnamable miscreants and blasphemers as might, in certain far-away localities, dare to question the existence of a Triune God. Shouts of "Glory!" "A-a-amen!" "Bless His name!" and other wild cries and groans arose on all sides, so as to drown the speaker's voice at the close of certain sentences full of blood-curdling sentiments regarding the ultimate fate of these distant monsters of Iniquity. Every heart in the crowded house was carried along in the torrent of the preacher's eloquence — every heart but one, a large one under a small bodice, which only murmured "goose" in response to him, and "geese" in protest against them.

After "meeting" was over Masten escaped from the throng about him to ask Anne if he might walk home with her, but she said as she was still delicate she was going to accept a seat in one of the wagons. He probably did not imagine that she could see how his countenance fell at this, but she could and did. He strode out stoutly, however, and when the wagon she rode in approached and passed him she could not help observing how tall, and even handsome (in his way) he looked, strong in body and mind, and (as she added to herself) utterly unlovable. He looked up for her bow, but her face was turned far away on the other side, so he could only smile on her companions.

She did not come out again for the afternoon meeting, and the hearers marked a great falling off in the preacher, scarcely a groan or shout broke the oppressive coldness.

Masten could not let the week go by without a visit at the tavern. If Anne had been in her own room she would have excused herself, but it happened that on that evening she was in the "settin'-room" with the innkeeper's family, so she welcomed him with the rest. The woman of the house wanted to withdraw, discreetly, to leave the young folks together, but Anne managed to drag her into the conversation and hold her there, *vi et armis*: and when finally she insisted on tearing herself away, behold, the unruly young woman must needs retire also, to the preacher's manifest discomfiture.

Two visits by one marriageable man to one marriageable woman, plus one neighbor looking out of window, amounts to a reported engagement in any frontier town. So "preacher he 's a sparkin' scule-mom," was the news in Wayback instanter. It did not affect anybody particularly, except poor gentlemanly Johnny McVey, who presented to the world, about these days, an effigy of despair. As Tom Lackner, the storekeeper, said, "Johnny looks like a stuck pig. He hain't cracked a smile for a week."

Even Anne noticed John's melancholy, and said to herself, "John is a faithful soul. That tiresome Masten, who knows everything and so much more, — *he* would never grow pale and thin for me or any other woman."

If Masten did not pine, he at least showed other signs of interest, the most marked was an appeal for advice to Prouder. Zury listened to him in grave silence, and after a minute's pause said simply, —

"Give it up."

"Give it up? Why give it up brother Prouder? She is the very person to aid me in doing the Lord's work, here or elsewhere."

"Mebbe so. But give it up all the same."

"Would not such a union meet the views of my flock?"

"Like enough."

"Then who is there to object?"

"Wal, thar 's Miss Sparrer fer one."

"Oh!" rather faintly, and much dismayed. "Perhaps she can do better?"

"Perhaps — or wuss."

"Do you think that, at the East, before she came here" —

"Mebbe so. She hain't never seemed to congeal with none o' the fellows West." To be congenial he meant.

"Well, brother Prouder, I shall consider your advice carefully — prayerfully. I shall take it to my closet. And I shall not decide hastily."

But at the same moment he had quite decided to try his luck with the school-ma'am herself before he was a day older, if possible. Not caring to assail the tavern again, he engaged the willing services of Sister Anstey, found just when Anne was to be at her house, and called there at that time.

Anne knew he "meant business" the moment she saw him, that they all "meant business" in fact, that she was to be made Mrs. Masten, peaceably if they could, forcibly if they must. The sweet Eureka had evidently fallen in love with the preacher as a husband for her darling preceptress. Anne had scarcely patience to put up with such perversity. What in the world she should do, she did not yet know; why would they persist in intruding suggestions of things she could *not* do? Vexation possessed her spirit, and her flushed face and bent brows as she promptly accepted Masten's escort for the walk to the village, ought to have sealed his lips regarding the thing he had to say. But they did not. As she said to herself: "Such men have just as much tact as a canal-mule."

"Miss Sparrow, I am a plain man, engaged in a great work." ("Of course you must begin talking about yourself!") "My education has been the best which my surroundings could afford." ("Pity you had n't learned common sense regarding women.") "My bodily health is perfect, I am informed by physicians that my life will probably be a long one." ("What a blessing!") "That is, if such be the Lord's will." ("Oh, if it is n't, you'll die sooner, I suppose.") "The life of a minister's wife no doubt has its trials and tribulations." ("How different from other women's lives!") "But they are sent by God." ("You should n't swear!") "And he does not leave the faithful without some compensations." ("Donation parties, probably.") "I presume you see the drift of my remarks?"

"I might guess that you intended to ask my advice about marriage. If I am right my counsel is ready; Eureka Anstey is a splendid girl, my favorite pupil, an angel in mind and body, heart and soul, and unquestioningly orthodox by birth, training, habit of thought, and conviction. I recommend you by all means to lay siege to her heart; slowly and carefully, so as not to offend her by showing expectations she may have given you no reason to entertain."

"Ahem — you catch the general drift of my thought, but not its particular direction. Perhaps my verbiage was not clear." ("*Verbiage* again! That settles it!") "What I meant to convey was, an invitation to you, sister Sparrow, to become a minister's wife — to be mine."

"Now Mr. Masten! — What can I say to you? I thought I had given you enough warning to spare me the necessity of this. I told you, at the outset, that I was not in sympathy with the most important part of your life. Is your piety such a shallow principle that you can forget it at a word, — ignore confessed heresy that must seem almost blasphemy in your view?"

"No, no, only error!"

"Error indeed! Your Calvin burned poor Servetus for such error! And you; the first sight of a face — a poor, pale, sad, freckly countenance — makes you ready to drop all question of faith and principle!"

"Oh, sister Sparrow! Who was it who was sent to call, not the righteous, but sinners to repentance? There is more joy in heaven" —

"There, there; never mind that. You are not sent to call sinners to repentance by marrying them — at least not this sinner! You orthodox saints seem to think that we heterodox sinners are only waiting for you to come along and tell us the news — to unfold your scheme of redemption that we may subscribe to it. You are mistaken — we decline your views because we know all about them and think they are *foolish!*"

"But, sister, if we are wrong we are still safe; while if you are wrong, where are you in the last great day?"

"Oh, don't try to bribe me into any belief by showing its advantages!" (He almost adored the way she said "advahntages.") "I suppose your entire interest in me arises from your fear that I am doomed to eternal torments."

She glanced up to see why he was silent; then down, startled by his humble look and words.

"No, Miss Sparrow; I feel that you will not perish. Whether by a change of heart under God's grace, or by some other gift of His infinite benevolence, outside my narrow vision, I cannot say; but you will be saved. I shall meet you in heaven if I am to attain thither — by some merit not my own. God grant it and amen! I would cast my lot with yours in this world and the next. But — I fear it is not to be!"

Tears filled his eyes, and his face looked pathetically altered with its loss of complacency and self-confidence. His unlovable good looks were gone.

Anne said: "Oh I'm so sorry — sorry I was rude!" But a moment later she thought, "You horrid man! You are going to make me cry, when I would much rather be angry! Why could n't you all let me alone?" And then she did cry.

"Do your tears — give me any reason to think — to hope — that you may bring your mind to a favorable answer to my proposal?"

So he was a good fellow at heart. Might be humble and loving, even under that sanctimonious smile! Of what consequence were "verbiage" and "a memoranda" after all?

"No, Mr. Masten. Now may I say something which I know will spare me any further questions and insure me your forgiveness and your friendship?"

"Alas, yes, Miss Sparrow! I could refuse you nothing just now."

"Well, then — *I am not free to listen to you.*"

A boy awakened much interest at home that night by a remarkable tale.

"I guess schule-mom she 'xperienced religion t'day daown in th' woods. I seed her 'n' preacher a-blubberin' like sixty, a-walkin' along th' road. I wuz a-plowin' corn 'longside the fence, 'n' I heerd preacher a-blowin' his nose like sixty, and I peeked threw th' fence, 'n' thar the' wuz, a-walkin' along, not a-sayin' a word, and both a-blubberin' like sixty!"

"Does look like she'd be'n convicted o' sin, 'n' 'xperienced a hope, don't it!"

CHAPTER XV.

KICKING AGAINST THE PRICKS.

"O-H-H-H, sister Anstey!"

"Why, sister Praouder! Thet ain't never yew, is it! 'N' Zury tew, I dew declare! Wun't ye light 'n' strip?"

"Thankee no. We wuz jest a-joggin' t' taown."

"Haow 's things aout on th' parayra?"

"Oh, same old rut. Ye heerd haow th' blacksmith's wife she 's pootty low?"

"Ya-as. I heerd. Haow dooz it look with her?"

"Oh, bad enough. Physic don't seem t' take no holt on her. Blacksmith 'llaows 't ef she lives till th' change o' th' moon she may git well, but ef not, why he hain't much hope o' her ever bein' any better."

"Hev the' tried slipp'ry ellum peeled in th' dark o' th' moon?"

"Slipp'ry ellum! Why the' 've had the new doctor, 'n' real store drugs! *They 'd* a pulled her threw ef anythin' could."

(We will spare the reader the lists of expedients "they might have tried.")

"Wal, sister Anstey; them things might likely a helped her *some* ef it had a be'n th' Lord's will;

very likely I sh'd say. But that 's nuther h'yer ner thar. We 're jest worms o' th' dust, h'yer today 'n' come agin t'-morrer. We 're all in th' han's o' Him that 's like a squirrel in th' wall; He a-seein' us all th' time an' we a-knowin' noth'n' abaout it. But hev ye heerd what the' say *naow* abaout sister Sparrer?"

"S-h-h-h! She 's in the gardin' with Reekie. What dew th' say *naow?*"

"Why the' say she gin preacher th' mittin."

"Wal—I 'llaowed as much, jest from him a-comin' h'yer t' walk t' Wayback with her, 'n' never a-showin' up sence."

"Ye hain't as't her nothin'?"

"No. Nobody th't knows her 's well 's I dew don' dew much questionin' on her. Glad enough t' hear her talk on her own hook 'thaout a-puttin' in *my* oar much. Wal, she 's tew good fer him, —er any other man, fer that matter."

"Would ye mind a-hollerin' tew her? I 'd like t' kinder pass the time o' day with her."

"Sure-lye! O-H-H-H, Reekie! Yew Reekie Anstey! Come h'yer!"

There was no answer. Anne, who had spied the Prouders afar off, had artfully drawn Reekie back into the dim recesses of the "woods-lot" to avoid a meeting. But the energetic Mrs. Anstey "rewted 'em aout," as she expressed it, and they came forward and greeted the travelers.

"Miss Sparrer, we 're a-goin' toward th' tavern, 'n' I thought ye might like a lift that fur."

"Thank you, Mrs. Prouder, but I did not think of going for a while yet."

"Wal, anyways sune? I dunno 's we 're in any gre't of a hurry."

"Oh, not for a long time. I shall be going over about the time you are going back home."

"Wal — t' tell th' fact, — I did hev a leetle matter I wanted t' speak with ye abaout."

"Oh, very well, — then I 'll go, of course. Good-by, Reekie, we 'll settle that to-morrow."

"Settle what?" said simple-hearted Reekie.

"Why, don't you know? That matter I was going to talk over with you if I had stayed longer." A mysterious nod and frown failed to intimate to the unsophisticated younger woman that Anne wished to fabricate a plausible explanation of her first refusal of the Prouder's invitation.

"Naow, Miss Sparrer, Zury he 'llaows ye would n't jest nat'rally come up 'n' squat daown with us; but I tell him ye can't most ollers tell what ye kin least expeck abaout a young gal, not till ye ask her, 'n' not ollers then."

Anne shook her head in firm, silent negative. Mrs. Prouder was about to enlarge on the abundance of room and food on the farm, when her husband interrupted her.

"See h'yer, Flor. D' ye wanter bring me up t' th' poorhaouse?"

"Wal — not right off, Zury! Th' spare chămber 's idle 'n' useless, 'n' as fer feed, the 's more give t' th' dawg every day th'n th' little she 'd eat. 'N' ol' Shep he 'd orter be killed anyhaow!"

"Oh sho! Spare chămber h'yer 'n' dawg thar! It 's money I 'm a-lookin' at! Thar 's Thum a-owin' me — a-owin' me — wal, no odds haow much; an' th' debt a-growin' bigger every day more ner Miss Sparrer's keep 'll come tew; 'n' no arthly chance o' me ever a-gittin' it aouter him in cash. An him 'n' me 's fixed it up t' charge up folkses bills th't I send thar 'n' let 'em run on th' accaount; 'n' naow h'yer comes yew, persuadin' away th' customers thet 's a eatin' aout th' debt! It raily ain't right, Flory, — agin yer own husband, tew!"

"Naow Zury! Ye know I did n't go fer t' dew noth'n' agin ye! But could n't we have her t' aour 'us, 'n' charge it up agin my farm somehaow?"

"No, we jest could n't! Chargin' yew, by me, 's jest takin' money aouter one pocket 'n' puttin' it in another; whereas naow it don't cost me a blame cent!"

"Jest like Zury! Grippin' 'n' gripin' t' th' last, same 's ever!" Such was Mrs. Prouder's half admiring, half regretful thought; and such was the outspoken opinion of the neighbors when, in due course of time, they heard of the transaction. Anne's face was stonily grave, but her heart smiled a little.

After a pause Mrs. Prouder broke the silence again.

"Miss Sparrer, the' dew say ye gin the mittin' t' preacher."

"Does Mr. Masten say so?"

"He hain't said yes ner no, so fur 's I 've heerd. He hain't denied it, ner he hain't no cause t' aout with it — his face tells it plain enough." And the good woman laughed heartily, as if it were a fine joke at Masten's expense.

"I 'm not fit to be his wife — or any man's wife." Her voice sounded to Zury hollow and strange.

"Oh, ye 're a-gittin' all O. K. I kin see ye a-gainin' right along."

"Dunno 's I blame any gal fer not marryin' a preacher," said Zury. "Got t' be stuck up all yer life, 'n' nothin' t' be stuck up on! 'T ain't as though a preacher hed a farm, or even a good trade — blacksmithin' or sech like. But no, it 's talk, talk, talk, fust in one place an' then in another, a-suitin' folks or not a-suitin' 'em ; jest like a-sayin' t' everybody, 'd' ye like me? Then give me a shillin'!' Naow a farmer, ef folks don't want his truck he kin eat it himself; but a preacher, er a lawyer, er a docter, their truck ain't no 'caount unless it 's took — *they* can't live on it!"

"Eureka Anstey would make the best wife in the world for Mr. Masten."

"Oh, Reekie, she 's all right fer some farmer's boy. But the' 's a slew o' little Anstey's, 'n' th' farm mortgidged up t' th' handle a'ready. Th' haouse ain't none tew large, nuther, — though I s'pose the' could make another bed-place up garret by a-hangin' up comforters 'n' sich. Naow preacher he 'd orter marry some gal thet her father could set her off a leetle of a farm — er anyways a haouse-lot 'n' a woods-lot, 'n' some parster 'n' medder."

"That is true, and that would be a good reason for my not marrying Mr. Masten."

"Oh, yer school teachin' 'd help some," said Flora, — till th' babies begun t' come — 'n' afterwards, between whiles, ef ye warn't blest with many."

"What a vista!" thought Anne.

"Miss Sparrer," said Zury, "Johnny McVey is dead gone on yew. As the' say, 'his eyes is sot.'"

"Naow Zury, ye know ye allers 'llaowed, yerself, haow 't Johnny wuz weak in th' upper story."

"Wal — yes, in a way. I dew guess 't Johnny 'd weigh more ef his head wuz cut off, — but mebbe he 'd make all the better o' man on that accaount!"

"A husband? Oh, I *don't* want any husband!"

"Not want any husband!" and Flora looked at her newly won lord and master in wonder that any woman could talk so.

"Oh, that 's only her way. She 'll want one bad enough when she comes to think it over. Some folks never dooz wind up the clock till it runs daown."

"Johnny ain't much t' brag on, sure enough, but he 's a heap sight better 'n none. Besides, the' don't seem to none o' th' other fellers took a shine t' ye, 'xcep' McVey and preacher."

This brought plainly before Anne's mind the fact that any of "the other fellows" would be far more objectionable than gentlemanly Johnny.

"But of course," she said, with a gleam of hope, "he would n't want me now!"

"Would n't he jest? Ye don't half know Johnny — nor other men, nuther! When a man's eyes is sot, he don't care ef a woman wuz to turn aout — Apollyun!" This word Zury added after a vain effort to remember any female devil: there being none — in fiction.

"Johnny hain't a cent in the world!" objected Flora.

"Oh, I 've thought of that, tew. Yew leave that t' me," said Zury. "Polander Brothers, whar I buy my supplies wholesale, in Springville, want jest sech a man. I told 'em so, 'n' they did n't deny it. It 'll come handy, tew, fer me t' have a man o' my own, right thar t' headquarters whar my stuff comes from."

A little silence followed this, broken by Flora.

"Why! — I declare t' man if she ain't a cryin'! Be ye sick, Miss Sparrer? Thar, put yer head daown on my shoulder, so. Never mind yer hat; let it lay thar in th' bottom o' th' wagin. I 'll pick it up afterw'ds; 'n' I 'll dew up yer hair agin, tew! Thar, thar, *thar!* Dear heart! Don't, *don't* sob so! Ye 'll jerk yer insides aout! Jest come up 'n' live with us, 'n' be a darter t' me; 'n' don't never marry nobody till ye have a min' ter."

A shuddering negative was all the reply the kind creature could extort.

Zury's horses needed a great deal of attention; and the sun in his eyes seemed to trouble him, too. That night after supper he disappeared. The tenants on the Peddicomb farm were surprised to see him stalking, silent and alone, all about the place. He wandered over the whole quarter, half a mile square, with good fences and cross-fences; a grove of young black walnuts, an orchard only second to his old one, barns and house better than his, and bursting granary and corn-cribs, and stacks of hay in ranks; and fat live-stock here and there and everywhere.

Well, it was a nice farm.

And there was the poor girl at the tavern, her swelled eyes buried in her tear-dampened pillow.

The more Anne thought, the more she felt that her future was being shaped by a relentless fate outside of the scope of her feeble powers. Was the horizon opening out, or was it closing in? Her life had had a world of dreams; some very bright. She was to have been a writer; she was to have been the priestess of a coming revelation: even as late as her westward journey she was to have become a little queen among the rough people she was to meet in the wilds. *Now*, what was she to be after all her little attainments and fond hopes of greater? "Poor Mrs. John McVey!"

On the other hand, in her times of depression, she could no longer rush willfully headlong to the lowest depths, and grovel there; for unless McVey should desert her now, a life of usefulness and respectability was within her reach.

But would John marry her, after all, when it came to the point? It did not seem possible! In the still watches of a wakeful night, during which, after her usual fashion, she seemed to herself to shrink into helpless insignificance while the world, fate, and circumstances all became hideous monsters clawing at her; she concluded that she had only to take a step toward him to meet a contemptuous repulse.

Morning brought more courage and confidence; also more toleration of the thought that she might gain a little rest and comfort and sustenance by marrying poor faithful John. As the heroine in Hardy's strange novel, "Two on a Tower," says to her brother, "Anybody—even a tinker."

She certainly was not "in love" with John; but neither was she with any other man. He was more nearly sympathetic with her, at that moment, than any other person in that part of the world; more like her in education, language, habit of thought and feeling, than anybody of either sex whom she had met since she left New England. And then, too, his spaniel-like devotion had become the source of a kind of comfort to her under existing circumstances.

She had one more "bad quarter of an hour." It was when the thought struck her that she, the victim, ought to *adorn* herself for the sacrifice!

But she succumbed to the inevitable. She feared that Prouder would interfere again, in his masterful fashion, and in that way make her appear to herself acting under his influence or compulsion.

So one Sunday morning, with shame and misgiving she dressed herself a little more carefully than usual, and invited John to be her escort to church — the first time she had ever done him that honor. On the way she talked long, seriously, and doubtless fully with John.

The good fellow only tried to eat his humble pie as proudly as possible.

"Of course, it's proper to let the past be past. And then, as to the future" — He paused.

"I am not putting myself up at auction, nor offering inducements to strike a bargain!"

"Well, supposin' I was to make a proposition" — Another pause.

"I shall not consider any supposed case. If you have any proposition to make, unconditionally, make it; if not, let us drop the subject."

Johnny looked at her with dumb and unspeakable admiration. He thought to himself, "She's more of a man, if anything, than Zury Prouder himself!" The force of language could no further go than this.

Anne made as if to terminate the interview, and John was panic-stricken.

"You are as blameless as a woman can be, and I propose to — marry you."

She waited to see if there were to be any conditions. None came, happily for all concerned.

"Then I accept you, and will make you a true, honest, and faithful wife, as long as we both shall live." She gave him her hand and turned away her face, in trembling expectation that he would take some instant advantage of her surrender. But he only shook hands as on a bargain struck. And then and thenceforth she remained as to him as completely mistress of herself as this auspicious beginning presaged.

What a relief! None the less for the knowledge that her future husband had only hesitated for appearance' sake that he had never for a moment wavered in his absorbing wish to marry her — to tie his weak nature to her stronger one by a sustaining bond. After all, as a man was only a necessary appendage, the lighter the appendage the slighter the personal sacrifice. And if the chief question to be considered was "which is to be head of the house?" — she almost smiled as she propounded this simplest of problems, as between her and John Endicott McVey.

After "meeting" she, to avoid tiresome talkers, concluded to walk home; the way was a little long, and she took the arm of her affianced. He was very strong though so slender, and she had a perceptible satisfaction in leaning on him.

"Oh John" — the first time she had ever called him so — "make a home for me, quickly, and take me to it!"

"Well, after dinner I'll step over to" —

"No! never mind telling me where you go, or whom you see, or what he says. Just do the best you can; *at once*." This was not said imperatively, only urgently and pathetically. "I long for some place that isn't here, and some time that isn't now."

That very evening John called, full of plans. Mr. Prouder was to let them have a wagon, horses, and harness, to take them to Springville, and be sold or kept for use as they might elect; he charging the value of the outfit to the fund he should recover from the county on account of the riotous destruction. Whatever room was left in the vehicle he was to fill with household supplies from the farm, charging them to the same account. The balance he was to pay in money. Then he was to accompany them to Springville and install John in his employment as bookkeeper for Polander Brothers.

All well except the last clause. Mr. Prouder must not accompany them to Springville — not on any account. In fact, they would not do anything until John's position was assured. No; Anne would not see Mr. Prouder about it herself; she would rather depend entirely on John. She felt such reliance on his prudence and ability!

Well, then, John and Zury were to go to Springville at once and get to work, and then Zury would come back and bring Anne on and all her things — attend to everything for her. The marriage to take place at Springville.

All satisfactory except having Mr. Prouder troubled about Anne and her things. He and John might go to Springville as suggested; and then as soon as possible — the sooner the better — John could get leave of absence and come for her and marry her; and then they two could drive to Springville alone, for a wedding trip! She was sure John would not like to have his wife run after him all over the country! Otherwise John had arranged everything beautifully! No; she would not interfere herself. John must do it all. Only make haste!

So said so done. Anticipating a little, we may say here that all John's plans were carried out to the letter, and, while this arrangement was very advantageous to Anne and her husband, it turned out very much so to Zury Prouder too. The prices he charged were good, the money balance was small, and the county finally paid for everything, principal and interest.

"The' dew 'llaow 't Miss Sparrer she 's tuck up with Johnny McVey arter all said 'n' done!"

It was old Anstey who imparted this momentous intelligence to the astounded world — consisting of Mrs. Anstey and the family.

"Oh, father! Not really!"

"Wal — I met Zury Prouder, 'n' he wuz jest plum full on it! He 'llaowed he 'd taxed Johnny with it 'n' Johnny he never denied it; 'n' I axed Zury what on th' footstule the' 'llaowed t' live on, 'n' he 'llaowed the' wuz a-goin' t' Springville, whar Johnny he 's gotten a place a-clerkin' in a store."

"Don't ye know what 's done it — what 's made her take up with Johnny?" asked Mrs. Anstey. "Nothin' in God's world but larnin'! Ef Johnny 'd a be'n ign'rnt, low-daown trash like yew, 'Bijah Anstey, *she* would n't a never a looked at him!

No, ner his shadder! not ef he 'd a-had a hunderd dollars in gold!"

"A hunderd dollars is right smart o' money!"

"I don't c'yar! Larnin' 's wuth more ner a hunderd dollars. Right smart more." Of course Mrs. Anstey spoke under great excitement. "'N' yit I can't never git none on ye t' read yer book 'ceptin' Reekie. I 've a notion t' cut a good gad apiece fer ye all raound, 'n' mark yer names on 'em, 'n' jest wear 'em aout on ye so I will, t' see ef I can't git ye t' ten' t' yer larnin' when scule opens agin."

"Oh sho!" retorted 'Bijah. "Preacher he 's got larnin', tew, 'n' yit she upped 'n' mittened *him*. It wuz jest 'cause he couldn't talk like Johnny, 'n' say 'Boys ye cawn't fawncy th' advawntages of educat-i-o-n' like Johnny use' ter."

"'BIJAH!" cried Eureka. And she came at him as if she had been six feet high, with eyes blazing as if they would have set fire to his hair. He darted out of the door, then paused to call in through the window, —

"Oh, Reek, *yew* hain't no call t' beller. She 's left preacher fer *yew*."

Now she *did* "go for" 'Bijah. Around the house, through the garden, over the fence, and down the road, the strong youth, impeded by laughing, had all he could do to keep out of her reach. And when as a parting shot she threw a "chunk" after his flying figure, it almost struck Mr. Masten, coming to call for the first time since he had escorted Anne from there as has been told.

Yes, he did catch a glimpse of her eyes, before she turned and flew toward home. Who could could help it? They took up some space in the horizon, and possibly paled the sunshine a little.

Eureka in her Sunday-go-to-meeting best visited Anne, and her glowing account put the matter beyond doubt. Miss Sparrow looked almost as hearty as ever. Johnny had gone to Springville and begun clerking for Polander Brothers, and his salary, wonderful to relate, was fifty dollars a month! Such is the power of education.

Johnny was coming back some day next week — exact day uncertain — and the following morning Squire Brown was to marry them, and they 'd get started for Springville as soon after sun-up as might be.

"No party?" roared 'Bijah. "Then we 'll give *them* one, fust chance we git. A good one, tew. Chivaree ain't no name fer it. Whar 's my tin horn? Whar 's th' ole tin milk-pail with a stone in it? Whar 's th' ole shot-gun 'n' th' paowder-horn?"

"Wal, sonny, I guess I 'll keep th' shot-gun 'n' th' paowder-horn. I may need 'em. With that shot-gun 'n' a couple o' han'f'ls o' rock salt, I guess I mought take a hand in that thar chivaree that 'll s'prise ye some. 'N' ef rock salt won't give ye yer belly full o' fun, I 'll have a small charge er tew o' bird-shot th't 'll make ye sing laouder 'n' make right smart more noise th'n all yer tin horns."

Eureka did not tell how much of her talk with

Anne ran upon the subject of the Reverend Mr. Masten. But then, so did her talk with Mr. Masten run upon the subject of Anne Sparrow. So *that* could n't cut any figure, now *could* it?

CHAPTER XVI.

A NOVELTY IN NOVEL WEDDING-TRIPS.

A WEDDING and a bridal trip. What an opportunity for the romancer! How easy to enchain all readers, of any age, sex, color, or previous condition of servitude! No need to be graphic, witty, picturesque in order to be interesting, the mere theme does it all. No need to condense; the more diffuse, minute, circumstantial, familiar, and confidential, the better, with such events to tell about.

Now this was not exactly that kind of marriage and wedding tour. Yet it was better than none, and Anne was not unhappy. They talked about Boston, where they had a very few common acquaintances—notably the State House and Beacon Street — and this made a certain sympathy, of course. They talked of Wayback with an outside view of its peculiar characteristics such as no one else in that part of the world was qualified to take. This made more sympathy. Then when toward the end of the long ten hours drive, Anne grew very tired, and she clasped her hands on his shoulder and rested her head on them, it was with quite an affectionate feeling, certainly not wifely, scarcely sisterly, more, as she laughingly told him, as if she were his aunt. He did not object, he laughed too, and promised that if she would be an aunt to him he would reciprocate by being an uncle to her, and all went merry as a — bell of some kind not yet named.

When they began their residence in Springville, John was for keeping the horses, selling the wagon, and buying a carriage for their own use. Of course they were not always going to live on fifty dollars a month! He had vague expectations of additional income from sources to be opened to him by outside aid — "capitle" to be obtained.

But here he was firmly "sat down on," and the whole outfit promptly sold to reinforce the family exchequer. These avails, and Anne's other belongings, went far toward preparing for her (them we mean) a cottage where she (that is, they) started to keep house, and very nicely too. McVey accepted his improved fate without a murmur, avoiding all reference to any part of the past which Anne preferred to drop out of sight.

At the "let out" of the Wayback meeting on a Sunday soon after this, gossip ran thus: —

"What 's the matter o' Zury Proauder? He ain't opened his lips fer a coon's age!"

"N' more he hain't! Wal, naow; what 's up? Some misch'f in Zury's head you bet! He ain't a-makin' no big deal 's I know on."

"Not 's I know on nuther. Ef the' 's a hen on I hain't hearn a word of it."

"A settin' hen don't cackle. I bet ye hear on 't when she hatches."

"I b'lieve ye! Zury's long head don't work fer the fun of it."

"No man th't knows him as I dew won't buy ner sell with him when he 's the way he is naow."

"Ef my own mother 'n' law wuz a dickerin' with him now, I 'd caounsel her t' back aout."

Then another speaker volunteered an explanation of the phenomenon in question, which turned speculation into a new channel, and carried conviction to the minds of all.

"Oh yew smarties! Don't ye guess what 's the matter o' Zury? Ye dunno n' more 'n a last year's bird's nest! Reckon ye 've forgot the We'ns-d'y meetin' 'baout the school-haouse fire! Don't ye reckleck haow Zury wuz kinder druv t' 'gree t' settle that bill 'n' look t' the caounty for his pay?"

"Jesso, jesso, Tom! Ye 're right! 'N' naow he 's aout his money 'n' schemin' haow t' git it back."

"Mebbe so — mebbe so. Wal, ef so be Zury 's after Spring Caounty, Spring Caounty 'd better be a-hustlin' 'n' a perparin' to be picked up 'n' car'r'd off."

"Right ye are, pard! We 'uns better git all aour farms spiked daown tight, er Zury 'll hev 'em rolled up 'n' sold at sheriff sale, t' pay his claim."

But all the gibing wiseacres were wrong. Zury did n't himself know what was the matter with him, but he did know that it was not any anxiety about his claim for indemnity in the fire matter. On the contrary, the chief consolation he found in his glum and sulky state was the thought of having helped poor Anne out of her sorest straits. Every little aid he had ever rendered her he rolled as a sweet morsel under his tongue, and her gentle looks and tones of thanks haunted his memory, scanty as they had been.

A few months after the McVeys were settled, Prouder visited Springville on business. All the long way there his mind dwelt on the coming meeting with them, but a disappointment was in store for him. Anne met him at her door, her sewing in her hands, and greeted him kindly, but did not ask him in. She was really sorry to annoy and disappoint him, but she could not help it. If he would come with John at night she would be glad to see him, but just now she was — too busy.

He did not come, which made her glad and sorry together. He would have amused her, but she would have felt it rather awkward. As for Zury, he made his way back home in a very thoughtful frame of mind. His answers to the numerous questions put to him about Anne were reasonably profuse and circumstantial, but quite general; he did not tell that she had coolly dismissed him with as few words as civility would allow. Fortunately Anne's front door opened into the main living-room, so that he was prepared to give a highly satisfactory account of her surroundings — and to say that she looked remarkably well.

When John came home at night he said, —

"Zury Prouder's been at the store 'most all

day, and this afternoon I showed him the way out here."

"Yes — he called."

"Did he stay long?"

"No — he did n't come in."

"Not come in! The nati-o-n!"

"I did not ask him in."

John was rather dumbfounded at this. After a pause he resumed, —

"Well, we 're considerable obliged to Mr. Prouder."

"Yes — all we are ever going to be."

"Did he say anything about capitle."

"Of course not!"

Poor John was evidently quite disconcerted. Without sacrificing either himself or his wife, he would have liked to receive capitle from Zury, because capitle was what he had really needed all his life, and he saw no reason why he should not have it. Other men had capitle, and it seemed to do them all good. They liked capitle; so should he.

He secretly determined to broach the interesting subject of capitle to Zury again, the first time he found a good opportunity.

In this cottage Anne McVey's twin babies were born. She named them Philip and Margaret, her two favorite names, long prepared for use as alternatives and now, happily, both made available. Never, from their natal hour, were her "twinnies" aught but comforts and blessings to her.

Before they were a month old she found, to her surprise, that darkness had lost its terrors. She could "put her feet to the unseen floor" at any moment, in their service — Nature had become her friend, her sister in motherhood, instead of an alien and an enemy. Time passed, and she learned that Mrs. Prouder's motherly hopes were disappointed. Flora's experience was much the same as had been that of her sister Mary, only her baby had lived but a few hours instead of months. Anne's heart went out in pity and sympathy to the bereaved parents, and she sighed to think of that great, rich, childless household.

On a certain summer afternoon, when her little darlings were old enough to creep about, she sat sewing in the shade of the cottage while they played in the grass at her feet. She heard the gate open, and in walked — Zury Prouder.

"God bless 'n' presarve all here! Mis Sparrer — McVey, I should say — I don't s'pose ye 'll object t' my comin' as fur as this?"

She could not. He was there already. And if she had had an enemy in the world, and he were that enemy, still she could not have the heart to refuse him a sight of those treasures! What crime could any one be guilty of, that would merit such a punishment?

Zury sat down on the ground and watched the little ones long and in silence. The boy would creep up fearlessly, and climb with his fat hands on Zury's knees, but the girl kept close to her mother. Zury took up the little fellow and let him pull his hair, while he admired the sturdy limbs of the perfect child.

"Be ye happy with yer childern?"

"I ask nothing from heaven or earth except prosperity for my boy and girl."

"Looks like a little heaven here below!"

Zury scarcely ever in his life passed an hour, in company, so silently as this. And Anne sat there and dreamed out a future for her children. Why should not this rich man make them rich, when they grew older and needed money to secure for them a place in the world such as she could not give them? It did not seem wrong and inhuman to her to wish that an old man should die just in the very nick of time to benefit them. So one-sided is the heart and conscience of the natural mother! She would joyfully sacrifice her own life for them, if need be, — why not be equally willing that Zury should die in the same good cause?

"Be ye fixed t' suit ye h'yer?" She looked up quickly, and did not reply.

"I mean t' say, ef the' 's anythin' I kin dew — anythin' more — t' make up fer any trouble ye 've had" — An awkward pause.

"When I want anything from you I 'll ask you for it. And if I owe you anything I beg you 'll send the bill!" And her brows met over angry eyes.

"Ain't ye pootty hard on me?" he asked, "lonesome as I be! Ye 've got yer babes, 'n' I hain't got nothin' — 'ceptin' money! An' not much o' that, come t' think." He turned again to playing with the boy. She felt a touch of pity, and was sorry for her bitterness.

McVey came home while they were all thus engaged. He was delighted to see Mr. Prouder, and urged him to stay to tea. He accepted as soon as Anne added her invitation, and she left her precious charges to them while she prepared the meal. In the evening, McVey walked with Prouder to his hotel. When he got back Anne asked him what they had talked about. John hemmed and hawed, but made a very poor showing of the conversation.

As Anne composed herself to sleep, a baby on each side as was her wont, she said to herself: —

"Well, small danger of Mr. Prouder's wasting the children's fortunes in 'capitle' on poor John. But then John's asking him to do so is rather mortifying. On the other hand, let him do it! It will keep Prouder from any very frequent visitings, which would be intolerable." And so did things settle themselves down. Prouder's visits to Springville were not frequent, and his calls at the McVey cottage were equally irregular and not brilliantly agreeable; Anne refusing to see him when her husband was not present, and John making himself a bore when he was. Besides, as the years passed, the children were no longer quite so entrancingly interesting. Phil and Meg were like other children — when they first came, miraculous phenomena; when they grew up, interesting individuals; but between whiles nothing more than ordinary specimens of the young of their race: the boy often good, the girl never anything else.

When they were a few years older, however, something occurred which showed that Zury was aware of their existence. On a certain day, Anne while at the store, attending to some of John's work (as she often had to do now when he fell behind), was called to the door to see a friend. There, in Zury's wagon which had brought her all the way from Wayback, sat Mrs. Prouder, unmistakable, though she now looked a little like two Flora Peddicombs rolled into one.

"Well, Mrs. Prouder!"

"Wal, Mis McVey!" (These greetings were given in an affectionately pathetic tone, beginning high and dropping suddenly at the closing word —as if to say, "I 've waited long for this reunion, but now it 's come and I 'm consoled for all.")

"Bless yer heart! Ye 're a-lookin' peart."

"I'm always well. How well you look!"

"Ya-as. What there is of me, 'n' plenty of me sech as it is. Johnny well?"

"Very well. He 's gone down the river on a fishing expedition."

"Did yer twins both live? I heerd ye hed twins."

Did her babies live! What a horrid question! "Oh, yes — certainly. They are both alive and well."

"Boy 'n' gal, hey? Lessee, haow old be the'?"

"They are — about five."

"Oh, it 's six years this summer since ye lef' Wayback, ain't it? I often thought I 'd knit 'em s'm mittins sometime, ef I only knowed the'r birthday."

"Oh, Christmas is our great day. Six years — how time flies, does n't it! My heart did bleed for you when I heard of your disappointment, your bereavement."

"Thar, thar, thar!" And the poor creature sniffled excessively in the delay of searching for her handkerchief, — a delay which obviated any absolute necessity for its use.

"Never had no more, hey?"

"Never any more."

"Ye 'll 'scuse my not a-gittin' aout, wun't ye? I don't never 'llaow t' git in 'n' aout o' wagin more 'n wunst a day, an' me 'n' Zury we 'llaowed t' drive 'raoun' 'n' see ye shortly."

"How nice! I 'll hurry home and get ready for you."

The visit was pathetic. Zury walked about the little garden, while poor Flora went in and gazed tearfully at the children. They, with the unconscious cruelty of the savage in our nature, disliked and feared her. They clung obstinately to their mother, and Phil pointed at Flora and said in a loud voice, —

"What makes *her* cry so?"

"Because she has n't any little boy and girl, my son."

"Oh, is *that* all!" Then, after a pause, "I thought she had a great — big — stomercake."

"Margaret," Anne whispered, "Mrs. Prouder had a little girl once, but it died."

"Died? What is *died?*"

"Died, you know, and was buried — like your little bird, don't you remember? Now don't you think you could go over and comfort her a little?"

Thereupon the dutiful little soul, sorely against her will, stepped snail-like toward the large, repulsive visitor, her progress being at about the rate of one carpet-figure a minute. When she reached her, Mrs. Prouder took her on her knees, what there was of them available, and cried so much harder than ever that the child soon got down and retreated to her mother, fairly bawling, with knuckles buried in both eyes.

"Never mind, Mrs. Prouder. (There, there, my dear little girl!) They 'll come around in time to loving you as their mother does. (Now Margaret, that 's enough. You must be quiet. There — mother is holding you tight. Don't you both want to go out in the garden and see Mr. Prouder?)"

Phil escaped with a rush, but Margaret was far from flying present evils by rushing to others that she knew not of.

By turning Mrs. Prouder's thoughts to Wayback matters, Anne soon managed to dry up the geyser of grief and regret.

"Preacher 'n' Reekie Anstey upped 'n' mar'r'd right away after yew left. Th' ol' folks 'llaowed the' both hed t' talk abaout yew s' much 't the' hed t' marry t' git time fer it all. Then the' tuk th' scule t'gether, 'n' run it on yer own lines. Reekie she knaowed haow, 'n' the' run it splendid. Deestrick Number Seven 's got t' be knaowed all over the caounty, 'n' other caounties tew. Got t' be so 's the' hed t' set a day fer visitors: so many scule-boards wanted t' come 'n' see it, it interfered."

"Oh, dear! Now you make *me* cry. I have n't lived in vain, after all, have I?"

"In vain? Lived in vain? Not by right smart, I tell ye! Wal, 's I wuz a-saying, the' kep' th' school till the babies begun to come, 'n' the'r fust bein' a gal, the' called it Anne McVey Masten, as of course ye 've heer'd. 'N' then con-f'r'nce took a-holt o' Masten, 'n' give him a *big* lift. 'N' so we lost 'em, wuss luck!"

Now Zury looked in.

"Mis McVey, me 'n' Phil 's fixed it up t' take a leetle ride in th' wagin, 'n' bait th' team at the tavern, 'n' git a bite thar ourselves, 'n' then come back fer Flory, ef ye kin give her what leetle her stomick requires 'twixt naow 'n' night."

Anne was about to say *no*, suddenly and decid-edly. But Phil's dancing eyes and eager words prevailed.

"My little boy has never eaten a meal away from his mother in his life."

"I wanter go in the wagin."

"Why could n't you take a little ride and come back here before you go to the stable?"

"I wanter go in the stable."

"Or you might take the team to the stable and

then come back here for dinner instead of to the tavern."

"I wanter go in the tavern."

"Ye see, Mis McVey, Phil 's made up his mind it 's time fer him t' begin t' see the world."

"I wanter see the world."

There was no resisting this. So off they went two happy beings, it is hard to say which the happier.

"Remember," said Anne in kissing her boy good-bye. "Nothing but meat and vegetables and bread. No tea or coffee."

"I wanter drink tea an' coffee."

But here Anne drew the line. The wild license of this orgie must stop short of tea and coffee.

Flora's admiration of Anne's pretty household adornments — utterly simple and entirely home-made as they were — was gratifying. Said Flora, —

"Thet 's what it is t' live intew a city."

Anne was tempted to tell and teach the rustic that all this and much more was possible in her own ugly home, but as no instruction was asked, she saw that it would be bad manners to intrude even good taste and good sense on her guest. She had not lived at the West all these years in vain.

Next morning Mrs. Prouder called alone, while Anne was away at the store as usual. The visitor stayed long, and as the little maid-of-all-work indignantly reported, "she jest hung over them childern like the' wuz hern!" She was still there when Anne returned and they made their simple noon meal all together. Then Mrs. Prouder spoke.

" Ye know, Mis McVey, we 're pootty lonesome to our 'us; got tew much of mos' everythin' but childern. Naow h'yer, I reckon its jest t' other way with yew, though ye dew look so luxur'ous."

"Oh, we have enough of all we need, and none too many children." She looked fondly at her cherubs.

" Wal, naow, Zury 'n' me we 'llaowed 's haow mebbe ye 'd be willin' t' spare th' boy."

The mischief was out. It seemed to Anne as if they spoke of Phil as one of a litter.

"MY PHILIP!" She almost screamed her reply, and seizing the youth with a force and vigor which called forth vociferous protest, she glared over his red curls at the enemy, like a lioness at bay, guarding her cubs.

" Oh, wal, of course ef ye don't like the idee, when ye come t' think on it — I jist mentioned it to Zury last night, 'n' he seemed t' kinder fall in with it." And soon afterward she took leave, vainly endeavoring to make the parting affectionate.

In the afternoon Prouder called, and begged for a little talk "on business." She received him, but there was danger in her eye.

"Did you bring your wife here to steal my child? Did you lay out that fine plan, so that she would think it was her own idea, when you had plotted it all beforehand?"

"One thing at a time! Is it stealing a boy for

Zury Prouder t' adopt him 'n' make him his heir?"

"Yes it is! Money could not pay me for parting with him, and money could not pay him for parting with me! Do you think I want him to be the meanest man in Spring County? Or that my son would want to be? No, not if he owned the county!"

Zury was deeply offended. Never in his life had he received such an awful blow between the eyes. His face burned as if it had been lashed with a raw hide held in a woman's hand — and that hand Anne Sparrow's! He walked off in grim silence.

"Dooz she think she kin bully Zury Praouder? Thet he's in her paower 'n' can't say a word? Thet he never done a hand's turn for her, 'n' her triflin' husban' 'n' her red-headed brats. We'll see! we'll see! Meanest man in Spring Caounty, eh? Throws *that* at me, 's though I had n't said it more times than anybody else! Me-eanest ma-an in Spring Caounty!"

He repeated it many times, but it seemed to have lost its old soul-satisfying ring. His steps were directed at once to the wholesale house, with an intent most perilous to the future prosperity of the McVey household. There he found nobody save some underlings, the partners having gone home. So he was forced to suspend his vengeance till morning.

He told his wife of the result of his mission. She said, —

"Wal, poor creetur, I don't wonder! What 'd buy one on 'em ef the' wuz mine?"

In the evening Zury walked out, and quietly bent his steps toward the McVey cottage — for what purpose he did not know; perhaps to nurse his wrath and keep it warm. He leaned on the little picket fence, nicely whitewashed. Thought he, —

"That doggoned ornery trifling McVey never whitewashed that fence, ner that house; ner planted them posey-beds 'longside the walk; ner handworked them curtings the lamp shines through so peart; ner thrummed that foot-mat that lays in front o' the door; ner fixed up that low swing that hangs clust t' the laylock bush!"

But then, neither had McVey insulted him. He would n't have dared, even if Zury had given him cause!

Next morning he walked with dogged steps to the store, and sought out the proprietors.

"Haow dooz McVey do?"

"Oh — he don't 'mount t' shucks! Hain't got no grip — no git up 'n' git, tew him!"

"'Baout 's leave ship him 's not naow, would n't ye?"

"Why 's fur 's he 's consarned, 'tain't noth'n' but your recommend that 's kep' him on 's long as we *hev* kep' him. But his wife — that 's another story. She 's a gray hoss of another color."

"Wal, what of *her?*"

"She 's wuth her money *every* day. Right up 'n' a-comin'! Wuth a hull bilin' o' his kind o' stock."

"Wha' 'd ye pay 'em?"

"Fifty a month."

"That ain't no pay fer 'em!"

"Plenty fer Johnny."

"But ye seem t' have him 'n' her both — more o' her ner o' him."

"Wal, it 's all they 've asked."

"Cal'late t' keep 'em on don't ye?"

"Wal, that 's owin' t' haow the cat jumps."

"I wuz a-goin' t' say, ye 've done fair by me; 'n' 's long 's ye sell 's low 's anybody else will — er lower — I 'm willin' t' give ye fust chance at my trade."

"Oh well, we don't cal'late t' bounce Johnny yet a while."

"Haow 'bout sixty a month fer Johnny?"

"We 'll hev a talk with Mrs. McVey in the mornin'."

"But not ef the ten dollars a month 's a-goin' t' be tacked onter my bills!"

"Trust *yew* fer that! It would n't work on a close buyer such 's *yew* be, not fer a half an hour, before it 'd be knocked galley-west!"

"Well, I try t' hold my own. Ye know I 'm the" —

He did n't finish the sentence, for some reason or other. But his vengeance had all "petered out."

It was with a pale face, round eyes, expanded nostrils, and tightly drawn lips that Anne, in the morning, learned that both of the partners wished to have a little talk with her on business. Could such meanness live as would lead Zury to strike a blow at her and her babies? The ringing in her ears was growing perilously loud — she must sit down and bear whatever might befall.

Then when the interview was over, the dizzy ringing was cured; only tears, happy tears, remained to be struggled with. Ten dollars more a month! One hundred and twenty dollars more a year! Affluence! Meanwhile the Prouders were well on their way toward Wayback.

But Zury called no more at the cottage. The sting remained, though no vengeance was taken — perhaps all the more for that reason. On the other hand, he had one more sweet morsel to roll under his tongue when he felt blue, as even he often did now. *He* had forgiven *her* something! *He* had rendered *her* good for evil!

John Endicott McVey has begun to slip out of this story. It takes a muscular grasp to hold his still handsome head above the waters of oblivion. Lacking the solid qualities which thrive upon hardship, he weakened under training. He kept his drawl, but lost his good English. He looked shabby, though spending more on his clothes than men about him who looked well. He might have earned a partnership — but not by being the last to come to the store and the first to hurry away.

For a year or two or three he kept up a fair show of service; then his laziness allowed the accounts to get into arrears, and he used to bring home the books for Anne to work at, write them up and take off trial balances. It was mere child's play to her, and she fell into doing more and more of it, at home and at the warehouse.

Anne was patient and tolerant with her husband; but when she found that he was surreptitiously chewing tobacco she "drew the line." It was the last straw; and happened to show which way the wind blew too. Was her son to grow up *such* a man? What right had John McVey to be a disadvantage to her children?

John would go off "down river" for days together, and come home with the ague, ruined clothes, and forty cents' worth of fish, of which he was quite proud, although the biggest had always got away. He bought a patent right, spending a whole month's wages in the purchase and a whole month's time in hunting for "capitle" to get up the necessary machinery. In this pursuit he had visited Zury Prouder on his farm.

"Did you see Mr. Prouder, John?"

"Yes. I saw him."

"What did he say?"

"Oh, he did n't seem to grasp the subject at all. Said it looked to him like the Dutchman's grist-mill — a first-rate grist-mill — O. K. and A 1 in every particular, — was n't a better grist-mill in the whole state, — only it would n't work."

"Nothing else?"

"Well, he called it a 'perpettial motion,' and — well, he did n't grasp the subject at all."

"How did Mrs. Prouder look?"

"As if she weighed from a quarter to half a ton."

"Did Mr. Prouder — ask any questions?"

"Yes. He inquired if the patent had ever been tried. I told him no, and that he could n't tell whether it would be profitable or not until he tried it. He said he could n't try it until he could tell whether it would be profitable or not. And so I gave him up, and came away."

John's report of Zury's remarks was imperfect, to say the least. More fully rendered, they would read thus: —

"Sonny, if ye kin git enough perpettial motion inter yer legs t' take ye back to Springville, 'n' then sufficient perpettial motion aouter yer head t' let ye keep yer eye tight open on yer work in th' store, ye may possibly accumle-ate enough capitle t' keep yer fam'ly till next blackberry harvest — if ye have luck."

John continued: —

"He gave me a letter to a party who resides down river a piece, who owes him a horse; and he told me that if that party would give me the horse, I might have it and give Zury my note for a hundred dollars and pay it out of my wages at the store."

"Of course you declined."

"Well — not yet. There's a party going to start for California next week, and if I had that horse I could get to go along."

Anne started — almost a guilty start — at the thought that filled her heart and brought a flush to her face.

"How would that strike you?" he added.

"Of course — if you thought it would be advantageous" —

"Well, everybody seems to be going."

So John went to California. Anne made the greatest efforts to provide her husband with his outfit. Few travelers started so well supplied with clothing and all the comforts a woman's hand can prepare. She dispatched him on his long, blind journey with a feeling of relief that made her reproach herself as a heartless woman. But then, was he not a drag and an increasing disadvantage to her children? A positive peril to their future. And was not this a justification for anything — any hardening of her heart?

John got the horse and the passage to the new El Dorado. Prouder got his note for a hundred dollars, and later got the money with interest. California got John, and John got — the cholera. Nobody mourned for him except little Margaret — the gentlest soul that ever put on childish form — who wept to see that nobody else did. Years passed, during which even she grew out of all memory of poor "gentlemanly Johnny."

Anne's health and her children's being excellent, she had no trouble in maintaining the family in comfort. Clothes cost little, food less, and education (public school) nothing. Phil had a genius for mathematics and was what is called a "natural mechanic." Margaret had a genius for faithful work at whatever her hand found to do.

Before Phil was ten years old he knew by heart all the mills within reach: the old breast-wheel grist-mill and the new overshot grist-mill, and the undershot saw-mill with its mechanical expedients, so few and simple, yet so ingenious and effectual. Then, when a railroad was built to Springville (which was before one came to Chicago), what rapturous delight encircled like a halo the first locomotive! He was the very earliest apprentice in the machine-shop, and days of labor between nights of study were his regular experience for years together.

During all Anne's Springville life and service for Polander Brothers, Zury was a frequent visitor at the warehouse, but never at the cottage after his disastrous castigation at her hands. At just about regular intervals he found it convenient to visit his merchants, and he always spent some time leaning on the railing that barred her from the outside world, and talking with her about the children and about Wayback matters. His unassuming, persistent cordiality won upon her. She grew to expect him, to rely on his cheery voice and strong nature as a part of her life. She flushed with pleasure when he came; she greeted him with her well-remembered smile; she pressed his hand with her soft, inky fingers at meeting and parting; and if he stayed away longer than usual she wondered at it and let him know, next time she saw him, that she had done so.

So constant and so deeply crafty is mother-love! Have you never seen a mother-bird try by simple strategy to protect her nestlings? I have. She spreads one wing and drags it on the ground as if she were wounded and almost ready to be caught; and only when she has tolled you far away from their hiding-place does she mount gayly to a tree-top and wait until you have given up your supposed inimical designs.

This summing up has taken us some years ahead of our story. Let us go back for an incident that occurred when the twins were entering their teens.

CHAPTER XVII.

ZURY FOR THE LEGISLATURE.

"HAOWDY, haowdy Mis Sparrer—McVey I should say."

"Good morning, Mr. Prouder. Glad to see you! How is your wife?"

"Middlin', middlin', I thankee. Yer babes peart?"

"Yes, they 're well—not exactly babes any longer."

"No, I expect not. Time flies. Ain't it amazin' haow it buzzes? Th' days use 'ter tarry like a meetin'-haouse clock; naow they spin 'raound like a buzz-saw."

"That 's very fine! Mr. Prouder, you were cut out for an orator."

"Oh, naow let up on me, 'n' quit yer foolin'!" said Zury, though he was pleased, and showed it. "But by th' way, some fellers that 's got some kind of a grutch agin me, I expect,—tho' I dunno 's I ever harmed 'em nuther—dunno 's I did 'n' dunno *as* I did,—they 've pitched on me t' run fer the legislatur'."

"Capital! You 'll make a good legislator!"

"Bless yer simple soul! Make one? Not ef they know it! They look t' be beat in the race, and that 's why the' pitch on me! Th' deestrick 's agin' aour side; 'n' besides, this h'yer free bankin' question 'll kill us. Th' fellers on th' other side is all fer it, 'n' of course we 're agin it."

"Oh, I see! Want to get you killed off to make room for somebody else."

"Eggzackly! An' pay fer the rope t' hang me, tew! Reg'lar turkey shoot, 'n' me th' turkey, tied t' a stick at th' lonesome end o' th' shootin'-range."

"What do you say to that?"

"Wal, I hain't said aye, yes ner no tew it yit." Then sinking his voice slightly, so as to make his words indistinguishable (though not inaudible) to the people about in the warehouse, "Ef I hed your brains, and my body, tew, I 'd turn the tables on them smart Alecks!"

"My brains? Have them knocked out instead of yours?"

"Nary time! Use 'em! I 'd make them fellers see stars!"

"How do you mean?"

"Carry the deestrick in spite of 'em! Farmers ain't no fools. They 'll listen tew reason."

"They 'd never listen to me!" she said, with a sigh. "I 've tried them once, with all the brains and all the arts I had — and they drove me away!" The tears filled her eyes at the recollection of her mortifications.

"What! Them fellers that was intew the burnin'? Nary a one on 'em left abaout th' diggin's! Don't ye charge Wayback Deestrick with that thar jawb! Why they jest could n't stay 'raound! The place got tew hot fer 'em — hotter 'n ever that dry tree got th't your money was hid intew! The' ain't no trace left on 'em, no more 'n the' wuz o' them bank-bills."

"Well. I'm glad they are gone. But it was n't they alone. All the people, women and men, gave me the cold shoulder; all except my dear scholars!"

"Thar it is agin! Yer scholars naow is jest a-gittin' along — up 'n' a-comin' — rulin' th' hull neighborhood, on yer own lines."

"Indeed? Well, I hope they won't follow in all my ways." Then hastily: "But it makes no difference — I am not you and you are not I."

"No! Wuss luck! Ef I wuz, I'd knock things galley-west! I'd rare right up on my hind legs 'n' paw the air! I'd range through that neck o' woods head 'n' tail up, like a blaze-faced bull in th' corn!"

"Now," said she, purposely raising her voice, "tell me about the Waybackers — all of them."

"Oh, they 're all O. K. Don't ye want t' ride over 'n' see 'em?"

"I should like it of all things, of course. We always want what we can't get."

"Can't git t' go t' Wayback? Why not, I'd like t' know? My team 's pootty stout, 'n' I kin spare 'em an extra ear o' corn apiece t' make up fer your weight in th' wagin."

"Oh, the team 's all right — and the wagon,

and the driver. But the passenger can't go all the same."

"Why not?" he persisted.

"Well, for one thing, my daily toil for daily bread."

"Oh, I'll fix that all right!" And he strode away to speak to the storekeeper, unheeding Anne's urgent and repeated calls to refrain from doing so. In a few minutes he returned with one of her employers, only too anxious to comply with the request of their powerful customer.

"Now why did you take all that useless trouble, Mr. Prouder? Because I cannot go, and that is the end of the matter."

"Why not?"

"Well — I have my children to care for."

"Fetch 'em along! Hog 'n' hominy 's plenty yet onter the Praouder farm."

Anne only shook her head and turning her back on him, resumed her book-keeping. Pretty soon the headstrong, petty tyrant, unused to failure, came back and renewed the attack.

"What else ye' got on yer mind, besides yer business 'n' yer childern?"

"Myself."

"Yerself?"

"Yes. You take precious good care of yourself: I take pretty good care of myself. Not always, but generally."

This seemed to puzzle him, and he went off to think it over. In the coarse and unconventional, though moral atmosphere wherein he had been brought up, such feminine exclusiveness had never come under his notice (except in Anne), and he did not yet quite recognize it when he saw it. In his bewilderment he sought counsel from one of the storekeepers.

"Oh, yes — you bet she takes care of herself! She ain't no slouch! Many's the feller 't would a liked t' took th' ha-ansome widder aout sleigh-ridin' or buggy-ridin', but no sirree! Nary a one on 'em! Not even *him*." (Indicating his junior partner.)

"Wal, I should think not!" said Zury, with jealous though illogical heat.

He mused long and silently. After an hour or so he once more approached the subject, but in a roundabout way.

"Mis Praouder she 'llaowed t' come t' Springville with me, shortly."

"Did she? Well, I shall be glad to see her."

"Would her bein' along make any difference abaout yer a-goin' home with us?"

"Being along? No."

"I did n't know but what — on her invite" —

"Well, I 'll wait till she asks me, at any rate."

Anne thought it extremely improbable that Mrs. Prouder would ever join Zury in asking her to Wayback. "I 'm sure I should n't, in her place," she said to herself.

But she reckoned without her hostess. In a week the large, fat, homely face of that dull person appeared at the store, as fully bent on having Anne make her a visit as Zury himself was, allowing a "personal equation" for the difference in their two most dissimilar natures. Anne accepted the invitation, for herself and her children; but later her heart misgave her regarding the little ones. Margaret was all right, but she looked sharply at Phil, as with a stranger's eyes, and decided not to present him to the Wayback public. He was better in the machine-shop. (He had never seen Zury since he could remember.)

As to Margaret's going, she would leave that to Margaret. Now that devoted young person took the idea that she might be useful to her mother and the world by doing some of her mother's work at the warehouse. She could practice what book-keeping she already knew and learn the rest; and mamma, when she returned, would find but little accumulated work awaiting her. Phil, with his mathematical mind, could help her in the evenings. *But*—the plan must be kept a dead secret, for if her mother found it out she would insist on Meg's going.

"Well, mother, the girls are just going into algebra; unless you really need me very much, I think I'll just, naturally, stay at home."

Her mother regarded her suspiciously. She was much disposed to imagine some nefarious scheme of self-sacrifice on the part of that artful creature Meg. For wily craftiness in that line, she certainly was "the beater." At any rate, perfidy prevailed this time. Anne fell into the trap and left Meg at home; and oh, the inky fingers and corrugated brows that adorned the dear young toiler during the ensuing fortnight!

The simpler first steps, such as she had already learned under her mother's tuition, she went through trippingly every afternoon. Then, the more occult classifications and postings, she achieved at home in the evenings, with Phil's guidance and assistance.

One evening, after hours of application, ending with the unraveling of a tangle — one of those compensations that make book-keeping so fascinating — Meg said, —

"Oh, Phil! Suppose we could manage a trial-balance at the end of the month!"

"Meg, you 'll come down with a brain-fever, first you know. That would be a trial without any balance."

"Stuff! your face is redder than mine, this minute."

"No stuff about it! Your forehead is hot; and that indicates brain-fever." (Kissing her.)

"But your nose is cold, and that indicates a healthy dog. We *will* get off a trial-balance! Mother always had hers ready on the first of every month; we can surely make it by the second. Then we can send it to her by mail."

"And pay twenty-four cents postage? Then she 'll *know* we both have brain-fever, or something dreadful!"

"Well, we 'll see about surprising her with it. Better not cross that bridge till we get to it."

Meanwhile Anne sped finely with her "outing." The journey over was pleasant. They took along a basket of luncheon prepared by Anne's careful hands, and stopped to bait the team and refresh themselves in a charming shady nook on the banks of a prairie creek.

Zury talked politics from time to time, and showed plainly in his quiet, shrewd remarks, that he really cherished some "views" outside of party fealty.

"Them fellers that thinks the world would be twice't as rich if th' wuz twice't as much money; the' always remind me of the calf that would n't eat his pail o' milk onlest the' wuz a pail o' water put with it. Money! The' dunno what the' 're a-talkin' abaout! The truck they 'd like t' flood the kedntry with would n't be no *money*, no more 'n nothin' in the world!"

"Now, Mr. Prouder, all you need is to say those same things on the stump, to be the best public speaker I ever heard."

"Oh, the' would n't amaount t' nothin'; not th' way I put 'em. My speech 'd last abaout six minutes by th' watch. The' folks 'd be all a sayin,' 'What be we h'yer fer? Come all this way 'n' not got more 'n half unhitched afore its time t' hitch up agin; cause the speaker's feed-bag 's run aout! Zury better hire somebody t' dew his talkin' if he 's so short-winded!' Ye see the' come a long way, most on 'em; give up a half-a-day's corn-plaowin' tew; 'n' the' want not *less* 'n' an haour 'n' a half afore the' feel t' got ther money back. But then what the' r'aly like is t' have two fellers git t'gether 'n' discuss: fuss feller an haour, seck'n feller an haour 'n' a half, 'n' then the fuss feller a half an haour t' reply! That suits 'em up t' th' handle! What with two er three extry, cross, back-firin's, 'n' a few volunteer speeches from aoutsiders, 'n' a vote o' thanks t' th' jint c'mitty th't gits up the hull thing, a long summer afternoon gits knocked endways 'n' the fellers go hum feelin' the' 've hed a free show 'n' noth'n' shorter! Why the'r minds runs on what wuz said that day clear on t' 'lection — mebbe longer; mebbe long 's the' live!"

"It looks as though they cared more for quantity than quality. Now I 'd like better to hear the first man to say black 's white, and the second man to say white 's black, and then run home and 'tend my children." (Anne gave a little sigh as she named her deserted treasures.) "And then I should think it all over and conclude that black and white both were — about gray after all!"

"Ha-ha! That 's pootty near the upshot on it, by 'n' large. But that kind o' fodder 'd never do in the world fer that kind o' cattle. Don't ye know what happens ef ye feed a mule all corn?"

"I don't know. I never was a mule since I can remember."

"Ye allers wuz a hull team, 'n' a hoss t' spare! But not a mule — mebbe a little bit muley sometimes. Naow the fact is, a mule, er a hoss either, ef he 's got all the corn he wants, 'n' noth'n' else; why he 'll eat up his beddin', 'n' his gears, 'n' his mate's mane 'n' tail, 'n' his feed-box, 'n' th' hull stable, 'n' the groun' he stan's on, but what he 'll git suth'n' intew him t' die-lute his corn 'n' fill up his innards."

"Poor beast!"

"Poor beast! Ye'd think so ef ye heerd him holler 'n' beg when he's hay-hungry like that."

"I'd put green spectacles on him and give him shavings."

"He'd eat 'em fast enough! 'N' the spectacles tew, soon 's he could wipe 'em off with his hind huffs! Wal, folks is the same way. If ye feed 'em tew rich they can't die-gest it 'thaout mixin' in a heap o' fillin'-up-stuff. Lucky fer the preachers, ain't it! Great Scott! If the' didn't give Christians some pootty pore spiritial food the'r fahm'lies 'd have pootty pore pickin's in temp'rals!"

"Naow Zury!"

"Oh, I ain't sayin' a word agin the preachers, wife. They give what the' 've got, 'n' what 's wanted, tew. Same 's I dew t' *my* mules."

"Lucky for us women, too, Mr. Prouder. Suppose nobody would listen to us except when we had something to say!"

"Wal — yes — in a way."

"Come to think, when we are tired of sensible talk we 're very like the mules — we turn to our gears, quite naturally."

"Good agin! Gears! To be sure! Gnaw 'n' nibble at yer mates some, tew, I guess!"

"Naow Zury!"

"Oh, I ain't a-sayin' nuth'n' agin the women, nuther. Salt o' th' yearth. 'Thaout them we men 'd all be gomorrahed in fire 'n' brimstun — er desarve t' be. But the' dew furnish plenty o' talk. Shavin's 'n' sawdust enough t' average daown a good deal o' hard sense. The' 're so built by th' Allwise, in His inscrutable ways 'n' past findin' aout, th't the' 've got ter talk er go crazy. Put a woman in a lonesone spot 'n' she 'll jes' barely save her life by a-talkin' to herself, a steady stream. Many 's the time I 've come up quiet tew a aout-lyin' farm-house, 'n' thought th' wuz a taown-meetin' er suth'n' a-goin' on inside; 'n' come ter fin' aout 't warn't noth'n' but th' ole woman a-discoursin' tew herself!"

"Naow Zury!"

"Fact, wife! Haow else 'd the peddlers live? Ef it warn't fer the lonesome houses they 'd starve t' death. Think the peddlers dew the talkin'? No sirree! All *they* hev t' dew is t' listen say half an haour, 'n' then make as ef they wuz a-goin', 'n' the woman 'll buy, er sell, er trade suthin' t' keep 'em on a while longer. It 's talk 'n' sell some mantel ornaments; 'n' talk 'n' buy some goose-featehrs; 'n' talk 'n' sell a paper o' pins; 'n' talk 'n' trade some tin pans fer a jar o' honey — ontel it 's time t' blow the dinner-horn."

When the wagon was again on the road and jogging merrily along, Zury cautiously and awkwardly got back to the deep thoughts he had evidently been harboring for weeks.

"Speakin' o' women, 'n' mule-feed, 'n' one thing another; me 'n' Flory h'yer 's be'n a-talkin' abaout this speech-makin' job." And he looked anxiously at Flora for confirmation.

"Ya-as. I was a-tellin' Zury 's haow 't would n'

be no trick at all fer yew t' work up a good *discourse* — with yer book-larnin' 'n' all; 'n' so" — She paused as in a quagmire.

"Long 'n' short of it is — I know what to say, but dunno haow to say it. Yew tell me haow t' say what I 've got in my head, 'n' — I 'll be in the legislatur next winter." And he turned to his horses and began, in his embarrassment, to whistle a succession of tuneless notes, as if he had completed his task and had no further interest in it.

"I to write a speech and Mr. Prouder to commit it to memory? I could n't write it; he could n't learn it; and it would be a dead failure if we could." Zury seemed not to hear and kept on whistling. "His own plain talk is the best speech that could be made on the matters; and if people don't like it, that 's their own foolishness." More whistling. "I can fancy his thoughts and images used by some practiced speakers I 've heard, and being very effective."

Then, finding that she was drifting rather in his direction, she held her peace. Zury got tired of whistling (as even the very worst of whistlers will in time), and a thoughtful silence fell upon the trio. Then Zury began talking politics again.

"This h'yer nigger question 's li'ble t' come up, tew. We 're jest on the divide h'yer, betwixt th' northern and southern viws. Th' hottest talkers on one side is fer lettin' slavery spread; 'n' on th' other side fer 'bolishin' on it altogether; 'n' the the coolest hands is fer keepin' on it where it is a'ready. I don't hardly know what t' say. Jule he 's a likely nigger; but yet he ain't no more fit fer an American citizen 'n' a voter, th'n a ring-tailed 'possum with one eye. Ye 'll hear fellers that 's ben daown South 'llaow 't th' niggers is the happiest critters on top o' God's green 'arth; 'n' the wust luck 't kin happen tew 'em would be t' be sot free. Wal, then, that settles it — all we got t' dew is t' 'bolish the fugitive slave law; let 'em come up 'n' larn the fax; 'n' then keep the bars daown fer 'em t' git back t' all the blessin's o' civilization 'n' sugar-plantin', jest as quick 's Goddlemity 'll let 'em. Wun't they hurry South! Wun't they come a-runnin' back t' the'r masters! Oh, yes — yew bet!"

"Slavery! Does anybody defend negro slavery? Every man who owns a slave is a robber! I don't see how any man or woman can sleep or wake in peace who traffics in human bodies and souls! Ugh! If I were a slave I know my master would n't enjoy life very much or very long!"

"No," said he, looking back at her, "you 'd never make a very comf'table chattle! But s'posin' y' owned a lot on 'em, haow then?"

"Why I 'd set them free, of course! I thought everybody knew that that is the proper thing to do!"

"Wal, thet 's Massychusetts all over! Yew step daown South 'n' ye may happen t' find some perfessin' Christians — ministers o' th' gospel 'n' others — th't ain't quite perpared t' agree with ye. In fact, ye need n't go so fur, 'n' ye need n't go Saouth nuther. Ye 've seen 'em, 'n' shook han's with 'em tew. That thar brother Stokes, Presidin' Elder o' the feet-washin' Baptists — he 's a bright 'n' a shinin' light fer the Scripter authority fer slavery. He 'll preach ye a sermon from 'Cursed be Canaan,' thet 'll prove it t' be one o' God's holy ordinances; jest 's clear 's 'riginal sin, 'lection, 'n' predestination, 'n' just'fication by faith."

"Faugh! I 'd like to give brother Stokes a piece of my mind."

"I don't doubt but you could spare enough to double his 'n' never miss it." After driving on in silence for a while he added, —

"I guess them slave-holders better sing small ef they know when the' 're well off. Ef they try t' run things *tew* much, they 're liable t' find they 've bit off more 'n they kin chaw. But then, of course, I ain't no abolitionist. I don't believe in mixin' up blacks and whites till ye can't tell 'em apart — marryin' t'gether 'n' all that — let blacks be black 'n' whites be white; 'n' each keep t' his own race, says I."

"Mixing up? Who talks of mixing the races? Not the Abolitionists, so far as I know! And who is doing it without talking about it? The slave-holders! In a few generations there won't be a full-blooded negro left in slavery!"

"Jesso, jesso! Ye 've hit it right, sure enough! Thet thar idee is am'nition fer me, when the question comes up!"

The drive and the shadows grew long. Sometimes for miles the road led through open prairie

— wide open — "out of sight of land" as the expression is, describing the spaces (then plenty, now rare), where naught but land was visible in any direction; no tree, fence, hill, nor house to break the prairie horizon on the north, south, east, or west. At this present writing, almost every farmer has a plot of growing black-walnut or some other valuable tree; or at least an orchard. Since the prairie fires have been checked by the circumscription of human influences, these trees do very well in places where, as late as "the forties," the undulating surface was as naked as the heaving ocean, or the blowy, moving desert of sand.

In one of these stretches, Zury asked Anne for a song, and once more had the pleasure of hearing "Home, Sweet Home," in her best treble. Then she gave them "Araby's Daughter," and the "Mistletoe Bough," which last touched their hearts almost to the melting point — though they *were* Western pioneer settlers. After these, Anne asked Mrs. Prouder to sing; and she, nothing loath, struck up, —

"Hark, from the tombs a doleful saound!
  Mine ears attend the cry.
Ye living men, come view the graound,
  Where ye must shortly lie."

Each note she approached from several tones below, reaching it with a kind of gouging curve of sound, typified in nature's voice by the festive bull-frog, what time the full moon rises over the lonely marsh-lake.

Then fell a long silence, broken only by an

occasional creak of wagon or click of harness. Then the lights of Wayback, then a stretch of bottom-land and woods familiar to Anne's memory — Anstey's house and the school-house passed in silence — then home; tired, hungry and very ready for supper and a dreamless sleep.

As they said good-night, Zury called after Anne, —

"By the by, I'm a waitin' all these years fer the nub of that thar wall-paper story!"

"Goodness! What a dreadful memory you have! Well, I'll write it out for you some time."

"Wal, jest please reckleck th't some time don't mean all etarnity!"

CHAPTER XVIII.

ELECTIONEERING.

When morning showed the Prouder homestead it looked so utterly unchanged that Anne could not realize that so many years had passed since she saw it last. The same ugliness grown a little uglier, shabbiness a little shabbier, apple-trees a good deal larger, barns a good deal more numerous, the old log house still standing, though almost audibly begging to be killed and buried as they say aged savages do. It was all a large busy, prosperous, childless, pleasureless, laughterless desert.

Anne met with as much of an ovation as can ever be extorted from the undemonstrative frontier folk. Smiles, kisses (from her old scholars), tears even, here and there from women whom she had "boarded 'round" with or otherwise become better known to. These had already grown to be old in the rapid wear and tear of farm work, unwholesome nourishment, tooth-pulling, and medication. Poor old Mrs. Anstey was quite a wreck, but as faithful to her nostrums and as loving to Anne and as talkative to everybody as ever.

"Ya-as, Reekie she 's mar'rd 'n' gone, 'n' dewin' splendid. As fer me I can't say but I ain't no better, not t' say better, though I am a tryin' a pain-killer, 'n' a sass'p'riller, 'n' a collygog. Looks 's though some on 'em 'd oughter help me. Lucky the boys ain't had noth'n' much the matter on 'em lately, fer ef the' hed the' 'd a died sure, 'cause hearin' yew talk agin physic sot 'em agin it wonderfle. I 'xpect I 'd give 'em enough before t' keep 'em well so fur, but I look t' see 'em break daown any minute quick 's th' ole healin' paower gits clean wore aout by time."

"Maybe it is as I always said — better health without physic than with it."

"Ah, yah! Looks likely don't it? Think th' Lord 'd 'a' sent all them good paowerfle drugs ef the'r hed n't a-ben no use fer 'em? Doctors tew! Think *they* go t' colleges 'n' read mons's big books (so I 've heerd — big 's a half-bushel measure) 'n' all t' larn th't the' dunno noth'n' when the' git threw?"

"They say the older and wiser a doctor gets, the less physic he gives."

"Ah, yah! Ef one on 'em wuz t' come h'yer 'n' not perscribe no physic fer me, I 'd send him a spinnin' daown the road. Yes I would. 'N' mighty quick tew. No matter ef he wuz 's old 's Methusalem 'n' 's wise 's Solomon. I want suth'n' I kin feel right threw me, minute I take it."

In some respects the region had grown a little. Many of Anne's old scholars had homes of their own, and kept up some neighborhood cordiality of tea-parties, picnics, quilting-bees, and such like mild gayeties which had been almost unknown in their own childhood. Scarcely a day passed without an invitation to Anne and her hosts, calling them to some such entertainment. Her visit was made the occasion of an outburst of dissipation such as Wayback had hitherto never witnessed. Zury, too, had turned over a new leaf — went everywhere with his wife and her friend; talked with everybody; laughed, joked, learned to listen even when he differed, to argue where he was well-informed and his opponent ignorant, to greet civilly when he despised, to affect interest in affairs of others, to remember one day what his interlocutor had said on some other day, to give promises on conditions which could never become realities, to withhold promises where the conditions were likely to come to pass, — in short to *electioneer.*

Each night, when they got back to the homestead, they had a long talk on "the situation" — though that expression had not then been transplanted to the vernacular. Anne found herself insensibly, and not unwillingly, drawn into the task Zury had laid out for her — putting his ideas into shape for use "on the stump."

The great trouble was, to dilute them sufficiently for the coarse mental digestions of his prospective audiences. No orator ever sought for brevity more earnestly than these schemers did for diffuseness. How to fill the necessary hour or two of a country afternoon mass-meeting was the problem to be solved.

After "the hands" had gone to bed, the three — Zury and his two faithful auditors — would have a little meeting all to themselves.

"Now Mr. Prouder, look at the clock. Just eight, you see. Get to work, convince us two women that black is white, and don't let us hear you dare to be silent for the next thirty minutes by that clock, or we 'll go home and vote against you."

Then Zury would begin, drawl and dawdle as much as he could (repetitions were barred), and tell every illustrative story as diffusely as was possible to his practical mind, and then after reaching and saying by rote the prepared peroration, would look up at the clock. Alas! Only twenty minutes after eight!

Then it would be Anne's turn again. With much raillery and good-natured ridicule, she would take up his theme, give all his words, together with as many more, throw in personal hits which had perhaps been suggested by the day's conversations outside, and by the time *she* had dispatched the subject nine o'clock and bed-time had come.

Next evening Zury, an apt scholar, would take the laboring oar again, and before many lessons he managed to fill an hour very comfortably.

One of their excursions was over across the river to the neighboring county of Posey where a meeting of the other party was to be held. Zury did not tell Anne that it was on the picnic ground of so many years before, and she was somewhat disconcerted to find herself traveling the same old road, remembering the woods-fire and the walk of terror to the coal-mine on the river-bank. Neither of them alluded to it in any manner, and Anne's embarrassment passed off unnoticed.

The meeting was well attended, and many loud jokes were passed upon Zury, regarding his present incursion into the enemy's camp. Did he expect to steal their thunder? Or lose his own scalp?

"Neither one ner t'other, my friends. Jes' thought I'd drop over — my wife wanted t' hev a ride — 'n' Mis McVey h'yer — Did n't know but what I mought larn suth'n': mought git converted, 'n' vote agin myself come 'lection-day!"

The pro-slavery, pro-shinplaster harangue of brother Stokes displayed a folly, an ignorance, a bigotry, a wrong-headedness, that set Anne's teeth on edge, and made her want to arise and protest, then and there, against its horrible teachings. At this day of freedom, of sound currency, of political virtue, at least in professions, one of the political diatribes of 184– could scarcely be believed to have been seriously uttered.

The experience was, however, a very valuable one for our practicing political debaters. At home, that night, they tore the unconscious Elder Stokes to tatters and swept the ground with his remains. So voluble was Zury in his scorn and indignation that he scarcely needed any prompting, and nine o'clock came almost before they began to be at a loss for ammunition with which to carry on their sham battle.

The crucial test was fast approaching. Zury's first mass-meeting was set for a Saturday afternoon — the last of Anne's stay. It was called to meet at the school-house, with the modest view of not appearing to expect more than a room full to be present. But, by a strange coincidence, one of Zury's wagons, loaded with good apples, happened to break down just in front of the adjoining cleared field; and there it was when the crowd began to gather. Lucky, too; for the school-house overflowed before a third of the hearers arrived, and then what more appropriate than that the orator should speak from his own wagon-bottom?

"Kivered with apples? So 't is! But, friends, if it stays so very long, after you 've come h'yer by my invite 'n' I want room t' stan' up 'n' talk t' ye in — why, thet 's yewr lookaout 'n' not mine."

Then followed a good-natured scramble, a munching of fruit, a filling of pockets and a general warming up of the cockles of the heart. Folks are never so hearty as when they eat together. How the boys did distribute those apples! And the girls! They estimated their store somewhat in the same light that "society girls" do their cotillon favors after a ball, and every mother carried home some for her little ones.

On the way over Anne had been coaching Zury as to his start, knowing that once fairly under way he would gather force and do well. So she had devised a phrase or two that would sound half-way familiar and half-way new — just what sluggish hearers like — and break the ice for his further strokes.

"Friends and fellow-citizens! When in the course of human events it becomes necessary for one man to offer himself to his fellow-men, as a candidate asking for their votes, a decent respect for the opinions of mankind requires that he should give them such reasons for granting his re quest as he may be able to present, be those reasons good or bad."

This sentence was so well turned, so formal, so respectful, so far from the free-and-easy patronizing kind of talk the hearers had expected, that they were taken with a pleased surprise, and even at that early stage, gave him a cheer — a most effective fillip to the doubting heart of this tyro in oratory. The phrases were shrewdly adapted to taking the simple hearers captive, for they assumed a gravity and reasonable discrimination in the audience. No more fatal mistake could Zury have made than to underestimate his public and let them perceive that he did so.

Later, however, he fell into more familiar and jocular strains of thought and speech. Said he, —

"These h'yer money-cooks, they dunno whut they 're' a-talkin' abaout. Money! They dunno whut the word means! Banks can't print paper and make it inter money — it 's only a promise t' pay money, arter all, 'n' sposen y' hev a pocket-full on it 'n' th' bank can't or wun't redeem it, — wun't perform its promise, — whar be ye? Farmer's Bank o' Milksick Centre, Fever Caounty prints a wagin-bed-full o' bills 'n' calls 'em *money;* yew farmers go t' th' bank — Farmer's Bank, ye know — ye go t' git some o' th' *money;* th' bank cashier — store-clo'se 'n' stan'-up collar, straps on his pants 'n' lard on his har — sez he, 'Yes, sutt'nly. Jes' morgidge yer farm 'n' ye shell hev yer *money.*' Yew smart Aleck out with yer morgidge — hand it over and git yer *money.* Cashier trades yer mortgidge to some Eastern shark 'er other fer *real* money (hard chink) t' move t' Noo York with. Ye 're orfle rich with yer *money* till ye come t' pay the shark yer morgidge interest, 'n' find he wun't take Milksick money! Oh, yes — he 'll take it — as the Missippi woodyard man told the steamboat cap'n he 'd take some o' th' same kind o' stuff in pay fer wood — cord fer cord!

"Why, I tell ye, feller-citizens, things would sune come to jes' sich a pass as 't wuz in Michig*an* in 1838, when a Massychusetts caounterfeit one dollar bill wuz worth more than a ginuyne Mich-ig*an* ten!" (Loud applause and laughter.) "'N' s'posin' ye go daown to t' Milksick Centre with a boot-leg full o' the *money* th't come fr'm thar — what then? Tho' won't take it fer yer hoss-bait! Bank 's closed. Ye can't even git a Fever Caounty jury t' give ye judgment agin a Fever Caounty Bank! What dew ye git fer yer trouble? *The agur!* Traded off a good morgidge on a good farm fer a fuss class fever 'n' agur!

"No sirree! Them bills ain't *money* no more 'n pig's tail 's my elbow! *Money* 's a thing that can't be manufactured by a sharp in an office — its suth'n' th't 's got t' be dug aouter the graoun' 'n' then traded off fer suth'n th't 's growed a-top o' graoun': corn, hawgs, wool, — suth'n' 'r other th't takes labor. All other kinds o' *money* 's jes' a scheme t' git aour hard-arn't prodooce fer noth'n'! Talk abaout the kedntry need'n' more sucklatin' medium! S'posin' the' hed more, say tew dollars fer one, haow long 'd that dew 'em? Any place on the hill 'll dew t' start that stone a-rollin' but no place 'll dew t' stop it when its started except the ditch at the bottom!"

Here occurred an interruption — one of these occurrences that threaten disaster to the unready orator, but which are turned by the ready one to double account.

"Say, Zury; when I as't ye last week t' lend me forty dollars, ye 'llaowed money wuz tew sca'ce jest naow. Mebbe if ye 'd a hed yer pocket full o' shinplasters I mought a hed better luck."

"Yew, Joe Felser! Ye 're mighty right abaout that! Friends, can't ye see whut Joe Felser wants a lot more bank-bills printed fer? I 'll tell ye! He wants bank-bills t' be so plenty th't a feller 'd druther hev Joe Felser's promissory note fer forty dollars th'n t' hev forty dollars in bank-bills! Wun't bank bills hev t' be pootty plenty 'n' pootty cheap afore we see thet day? Cheap 'n' nasty — cheap 'n' nasty 'll be the bank bills we don't vally higher ner whut thet comes tew." (This rude personality tickled the rustic crowd more than it deserved by virtue of its wit.)

"The minute ye go t' increasin' paper 'n' callin' it *money*, then it begins t' go daown hill; prices goes a kitin', 'n' pootty sune the cry is fer more paper; coz it takes more at high prices than at low prices t' dew th' same work. Thet 's whut 's called inflation. Nex' thing is, — more yet. 'N' so on, till ye 'll hev t' tote a basket t' pack yer *money* t' mill, 'n' a gourd 'll fetch back all the flour it 'll buy!" (More laughter.)

"Why, friends, ye 're some on ye farmer's boys, 'n' the rest on ye hev ben — 'er gals, one er t' other, fer I 'dress my remarks to the ladies present as well as the rest. Wal, did n't ye never wean a calf by hand? I did, 'n' many a one. Daown in Pennsylvany, whar I come from, we could n't afford t' let caows run with th' calves. I useter go aout a milkin' early o' frosty mornin's, afore sun-up, 'n' scare up th' caows easy like, so they would'n' move away so but whut I could milk, stickin' my cold toes down in the warm place they 'd laid in. Then I 'd mix s'm meal in 'n' feed the calves. Six quarts o' milk fer a starter, is a square meal fer a calf. Naow, s'posen some calf is such a dod-gasted fool of a calf that he turns 'inflationist' — that is a paper-money calf. Fust thing ye know he wants six quarts o' water with his six quarts o' milk. Down goes twelve quarts o' th' inflated milk. Still he baa's fer more, so yew double it again 'n' daown goes twenty-four quarts o' skyblue mixtur'. Same time don't ye see he don't git a drop more milk than he did at the start? But naow the' 's no stoppin' on him, he cries again for more currency; 'n' pootty sune he 's got t' git 'raound a bar'l full o' water t' dygest his six quarts o' milk! Whut 's the upshot? Why that thar calf 's got t' BUST. 'N' so must any calf er any c'munity th't sets abaout die-lutin' good milk with poor water, er good cash with poor paper."[1]

Laughter loud and long followed this homely illustration, and Zury had time to refresh himself and gather new strength for new triumphs.

Passing over his talk on some local themes which would mean nothing to us, we will try to give an idea of what he had to say about the "Nigger question." He had associated so much with Jule in the early days that he could give a fairly graphic imitation of negro dialect and pronunciation, the latter seeming to be the product of soft flabby organs too large to be comfortably managed and used in the mouth that contains them.

"Makes me laugh t' hear brother Stokes blow abaout the niggers bein' a heap better off in slavery th'n what they would be ef th' wuz free! Reminds me of a talk our darkey Jule hed with one o' them 'postles preachin' the gospil o' slavery fer the good of the nigger. H'yers abaout the way the talk run: —

"'Wha' d' ye run away fer, Jule? Did n' ye have a kind marster?'

"'Oh, yes, baus; ole marse wuz kin' 'nuff, I speck.'

"'Did n' ye hev enough t' eat?'

[1] This illustration is adapted from a stump speech of Representative Horr, of Michigan.

"'Oh, yes, baus; s'peck we 'uns hed all 't wuz goo' fer us.'

"'Medicine when ye wuz sick?'

"'Oh, yes, baus; plantation docter ollers raoun' when we wuz off de wuhk.'

"'Clo's all furnished free?'

"'Yah-yah! Din' take much clo'se in de cott'n fiel' in de sunshine!'

"'Liberty-day now 'n' then?'

"'Oh, yes, baus; when da wahn't nuffin' t' do, din' do nuffin'.'

"'Then whut 'n' th' nation 'd ye run away fer? All them blessin's is a heap sight more 'n most of us fellers gits up h'yar.'

"'Yah-yah-yah! Tell ye w'ut 't is baus, ef de place suits ye, I guess it's open yit! I'll gib ye de d'rection; ye kin pile right daown dar!'"

This was another story that "went to the spot" with those workers in glorious freedom, Western pioneers whose muscles were driven to the verge of desperation, but whose minds were free from any suggestion of control. The sea of faces before Zury was now illumined all over by the welcome whitecaps of broad grins.

"Dew I hear anybody askin' me, 'Zury, be yew an abolitionist? Would ye like yer darter t' marry a nigger?' Ef I don't hear this old circus conundrum, it 's jest coz the' ain't no Posey Caounty politicians in hearin'! Over t' Posey, th' other day, whar I wuz, ye could n' throw a stone 'thaout hittin' half-a-dozen fellers askin' jest that rebus offen somebody. My answer 's ollers ready to sech questions. I say I want every race t' keep t' itself 'n' work aout its own salvation best way it kin. Thet 's why I don't want no extension of the blessin's o' slavery intew Illenoy. Talk of 'malgymation! Whar dooz it flourish? 'Mongst th' abolitionists, er 'mongst the slave-holders? I hain't heerd o' Jule's 'malgymatin' t' no gre't 'xtent sence I fetched him up h'yer, goin' on twenty years ago! 'N' ef he hed, I guess I 'd a ben likely t' a-hearn tell on it! Same time, daown whar he come fr'm, marsters 'n' slaves is pootty near all of a color a'ready, 'n' gittin' more so right along! Why, th' State o' Kentucky 's plum full o' bleached darkey babies, so white ye can't tell t' other fr'm which!"

More laughter greeted this sally, and when it had died away Zury proceeded to the combination of his various branches of talk into one edifice.

"Naow, friends, I 've paid my respecks to the various loonatics the' is a doin' business in the p'liticle market; 'n' I want t' see you 'n' me 'n' all aour kind ockepy a stan' whar we kin look daown on th' hull caboodle on 'em. H'yer 's th' way it is — the Demycrats kin beat th' Whigs, 'n' th' Free-bankers kin beat th' Demycrats, 'n' th' Whigs kin beat th' Free-bankers. This ollers reminds me of our ol' hen-haouse tew hum.

"Ye see th' black hen she c'd whip th' white hen; 'n' th' white, she c'd whip th' ol' speckled hen; 'n' th' ol' speckle, she c'd whip th' black. Wal, ye know it 's th' natur o' hens t' want ter roost near th' ol' rewster. (I 'm naow speakin' only of two-legged hens.) So when th' ol' rewster he 'd fly up ontew th' perch, come sundaown, mebbe th' black she 'd up 'n' set daown next him, 'n' stay thar ontel th' speckle upped 'n' drove her daown flippity-flop. Thet wuz all right ontel th' white she 'd go fer th' speckle 'n' aoust her, hoss, foot, 'n' dragoons, 'n' set in th' seat of honor herself, ready t' be druv off a whoopin' 'n' a squawkin' by th' black. 'N' so the' 'd keep it up f'm sundaown clean on to dark night; ontel th' ole rewster he 'd git tired of it, 'n' rare right up on his hin' legs 'n' put a stop tew it — knock 'em all off f'm th' perch — pick aout fer his neighbor a pullet th't warn't neither th' white ner th' black ner th' speckle, give *her* the ch'ice location, 'n' reach over her with a smart clip at th' fust one that tried t' raise a disturbance. Naow s'posen we call th' white th' Whigs, 'n' th' black th' Demycrats, 'n' the speckle th' Free-bankers — who 's th' *ol' rewster?* Yew be, my friends; the thoughtful voters, the free 'n' independent farmers of th' State 'n' th' Nation! *Yew* 'll stop ther squawkin' 'n' ther squabblin' jes' 's sune 's ye git a good ready. Wanter know when that 'll be? Next 'Lection Day! Then ye'll whoop 'em up! Daown the' go — Black, White, 'n' Speckle, 'n' ther master — th' people — will have peace at last!"

After the roar which greeted this had subsided Zury returned to the more dignified, measured, respectful strain, and finally he gave the prepared peroration in a high, serious tone, without gesture or smile, gazing far away above the heads of his hearers, who listened in breathless silence. He only brought his look down to their eager faces as he gave them thanks for their attention and bade them farewell.

The speaker seemed dazed by the storm of cheers that followed. He sat on the wagon-board, with his eyes closed, his head on his hand and bowed upon his breast. Then the enthusiasts insisted and persisted until they could get hold of his hands; some on one side and some on the other, and shake them to a degree that finally broke his revery into a cheerful laugh.

"Heavens 'n' arth, Zury! Where ye be'n a hidin' yer light all these years! Why ain't ye Guv'nor of Illinoy?"

"Yes; er President of the United States?"

"Oh, I ain't noth'n' but a poor ign'r'nt farmer, pards. It 's th' fax thet 's strong — 't ain't me, ner th' way I putt 'em." Then his eyes sought for Anne as the true source of his success; but she had prudently withdrawn somewhat — in fact, her own feelings were somewhat excited and overwrought by hearing her words used in public, and the public so moved by them. She had exacted a promise from Mrs. Prouder that no sign or hint should get abroad that she had even known what Prouder was going to say. Zury did not need to be urged in this direction, but it would have been just like his simple wife to tell the whole story.

They drove homeward through the cooling airs of evening, and as they passed the gay groups they were greeted from all sides. "We 've got 'em, Zury!" "Hurrah fer th' Wayback candidate!" "That calf 's busted a'ready, Zury!" "We 'll knock them ol' squawkers all offen th' perch come 'lection."

Beside the two women he brought over, Zury carried back as many of the folks going his way as his wagon would hold, so there was no chance for any exchange of private views; and in the evening, when Zury hoped to have it all over in a long talk with Anne, she was conveniently tired and went to her room almost immediately after supper. She had an instinctive repugnance to thanks and explanations. When the next evening arrived, she had no longer any practicable excuse for not having the customary sitting-room conference, but then time had calmed the too effusive feelings that followed the stunning success of the meeting, and all was plain sailing.

"Wal, Mis McVey, Zury 'n' me we 've be'n a thinkin' whut on th' yarth we kin dew t' pay ye up fer th' help ye 've be'n tew him."

"Help, Mrs. Prouder? Pay? Why, that 's all nonsense! When I want anything you 'll know it, I assure you. Till then I hope you won't think of any such foolishness."

"Wal, ye know I ain't no scholard, ner much of a c'rackter anyhaow; but Zury, he 'llaows the speech wuz yourn, 'n' not his'n, 'n' it 's yew 't 'd oughter go t' th' legislatur' ef anybody!"

"I 'm not a candidate, I thank you! The speech was his speech, and his alone. It 's just as sensible to call it mine as it would be to say that a man built a house when he only whitewashed it."

"Whitewash!" cried Zury. "Whitewash? Why, I did n' dew no more 'n dig th' cellar 'n' lay th' faoundation! Yew built th' haouse 'n' furnished it! 'N' it 's me th't 's goin' t' live intew it — ef I git votes enough. So yew 'n' me ain't square, not by no means."

"Well, if I have done any good, I 've just done it to the country in the only way a woman can do it — or ought to wish to do it, according to my present way of thinking — by influencing a man's election or his actions after he 's elected. Nobody can ever pay me for that any more than a man can pay you for your actions in the legislature — after you get there, as I hope you will."

"Looks pootty like it, by what I 've heerd talked 'raound to-day. Big meetin' aout t' Danfield nex' We'nsd'y, 'n' 'nother some'rs else the Sat'd'y arter."

"Heavens and earth! Have you to get up all those speeches?"

"All those speeches! Bless yer simple soul, d' ye s'pose the' want any diff'rent speech f'm what I give 'em t' th' scule-haouse? Not a bit on it! The' would n't hev no other, not at no price! S'posen I hed another, jest 's good 'n' better; the' would 'n' never stan' it! The' 'd be a hollerin' 'n' yellin' all over th' place, 'Give us the busted calf, Zury! Oh, Zury! Haow 'baout them three hens! Tell us 'baout them nigger babies, Zury — can't let ye offen th' nigger babies!'"

"Why, will there be a fresh lot of people to relish the old stories they 've heard about?"

"Partly a fresh lot — mainly th' same old fellers, though. But the' 're like th' chil'n 'n' the'r mothers: the babes ollers wants t' hear th' same old stories, told in th' same ol' words. So does th' common run o' folks. *Yew* notice what jokes takes best in a craowd. Th' ones the' laugh at most is th' ones the' 've be'n most useter laughin' at."

So by cleverly turning the subject Anne had escaped the matter of thanks and "pay," as poor, awkward Mrs. Prouder rudely phrased it. Zury's ambitious soul was easily floated away from shallows of the past on the waves of the imaginary future.

But in at least one house the subject was more fully treated. It disturbed the privacy of the Anstey connubial chamber.

"Anstey — oh, Anstey — be ye asleep?"

"Jest a sugarin' off. What 's up?"

"Why, don't ye know what 's th' matter with Zury Praouder?"

"Zury? Why, he 's jest struck his gait. Fust chance he 's hed t' show what 's in him. *I* seen it all along. Could n't tell me noth'n' abaout Zury Praouder! Ain't noth'n' Zury can't dew! 'N' ollers could. 'N' I knowd it all fer this last coon's age!"

"Oh, yew sho! Ye ol' fool! Ye 're ollers a knowin' lots, fer a coon's age, arter it 's all come aout, specially ef it ain't so, arter all."

"Ain't so? Zury not a hull team 'n' a hoss t' spare 'n' a" —

"Zury here, 'n' Zury there; what's that got t' dew with his speech?"

"Why, I'm a tellin' ye, he's jest th' man t' make jest sech a speech, 'n' I ollers knowd it, 'n' so on."

"Yes, 'n' I'm a tellin' *yew* ye're an ol' fool, 'n' blinder 'n a bat, besides. Zury's speech! Pickled eel's toes! Anne Sparrer McVey's speech is what I 'llaow!"

"Sho t' man! D' ye b'lieve it?"

"B'lieve it? Don't hev t' b'lieve it, I know it! Tell me! Yah, yah! I wondered whut wuz up when she come daown h'yer 'n' went t' drivin' abaout with them Praouders, lookin' all over th' lay o' th' land 'n' not a-sayin' nothin', all 's innocent 's a pig in a garding."

"Wal, he-he! Ol' woman! Yew hev got a head onter ye. It's nex' thing t' Zury's own head 'n' I know it. Knowd it fer a coon's age! Dunno but ye 're right, dunno but ye be. Never 'd a thought it, though. Never mistrusted a blame thing."

"Mistrusted nothin'! 'Course ye did n't, ner none o' th' rest o' th' folks. The' 'd never notice ner mistrust noth'n', not ef the' wuz t' meet a wagin-load o' brass monkeys with the'r tails burnt off. I keep my eyes open, thet's all; 'n' *I* tell *yew* them idees 'n' them words wuz all Anne Sparrer McVey's idees 'n' words. Zury Praouder could n't never hatch aout no sech a brood 's thet, smart 's he thinks himself, 'n' many 's th' farms as he's got, 'n' morgidges on other folkses farms."

"Wal, is he t' ride inter th' legislatur on her wagin? Haow on th' yarth kin you 'n' me let folks know who actially made the speech, fixed th' way we be, in regard o' Zury, 'n' th' morgidge behind?"

"Oh, we hain't on call t' interfere. I speck she wants him t' git in; so ef we wuz t' upset his 'tater cart, we'd be a runnin' agin her; 'n' we ain't on runnin' agin her, I reckon."

"No sirree! Ef she says so, it's all th' more reason t' putt him in. 'N' we kin dew it, tew. But he'd oughter pay her well fer makin' up thet speech fer him, ef so be she did make it up."

"Ef she did? Don't I tell ye the' ain't no mistake abaout it? But yer mighty right abaout him 'd oughter payin' her well fer it."

"'D oughter give her a good five dollars fer it, say I."

"Yes, ye better believe it. Five dollars in gold, tew!"

And with this munificent vision of golden guerdon for their beloved Anne, the old couple sank into rosy slumber.

CHAPTER XIX.

HOME AGAIN. — ZURY DEFEATED, THOUGH VICTORIOUS.

"Now, Mrs. Prouder, I have had a delightful visit, and I must be thinking of getting home to my children and my work."

"Wal, ye 're welcome t' stay jest 's long 's ye 're a min'ter."

"Yes, I know. You 've been kindness itself. But all things come to an end, and so must my visit. When can you spare time for a drive to Springville?"

"Wal, I warn't cal'latin' t' go t' Springville agin right away naow. Zury he 'llaowed t' take ye over any day ye like."

"Oh, Mr. Prouder. I see — yes, of course," Anne answered rather hesitatingly. "But I was hoping for the pleasure of your company."

"Wal, I 'd like t' obleege ye, but I don't hardly see haow I kin git away agin right off. Zury he 's got ter be in Danfield come We'nsd'y, 'n' we 'llaowed it might suit ye t' make it so 's he c'd take yew on t' Springville th' same trip, ef that 'd suit ye, d'reckly arter th' meetin'."

This would n't suit Anne at all. But how to make that great dull creature understand that under no circumstances would she travel for a day or more alone with Zury Prouder, including attendance at the Danfield meeting? And how to get home in any other way? Here was a dilemma she had never contemplated: a puzzling — almost distressing predicament. Her still smooth forehead took on an unaccustomed cloud, and her old teeth-tapping trick evidenced her puzzled condition.

Why was the Prouders' plan out of the question? She would enjoy the repetition of her experience at the Wayback meeting. There was an intoxicating delight in hearing her best words uttered in Zury's strong voice and masterful manner; in observing the listening crowd hang in rapt silence on their utterance, and then burst into laughter and wild applause at every opportunity. It was a perfect and unaccustomed treat that made her heart beat fast, her breath come full and quick, her cheeks glow, and her eyes shine with the new joy of oratory (albeit second-hand), and with sympathy in the delight of Zury's hearers — her hearers.

And then Zury's company — without doubt it was more interesting to her than that of anybody else in the world except her children. Many associations of various kinds gave him a great place in her Western life; and besides, she shared with the rest of his friends the feeling of interest and amused respect which his fresh and vigorous originality inspired.

No hour — no morning — no day — could be

more attractive than one spent in his society, listening to his talk, always the same, yet without sameness; often wrong, often absurd, often affected in its piety or cynicism, often false, to draw out his interlocutor, but never dull. She felt when with him that she was at her best, and that he was fully as much pleased to hear her ideas as she was to hear his. It was always a game of battledore between them, except when there came a silence, which, after all, was scarcely less interesting. This plan of his, for a long drive with her (as she smiled to perceive), was in view of these pleasant relations, and would have had all these charms to the full.

So she could not think of permitting it.

In the evening Zury tried to rally her out of her determination to hasten home.

"Naow, Mis McVey — what makes ye in sech an all-fired hurry? Can't ye put up with common folkses livin' no longer? 'Course it 's pootty poor pickin's — not t' be called fash'nable 's I know on — but then we might kill a hawg er suth'n' ef that 'd be any object!"

"Oh, dear," answered Anne with one of her merry laughs. "One reason I must go home is my fear of getting fat and lazy with idleness and feasting!"

"Oh, we kin fix that all right, tew! Set ye t' whitewashin' th' fence, er droppin' corn as fast as two men kin kiver it, 'n' then ferget all abaout dinner — jest braouse 'raound instead o' feedin' reg'lar. Guess ye won't fatten t' trouble ye much."

"Still, I should n't be altogether happy. Two anchors hold me to Springville; and you know the longer the cable you have out the stronger your anchor holds."

"Oh! Them troublesome twins! Could n't ye git 'em 'dopted aout some'ers?"

"Now, Mr. Prouder, it 's plain you never were the mother of two lovely children!"

"Wal, not sence I kin remember. But what of it? They 're weaned, I understand."

"Another thing: you never were book-keeper in a general supply store — you absent, and your work running behind! This very day, being the end of the month, there ought to be two hundred monthly statements of account all headed and started, and a trial balance nearly ready so as to be handed in to-morrow or the day after!"

"Sho tew man!" exclaimed Zury, who had all the ordinary layman's awe of the supposed mysteries of book-keeping. "Be *yew* up t' all them things? No wonder ye kin make p'litickle speeches! Er do any other yarthly thing ye set yer hand tew! Should n' wonder ef ye c'd keep a hotel!"

"Of course I could! How do you s'pose I get along? Do you think I 've been begging my house-rent, and fuel, and food, and clothing, and schooling, for my darlings? This is the hard and callous hand of toil?" And she brandished a hand still fine, plump, white, and dimpled. Her one surviving vanity was her hands; her children would not let it fade away.

"Thar 's a hand t' make a white-wash-brush turn pale! Wal, ef ye must go, ye must, thet 's all. I 've got a little business up in th' north end o' th' caounty to-morrer — be back a Tuesday — take ye over t' th' Danfield meetin' a We'nsd'y ef that 'll suit ye, 'n' git on t' Springville nex' day."

"Well, we 'll see, we 'll see," said Anne musingly. "I hope for a letter to-morrow, that may let me know more about things at home."

Next day, Monday, after Zury had gone, his wife drove over to Wayback with Anne. She found the letter, sure enough; a formidable document that almost took her breath away, until she opened it. There it was — in her dear girl's unformed though neat handwriting — a trial-balance sheet for the month just closed! She could n't believe her eyes. (Perhaps that was the reason they filled with tears.) Long rows of toilsome figures, the remains of some of Phil's bolder pencil-marks where he had helped Meg with the additions; and all complete and perfect without even a word of explanation! Her dear twinnies — hers alone — so bright, so good, and so devoted! Why did she ever leave them! What other dreams of happiness could she ever, *ever* harbor except to be always with them? The "mother hunger" arose in her heart in such a flood that it seemed as if she should drown in it.

She asked the postmaster about getting to Springville by stage, but learned that "the hack," as he called it, did not come nearer than Danfield. There it turned back, and the mail came the rest of the way on horseback.

Mrs. Prouder glanced with wonder at the array of words and figures in Meg's letter, and from them to Anne's tearful eyes. Her dull idea of tears was that they were the mark of grief.

"I'm afeared ye've mebbe got bad news!"

"Bad? Oh, no! Not at all, but quite the contrary." She was about to explain the book-keeping miracle when she bethought herself that this unknown mystery might furnish her the needed excuse for getting home before Zury's return.

"The news is not to be called bad at all, except that I must get over to Danfield to-morrow, and go from there to Springville by stage."

"Oh lauk! Be all them figgers wrong? Hev ye got t' go 'n' write 'em all over again right?"

"Well, I can't be quite sure until I get there. Then I'll write you. Now how can I get to Danfield best and quickest?"

Of course this was soon and simply arranged. Mrs. Prouder was delighted to have Anne's bright spirit all to herself through a long drive, during which she could exhaust and deplete it, as dullness does pull down brightness whenever it gets it in its power. Anne got away next day and reached home without accident; but what a blank look came over Zury's face when he found that she had gone! Seldom had the wife seen him so "savage" as he was for some days afterwards. And in her flabby way she wondered what was the matter. The wild idea of a woman's becoming necessary to the happiness of a man who is not her husband was so far beyond her scope of vision that she could not have grasped it even if some one had tried to communicate it to her. It would have been to her like a French riddle to an American reader: he cannot guess it, even when he knows the answer.

How would Anne have liked it had she also seen Zury's suppressed fury at his disappointment? Of course it would have confirmed her as to the wisdom and propriety of inflicting it upon him. But perchance there would have been a drop of consolation in it. Women are not much offended by men's insolent ways in insisting on enjoying their society. Indifference to it is more galling. And then, as we know, Anne had not had her fair share of masculine attention.

When Anne reached her cottage there was a wild scene, and it was some minutes before she and Meg could be disentangled from each other and got far enough apart for articulate and intelligible speech.

Then all was told and retold on both sides — the son and daughter proud of the mother's oratorical achievement, and the mother proud of her daughter's courage, industry, ability, and devotion; also of Phil's ditto, ditto, ditto, ditto; only great doings were the natural phenomena of the boy's life. After a day or two of excited narration, things settled back into their wonted routine, and it seemed as if Anne never had been away, never constructed a speech, nor heard one; in short, as if her later Wayback experiences were years and years old, along with her original ones.

When next Zury visited the store, Anne caught sight of his stalwart shoulders from a distance, and beamed with pleasurable anticipations of their meeting and the customary words, more full and interesting even than usual. But alas! She soon began to see that the great man was in high dudgeon at her escape and avoidance of him, and meant her to see it very plainly. He never came near her! Anger and disappointment were her portion all day, but perhaps he would come to the cottage in the evening. He did not. Perhaps he would remain, or would leave at the store some token of his appreciation of her services. How and in what words should she decline any "pay," as poor Mrs. Prouder had phrased it? She needed not to puzzle herself with any such problem: no "pay" was forthcoming, and he departed without a word.

"The great brute!" she said to herself, with flashing eyes. "Why did I ever forget how mean he is! Likely enough he is glad to have the excuse of the pretended offense, to get clear of an inconvenient obligation without its costing him anything!" At the same time she was ashamed to perceive how much she really cared about his treatment of her.

Anne's anger having been the last to begin, and being complicated with some anger at herself for being angry, was by much the longer-lived. When at his next visit he attempted to show her that he had forgiven and forgotten her offense, she received him with a grave, unresponsive calm that baffled him as a sandbank nullifies a shrapnel shot.

"Why, dew tell, Mis Sparrer — McVey, I should say! That ain't never yew, is it?"

"Why not?" And she laid down her pen and turned upon him two solemn eyes, that paused as if awaiting some important reply.

"Why, workin' h'yer, same 's ever, jes' 's though the' warn't no sech a place 's Wayback, ner no sech a thing as a mass meetin' 'n' a stump speech."

"Oh, is that all?" and she turned away and resumed her pen as if he did not exist.

"I thought ye mought like t' know th't we beat 'em so 't the' did n' know whether the' wuz a foot er a hossback."

"On foot or on horseback?"

"Yes! The' 'lected me, by near tew t' one!" Then he added in a lower tone: "'Lected yew, I should say."

"And how long does the office stay with you?"

"Oh, I've got two sessions, anyhaow — that makes it just two years from now — 'n' 'f I git a reëlection, which I don't expect, it 'll make it a good four years."

"Well, will you kindly come in and tell me about it as soon as your two years' term is completed? That is, unless you are, as you say, elected again, in which case I hope you will come in after the four years." And she resumed her writing, though with a trembling hand.

"Ki! Ain't she hoppin' mad!" said Zury to himself as he turned away, pleased and amused at her anger, — flattered by it, in truth. Did it not indicate irritation at his neglect of her? All through his presence at the store, Anne felt rather than saw his smiling glances in her direction, and knew that her rage had been a blunder, which feeling aggravated it. Yet it must be maintained. It was one of those blunders which, well stuck to, are the next best things to no blunders at all. So when Zury, before going away, made a second attempt at cordiality, she gave him another slap. She ignored his presence while deliberately finishing the addition (wildly wrong) of a long column of figures, and then, with a bored and weary expression, turned to him: —

"Are the two years up already?"

"Wal, it seems a good spell anyhow."

"Is it two years?"

"Ya-as, in a way, ye 've been mad enough fer tew hours t' last tew years, I sh'd say."

"Then make it four years, if you please. Give my best regards to Mrs. Prouder, and come in again in four years." Then, as he lingered with an irritating smile of superior good-temper, she was compelled to add: —

"Do you understand English?"

"Wal, not so well as yew do."

"Then I shall have to teach you a little — for once. Please understand that I wish to be left entirely alone."

"Goin' t' put me aout, be ye?"

"I can't put you out; but I can put myself out, and I shall do it, if I have to." And she dismounted from her tall stool and looked at him with flashing eyes, waiting to see what he would do.

"Oh, see h'yer naow, I kin fix it all right" — And she was gone to her little cloak-room and had shut the door.

"Great Scott! Don't that beat all? Temper! I sh'd say so! If she wuz my wife, I'd — Dunno 's I would nuther. Dunno 's I *could!*" And he stalked off in surprised irritation — and respect. Thus did she snatch a victory, albeit a dear one, from the jaws of defeat.

"'Course I 'm greatly obleeged tew her. But *then!* A man don't have t' stan' everything. Guess I kin put up with it 's long 's she kin! Mebbe she may want suth'n' some day. I kin see 't these h'yer fellers ain't a half payin' on her fer whut she dooz, 'n' 't would n't take but a word fr'm me t' help her. I wish 't she knowd what she 's a losin' by a-quar'lin' with Zury Praouder!"

Then, *more suo*, he tried to comfort himself with the glory and strength of his position — member-elect of the legislature; richest man in Spring County, and the meanest, too, where he had a mind to be mean, but having no mind to be mean to Anne Sparrow McVey, unless she forced him to it; and so forth, with weary and fruitless repetition: for it was nothing but sawdust-and-water to his hungry soul.

"Ki! Don't a man feel small when a woman

hits him! Seems 's though he 'd ben bit by a caow er kicked by a dawg, seein' 't a caow can't bite 'n' a dawg can't kick. Kinder s'prised t' see haow it hurts! Wish 't some man h'd gone fer me th' way she did! But her, a snappin' them eyes o' hern at me, 'n' a showin' her shiny teeth! 'N' a comin' aout fust best when I knowed I wuz only a playin' mad, 'n' she wuz good 'n' mad!"

He made some excuse to stay at Springville over night, and in the evening knocked at the cottage door, which Anne opened to him. She regarded him with cool surprise, and did not ask him to enter.

"Haowdy, haowdy, marm! Be all well h'yer?"

"Yes."

"Ye see, I thought I 'd jest kinder drop in, 'n' kinder 'pologize fer any 'ffense I mought a given."

"Apologize?" with a shrill laugh, as if the very idea was too amusing to grasp. "For what? There 's not the slightest occasion."

"Wal, ye see, I 'm 's li'ble t' be wrong 's any-body — mebbe more so 'n most. We 're all poor falliable creeturs. Ef we had our failin's printed ontew our foreheads, we 'd hev t' keep our hats on night 'n' day, 'n' Sund'ys, — 'n' well pulled daown over our eyes, tew." He paused for a little help and encouragement, but got none. "So I 'llaowed ye would n't bear no malice, 'n' — we 'd be friends, same as ever."

"Yes, surely, Mr. Prouder. That is all right. Don't forget to give my regards to your wife." (The door begins to close.)

"I thought ef so be the' wuz anythin' I c'd dew fer ye" —

"Do for me? Thank you. If there should be anything, I will certainly let you know." (Door closing slowly.)

"Down t' th' store, naow — be the' a-treatin' on ye square?"

"Perfectly."

"Haow much do the' pay ye?"

"They pay me all I ever asked them."

"I kin make 'em dew what 's right."

"Well, if I ask you to interfere, I have no doubt they will listen to you."

After an awkward pause, the poor, crestfallen fellow could only add: —

"Is that — all?"

"All, to-night, I believe. Don't forget my message to your wife." And the door, after allowing passage to a muffled "Good night," shut entirely.

Zury walked away too much hurt to allow room even for anger. "Got m' walkin' papers sure," said he. "Yet I meant well. I meant well."

Anne had to face her children and answer their questions.

"Mr. Prouder? Oh, mother! why did n't you ask him in? I 'm just wild to see him!"

"Why, Phil, he is very busy, you know, and has no time to give to poor folks."

"But what is he going to do to pay you for what you did for him? Did n't he even offer to serve you somehow? Then he must be as mean as he 's cracked up to be! Or meaner."

"Certainly, Phil; that is what he came for, to offer me help in any way I could name. Of course I told him there was n't anything. If I had n't you, now, to be sure it would be different."

"Of course!" said the gratified boy, with one of his rare caresses.

"But, mother," cried Meg, "what 's the matter? You 're as pale as pale! I believe he brought bad news, or said something unpleasant."

"No, you foolish child," replied her mother, forcing a laugh. "Nothing of the kind! But I don't feel very well, and I think I 'll go and lie down."

She went into her bedroom, and much to their amazement they heard her lock her door. They had never before known that it could be locked.

Once there, she fairly broke down, and cried on her pillow. (It is a pretty sight, — a woman crying for pain she has inflicted.)

"What a fool I am! Of course there was nothing else to be done! I wish I were really angry with him! But it is myself I am angry with; and it is he I punish for it! Well, it 'll all come right some day and somehow. I don't suppose he was ever so cut up before in his life! But it will do him good! The hateful thing!"

CHAPTER XX.

SHOOTING-MATCH. — CHOIR. — PASTOR'S VISIT.

ZURY now stayed away from Springville as much as he could, quelling his mortification by the help of increased attention to business. When he did visit the store it all came back upon him, and he looked wistfully toward Anne's desk to see if the disfavor he had fallen into was departing. But she remembered her inexplicable and inexcusable tears; so no sign showed that she was aware of his existence.

One day his restless discontent led him to try to steal a look at Phil. At least he should see her son! He strolled over to the railway repair-shops and entered the round-house, where six iron steeds stood backed into their stalls, their formidable noses all pointing to the turn-table in the centre. Around them hung the usual crowd of rustics, staring open-mouthed at the still unaccustomed sight of a railway locomotive. How huge they looked under cover! How heavy, helpless, sleepy, and peaceful compared to their raging force and speed when at work! Elephants in winter quarters must resemble housed locomotives.

Behind them, and in the adjoining shops and forge-house, were the anvils, planing-machines, lathes, work-benches and tools, usually well-manned with grimy mechanics, now almost deserted; for it chanced to be a pay-day and a Saturday half-holiday. The hands, in their better clothes, were most of them clustered about the pay-desk in one corner. One of them, a fine specimen of incipient manhood, Zury easily recognized as Anne's son: his level brows, bright eyes, dark red cheeks, curly hair, square shoulders, powerful limbs, and quick, strong action, would attract attention anywhere from any connoisseur in stirpiculture; and they somehow seemed to mark him out as the fellow Zury was wishing to know without being known by him.

Phil stood at a bench, engaged in the apparently childish occupation of rolling bullets one after another down an inclined board into a little cup, scarcely larger than themselves, ready to receive them at the bottom. About one out of four would miss the cup and drop outside it.

Zury did not ask any questions, but he was glad when some one else did. A large-eyed little boy ventured: —

"Say, Phil, what ye doin' that fer?"

"Oh, jest playin' marbles."

"What ye tryin' t' hit?"

"Them others in the cup."

"Lemme try wunst."

"All right;" indicating the ones that had rolled aside. The ambitious youth tried and tried again, but they all fell wide of the mark. A loud guffaw from his rude fellows greeted his failure, and he slunk back abashed. Phil's looks followed the little man, who was evidently a gentle soul, small of his age, and absurdly sensitive.

"Come back, Freddy," said Phil; but Freddy walked away, apparently bound for home and sympathy.

"Hold on, Fred, I want to speak to you;" then, as the boy kept on, Phil skipped after him, caught him affectionately round the neck, and led him back to the bench.

"Ye see, some of the bullets don't chill regular and even when they are cast — one side 's lighter 'n t' other, see? Coarser grained; kinder-dozy like — that makes it lighter. Those that 's that way roll wobbly 'n' crooked, see? 'N' a ball that won't roll straight won't shoot straight."

"Lemme try some on 'em outer the cup."

"All right!" And he had no difficulty in running them successfully. So was the tender spirit comforted, and the scoffers rebuked — and Zury pleased with Phil's kind-heartedness.

"Be ye goin' t' shewt?" asked Freddy.

"Yes. Some of us are goin' over into the woods by the river to try our rifles."

"Why don't ye take along the crooked bullets t' give the other fellers?"

"Well, ye see, I know if they have good balls that 'll go jest where they aim 'em, I can beat 'em shootin' every time. But if they have crooked ones, why they may chance to hit the bull's-eye once in a while, coz they don't aim at it."

With which sarcastic pleasantry he gathered

up the rejected pellets and popped them back into the melting-pot.

When the riflemen set out they were accompanied by a considerable number of the loungers, among whom Zury walked along unconspicuous. The place being reached, and the ranges paced off, the marks — a "blaze" in the side of a tree, and a charcoal mark in the middle of the blaze — established, and the order of shooting fixed by lot, the quick, sharp cracks began and followed each other in rapid succession — sounding almost like one side of a small skirmish between outposts. The shooting was not the modern style — telescopic sights, long distances, targets almost out of sight, rifles resting on knee or foot, or some artificial support. Each shooter stood in his place and raised and steadied his heavy piece by sheer force of nerve and muscle.

Phil with his iron biceps and forearm was easily first at all distances. At the short range, thirty yards, the outside of his bullet-holes averaged as close to centre as the inside of those of his best competitor, and the poorest shots of those two as good as the best put in by anybody else. The long distances, one hundred yards, showed about the same relative prowess; and after fruitless efforts to match him they all gave up the trial, and sat down to clean their guns and tell shooting stories. Of course these grew from fact to fable, and from fable to that wild, grotesque, caricatured extravagance which seems to be the type of American fun.

First there were the old tales — how one seeing a long line of pigeons sitting on a limb, fired, not at them, but at the limb — split it — and caught them all by their toes in the crack. Then, too, was repeated the old Munchausen story about sending a bullet with a string attached through a whole line of wild geese, which at once flew away and carried the shooter whither he would.

"Say, fellers, my dad used t' be here in Illinoy when th' wuz injins 'raoun'; 'n' him 'n' a ol' buck injin got t' firin' at each other f'm behind tew trees baout a quarter of a mild apart. They shot 'n' shot 'n' shot till th' trees wuz near abaout cut daown by splinterin' off th' sides. Dad's tree growed so slim th't 't would n't hardly hide his body no more, 'n' all the hind buttons wuz shot offen his pants. Then he thort he 'd fix Mr. Injin. He was orfle strong in his han's; 'n' so he jes' bent the muzzle of his rifle acrost his knee close t' th' eend, so 't th' ball 'd go straight ontel it 'd got 'most aout, 'n' then take a sudding turn t' sideways. Then he let th' ol' injin have it, 'n' sure enough th' bullet went straight ahead till it got past th' ol' cuss's tree, 'n' then it whipped raound 'n' killed him!"

"Oh you sho, Jim! That warn't much! Haow fur off d' ye say th' injin stood?"

"Mebbe a quarter, er so."

"Wal, mos' anybody kin kill a injin inside of a mild — jes' shoot so laoud it 'll scare him t' death! But wha' 'd ye think o' my dad killin' a feller clar off in York State?"

"Noth'n' very strange abaout that. That's why he hed t' leave thar I 'xpeck."

"No sirree! It was after he got here he shot back at him. Ye see the feller he owed dad money 'n' wrote him a letter sayin' he could n't 'n' would n't pay a cent. So dad he tuk th' letter, see whar it come from, tuk good aim, 'n' put the bullet in another letter 'n' sent it back by mail; 'n' it got thar in abaout six weeks 'n' killed him dead."

"No wonder, nuther! He jes' cast one o' your yarns inside 'n' it busted like a bombshell jes 's sune 's anybody took a holt on it, 'specially ef he tried t' swaller it."

"Thasso, thasso, friend Rice! Onless he had a bread-baskit 's big 's yourn, 'n' then it would n't a hurt him. Ef it busted in the middle the pieces 'd be all wore aout afore they c'd reach the sides."

"Lord, John. If ye could shewt as straight as ye kin lie! But then the trouble is ye kin shewt only jest abaout 's crooked 's as ye kin tell th' truth. Fellers, d' ye know why John sold his gun 'n' don't shewt any more? Tell ye haow it wuz. He tried shewtin' at a bar'l-head nailed ontew th' barn-door. Wal, he could n't hit it, ner find aout whar in the yarth th' bullets went tew. Then he went up closer 'n' jest aimed at th' barn-door it-self. No difference; he could n't hit it. Then he went up close 's he could git, 'n' shot at th' whole barn; but fellers, if ye'll believe me, he never hit it once ontel he went inside 'n' shut th' door!"

"Fellers, my dad war n't no gre't shakes with a rifle, but take a shot-gun — sakes alive! Could n't he jest *more* 'n' shoot! Tell ye what 's a fack. We come f'm Maryland, where th' wuz lots o' cherries — no trouble to make cherry-pies except th' cherry-stones. All th' other fellers used t' want t' git a piece o' my cherry-pie coz theirs wuz all stones, 'n' mine did n' never have a nary one. Know haow it wuz?"

"Yer dad uster stan' over ye with a gad 'n' make ye stone 'em all!"

"Gad thunder! Stone nothin'! Mother 'd jes' take a panfle of cherries up in the chămber winder; dad he 'd jes stan' off a right smart piece with his shot-gun; mother she 'd pour aout th' hull panfle o' cherries; dad he 'd shoot; 'n' sure 's yer born he 'd jes' put one shot through every cherry — knock the stone aout, 'n' let the meat drap daown inter a dish on the graoun' underneath! 'N' ef ye don't b'lieve it ye kin jes go t' Maryland 'n' see th' shot-marks in th' side o' th' haouse!"

"Speakin' o' shot-guns, pards, did ye never hear of a savin' cuss that uster go duck-shootin' daown on Spring River? He was tew mean t' spend a hull charge onter one duck: ef he could 'n' git tew in a line he 'd jes keep a cork in his teeth, 'n' when he shot at a duck he 'd hurry up 'n' cork up his gun-bar'l 's sune 's enough shot got aout t' kill that one; 'n' then when he got a bead drawd on another duck he 'd pull the cork aout 'n' let *him* hev the rest."

Zury reddened and ground his teeth at this pleasing tale, recognizing it as one of the countless yarns which had been told of him in his youth. Nobody knew him here, so he was spared any open mortification. But he felt that he would not have had Phil recognize him as the man who had been mean enough to start such stories of meanness at his expense — no, not for a good deal. Not for a good deal! Though he used to glory in that yarn among the rest.

"Say, pards: 't ain't no trick at all t' shoot th' bark offen a tree, but wha' 'd ye say t' splittin' a dawg's bark right in tew in the middle?"

"Less try it! Yew bark, Jim, 'n' we 'll shoot!"

"Oh, yew smarty! Jest lemme tell ye, boys, haow my dad did that trick. One night th' wuz a dawg ou'doors th't jes' kep up his yawp, yawp, so 't mam she could n' sleep no more 'n' a fish. So dad he upped 'n' tuck his gun, 'n' opened th' winder. It wuz darker 'n' a pocket, 'n' he could n' see a blame thing. So wha' 'd he dew but wait till the dawg barked, 'n' he *fired at the bark.* The' did n' h'yer no more o' th' dawg, 'n' nex' mornin' dad he got aout bright 'n' early, 'n' wha' 'd ye think he faound?"

"Faound th' dawg shot through the head, 'n' the bark gone?"

"Noap! Guess agin."

"Faoun' the dawg-gone dawg gone, 'n' the bark shot threw th' head."

"Noap! He faound th' caow shot threw the head 'n' th' dawg a eatin' up th' carkiss!"

"Sho t' man! Dew tell! I wanter know! Is that so fer a fack, Jim?"

"Hope I may die!"

"Cross yer heart?"

"Cross m' heart!"

"See it yerself?"

"Yes sirree, I jes' did that!"

"Ef ye had n't a seen it ye would n't a b'lieved it, naow would ye Jim?"

"Ye 're mighty right I would n't!"

"Wal, we did n't see it, so of course" —

"Say, Sam, d' ye wanter hurt my feelin's?"

"No, Jim, 'course not."

"Then don't call me a liar."

"Oh, sho! Ef I wanted t' hurt yer feelin's d' ye think I 'd try callin' ye a liar? No sirree! Fer that jawb I 'd jes' take a club."

When the guns were all cleaned, the restless spirits, gay with the mere zest of unaccustomed holiday, looked about for fresh worlds to conquer.

"Jesse, I 'll bet ye a dollar ye can't hit that crow, up on that thar dead tree."

"Bet ye a dollar I kin."

"Don't let 'em hurt the poor crow, Phil," whispered Fred. Phil glanced up at the bird and answered, —

"Th' crow 's safe enough."

Then, after a pause, he looked up again: —

"Jesse, ye can't shoot at that crow."

"Why not?"

"'Cause ye 'd miss it, 'n' then whar 'd the bullet go?"

"Dunno."

"It 'd describe a parabolic curve 'n' 'light jest forty rods and three-quarters east southwest by north from th' court house — that 's right in yer mother's back yard."

"I swow, Jesse, that was a narrer escape! Bet ye a dollar yer mother 's jest a-hangin' out yer biled shirt; 'n' ef *it* had got tored ye 'd a had t' go t' church t'-morrer stark naked!"

"Bet ye a dollar I could a hit the crow if I 'd a shot."

"Bet ye a dollar ye could n't."

"Bet ye a dollar ye hain't got a dollar."

"Bet ye a dollar I hev!"

And so, having come to a square issue, the discussion was dropped.

"Ki, fellers! Look-a-there!" said one, in an excited whisper. At a distance of some hundred yards or more there was a whitish object — an animal about as large as a cat, with fur of shining lustre. It was evidently a *Mephitis Americana;* sometimes (incorrectly) called a pole-cat — name of horror and disgust. Several hands were stretched out for rifles. Phil's among the rest.

"Hold on, pards. Let Phil do the business — rest of us 'll miss him, likely — he 'll fetch him sure!"

Phil slowly raised his gun, "drew his bead" firmly and accurately, and stood motionless.

"Shoot, Luke, er give up the gun," said one, using a slang phrase well known as a common fillip to a hesitating speaker.

Phil suddenly changed his aim and sent his bullet smack into an oak hard by, while the poor beast, alarmed by the report, scurried away to his aromatic nest in some sequestered hole — doubtless to communicate his adventures to an interesting family.

"Wha' 'd ye dew that fer, ye blamed fool!" "Why did n't ye give somebody else a chance ef ye thought ye wuz a-goin t' miss?" "Might a tried him, hit er miss." These inquiries, spiced with strong expletives, arose on all sides.

Phil kept quiet and went to wiping out his gun again. After an angry silence, one of the elder men asked, in a decently respectful tone, —

"Why did n't ye try yer luck, Phil?"

"Well, it jest struck me, after I 'd drawn my bead right dead for him, that I did n't happen to have no grudge against him. He never done me no harm that I know of. Not as I remember at this moment."

A loud burst of laughter met this avowal, and it nettled Phil. He reddened with mortification and rage at the general ridicule. His brows dropped until they almost joined in the middle, and his bright eyes shone under them with an angry light. He glanced at the laughers, one after another, until one big boor gave voice to the contempt of the rest.

"Ain't he mammy's boy? Should n' wonder ef he wuz afraid o' hurtin' his uncle."

Phil set down his gun and went up to the speaker.

"Boy enough to slap your mouth if you 'll stand up."

Thereupon the offender, still seated, began a loud abusive exculpation, which all the rest recognized as "a clean back-down," and turned their ridicule on him.

"Did n't have no sand in yer box, did ye, Jim?"
"*Boy* side-tracked ye, fust station, did n't he?"

Phil simply knocked off the boor's hat, which the latter picked up and put on sidewise so as to pretend to join in the laugh, saying at the same time, —

"Oh, that 's all right, pard! When a feller 'pologizes to me, *handsome*, like that, I don't never say a word! I ain't th' feller t' bear malice! Any time I 've said anythin' I 'm sorry fer, I 'm glad of it!"

Phil's forehead cleared as suddenly as it had clouded over, and he joined in the general hilarity.

Zury left them and walked back to town in deep thought.

"Beats me, don't he! I hate t' hurt a hoss, er even a dawg, but he wun't harm nothin'! Not a blame thing is tew low fer Phil t' remember it hez rights! Afore all the rest on 'em, tew! Oh Lordy, Lordy! Ef I only hed a holt on him! Wonder ef he don't want nothin' I 've got! 'T ain't likely — not a thing, not a thing, 'thaout it 's money, 'n' that I hain't got, not t' speak of.

"He wuz a-goin' fer that other feller hot enough, tew! Feller 's big 's tew on him, pootty near, but, Lord! that did n' make no diff'rence, — not t' Phil McVey! Ef he 'd a-ben a Goliath 't would a ben all one t' that little David!"

Then he had long, dim visions of what his life would be with such a son.

"He 'd cut me plum aout, like enough. I would n' be nowhers. Wal, let him. All the better. Oh Lordy, Lordy, ef I c'd only git him! He beats me, all holler. Sees me 'n' goes me one better. I would n't hurt a child, ner a hoss, ner a mule, ner a dog, ner a cat — he would n't even hurt a *skunk*."

The next day being Sunday, Zury contrived to see yet more of these three interesting beings with whose lives his thoughts were so much occupied. He went to church, took an inconspicuous seat, and watched for their coming. The effort was only partly successful, for Anne entered alone; and, as it happened, sat down where he could scarcely see her. So being disappointed, he attended to the service and observed the rest of the congregation. The choir was placed in a corner, beside the pulpit and on a level with it, and facing the congregation.

This arrangement has its advantages and its disadvantages. It lessens the "dead loads of fun" which have been the perquisite of church-choirs ever since they began to supplement the psaltery and shawm of primeval worship; or, if it does not lessen it, it makes it more public and less perilous. No more flirting behind the closely drawn curtains, no more whispered arrangements for homeward walks and other tête-à-têtes; no more jealousy aroused in the breast of the bass-singer by the conduct of the treble and the tenor. The minister does not probably miss any marriage fees, at any rate his sermons are listened to by the choir, in the full glare of public observation, with an exemplary attention quite rare in the old hidden bevy of youths and maidens.

On the other hand, the pretty singers have, as spectators, the whole churchful of their friends; so on the whole, their reward gains in largeness what it loses in intensity.

Zury was near to the singers, and gave them a fair share of his attention. The evidently conscious belle of the choir did not enchain his regards: they were devoted to a humble, modest, unassuming girl who apparently thought nothing of her looks, because she was well aware that they were not worth thinking of. Strong, tall, red-haired, almost or quite worthy to be called ungainly, she nevertheless struck him as the most interesting, the most trustworthy, the most conscientious, even the most lovable of them all to a middle-aged man like him. What was it about her that made his eyes and his thoughts turn to her plain face with a refreshing sense of rest, peace, and comfort? Could it be because it was evident that no one else was attracted by her? Even there, under the eyes of the world, one might see that some of the girls were more sedulously waited on by their male neighbors than were others. Some never had a chance to find their own places in the hymn-books and tune-books. Almost all had one or more of the other sex quietly observant and constantly serviceable. But Zury's favorite waited on herself with perfect sweetness and good-humor, even had time and thought to spare for her more favored and more thoughtless sisters in melody. And among them she evidently found regard and affection, however lacking she was in the qualities which could exact it from the other sex; the girls had each a smile for her whenever their eyes met.

When the last hymn had been sung and the last amen said, Zury made his way out with the rest, just in time to see Anne joined in her homeward walk by his friend from the choir. It was Margaret.

While Zury was still cogitating over the one-sided acquaintance he had thus curiously struck up with Margaret, the minister came out, and recognized him as one of the pillars of the Wayback church where he had sometimes preached. He was an elderly parson — one of the salt of the earth but of a pulpit dullness verging on the miraculous.

"Brother Prouder! This is a rare pleasure. Seldom do we see you at our Springville ministrations. How is the work of the Lord prospering at Wayback?"

"Middlin', middlin', brother. Same with yew I hope?"

"Yes, the Lord does not quite forget even the most unworthy of his servants. I have no reason to complain — no reason to complain."

"Folks take a-holt pootty good?"

"Well — not overly well — not overly well. Sometimes I feel a little disheartened by a certain deadness — but then I realize that the fault must be mine — the fault must be mine. I am charged with a blessed message, but lack the tongue of power to make it heard. When I hear of the glorious doings of brother Pratt and brother Blank, I feel ashamed of my backwardness."

"Oh, mebbe ef ye wuz a-flyin' 'raound f'm place t' place 's they be, ye might git up steam same 's they dew."

"Possibly, if Providence had seen fit to vouchsafe me a wider field to gleam from, I might have more sheaves to show — more sheaves to show — but I never can find time to stray away from my narrow sphere of labor."

"Wal, naow that reminds me of the boy they tell on; a feller come along 'n' see him a whalin' away at a stick of wood with an axe duller 'n' a hoe; 'n' the feller he asked him why he did n't go 'n' grind his axe, 'n' the boy, sez he; 'ef yew had sech a pile o' wood t' cut 's *that*, I guess ye would n't be monkeyin' 'raound a-grindin' no axes.'"

"Ha-ha! Well, I suppose I *am* a little like that boy! But God has not seen fit to furnish me any one to turn grindstone for me. I suppose the axe is not worth grinding. He will sooner lay it aside and provide a new one."

"Oh sho, Brother Kizer! Yew 're all right; it's yer hearers is in fault!"

"They don't think so. On the contrary, they

think that if there were more power in the pulpit, there would be more movement in the pews!"

"Ah yah! There it is agin! I 've seen it more times in my life 'n I 've got fingers 'n' toes! A preacher a-draggin' the hull congregation! One poor ole man strugglin' along between the shafts — his tongue a-lollin' aout, 'n' the sweat a-pourin' offen his face — 'n' the hull congregation, deakins 'n' all, a-ridin' on th' wagin! 'N' every little while somebody ups 'n' sez 's haow th' ole nag 's a gittin' slow, 'n' 'd oughter be touched up!"

"Oh brother, brother! Such words as yours are comforting to the soul! I wish there were more like you — that I had you in my own fold! I feel as though, if I had such a refreshing spirit as yours always within my sphere, even I might gain a certain freshness — the old axe might grow to be a little sharper! I doubt not but that you are a noble friend to the church in Wayback!"

"Wal, I guess I 'm a heap sight better hand at findin' fault with other folks, than I be a-doin' any better ner what they dew." Then after a pause, during which poor Kizer was ruminating delightfully on Zury's quaint words of encouragement, the latter went on.

"By the way, brother, ye 've got some of aour old Wayback folks amongst your hearers — the McVeys."

"Oh, ah! Superior people, I judge — decidedly superior."

"Mis McVey — dooz she seem to take a holt, good?"

"A Laodicean, brother — a Laodicean, blowing neither cold nor hot. Now the daughter, Margaret — ah, brother, that is a blessed soul! My pet lamb of the flock!"

"Haow abaout the boy?"

"Oh, as to him; we must only hope for the best."

"Old story I s'pose girl a lamb and boy a limb."

"No, no, brother. I should hardly call Philip McVey a limb — only a brand to be, in God's good time, snatched from the burning."

"The mother you c'nsider as a — superior lady you say."

"Decidedly so. In fact, so highly superior that I have hesitated to assume full pastoral relations so far as to make a pointed effort to care for her soul's welfare. But I have determined to postpone the good work no longer. I am glad that your expressions of interest in them have recalled me to a sense of my neglected duties — shirked — shrunk from, I may say; for which, sir, I shall this night, before I sleep, seek pardon at the throne — pardon and renewed strength."

Then they parted; the good man, though poor preacher, getting more comfort and consolation than he could have explained, by the sharp fault-finding bestowed by Zury upon his troublesome congregation.

Zury, too, was a little comforted by hearing how consistently Anne was holding her own against the rest of the world. *He* was not the only man baffled by her cool intellectual superiority! He was very far from envying brother Kizer his task of approaching her regarding the state of her soul.

On the next day Zury went home; and that same night the good pastor nerved himself for the effort to do his duty by his fair parishioner. He called and was received with a mingled cordiality and reserve which made him tremble in his shoes, although nerved by a stern sense of duty and responsibility. Meg's more humble greeting was slightly reassuring; but Phil's did not help him. Anne was sewing by one lamp, while her children were studying by another at a little distance.

"Sister McVey, will you join me in prayer?"

Anne was taken aback, and an awkward pause ensued, broken by an ominous snort of suppressed mirth from Phil, which was partially disguised by the hurried application and vigorous use of his handkerchief.

"I beg pardon, Mr. Kizer; but I — have never been accustomed to pray in public."

"True, sister; you have Scripture authority for closet devotions, but this surely does not exclude more public addresses to heaven."

Anne could scarcely forbid the old gentleman to do as he chose; so he kneeled down, while Anne rested her forehead in her hand, Meg kneeled, and Phil left the room. Brother Kizer "wrestled" long and fervently, with a direct personal reference that at first made Anne angry; but fortunately the exercise was so protracted that she had time to recover from the insulted feeling it aroused, and to recognize and do justice to the worthy, humble, self-sacrificing motive that prompted the act.

Afterward, the minister read a chapter from the Bible, and ventured upon some pastoral questions and exhortations which Anne sustained with what grace she could command. Later, Mr. Kizer fell into a more worldly tone, and Anne, animated by a womanly desire to avoid giving pain to an estimable old man doing his duty according to his conscience, exerted herself to please her guest and to remove any feeling of having been repelled and rebuffed in the main object of his visit. In such an effort she was certain never to fail. So they parted smiling friends; and the minister was able to give a fairly prosperous picture of the visit in answer to the pressing questions of his wife, who was, of course, curious as to Anne's manner of conducting herself. (She was "his third," and much younger than her husband.)

. . . .

"Well, no; I cannot say that she made any professions of a conviction of sin; but she showed a most intelligent interest in the church work—especially in the charitable work."

. . . .

"Well, no; I do not remember her using any expressions indicating a desire for a change of heart; but she seemed to sympathize in the observations I threw out regarding what seem to me the failings and short-comings of my congregation. She greatly enjoyed my repetition of brother

Prouder's remarks on the usual relations of pastor and people — received them with a relish that was extremely refreshing. Our laughter at his homely illustrations went to the verge of — hilarity; I really hope that no one of the good deacons happened to be passing by in the street, and recognized my voice!"

. . . .

"Well, no; she did not accept my suggestion regarding your Dorcas society; giving as a reason, her extreme preoccupation in the business wherein she is at present engaged; but she inquired with the most particular kindness after you, and each of our children. She has heard of them through dear Margaret."

. . . .

"Well, yes; I should say she enjoys a most abiding hope of salvation — amounting, perhaps, to an over-confidence."

. . . .

"Well, yes; I shall persevere, perhaps with more fervor than if I felt more certain regarding the state of her soul. You know there is more joy over one sinner that repenteth than over many that have no need of repentance. Yes, on the whole, I think that I shall repeat the visit soon; very soon indeed, and with frequency."

To the last observation the worthy Mrs. Kizer did not make any audible reply; but it is violating no confidence to say that if her response had been audible, it would have been short and impressive, and in these words: —

"Oh, *you will*, will you!"

CHAPTER XXI.

ZURY IN THE LEGISLATURE AND OUT OF IT.

ZURY had attended church conferences. He had also attended town-meetings. The General Assembly of the State of Illinois did not resemble a church conference: what it was like was a prolonged, exaggerated, disorderly town-meeting.

An army of spittoons, each serving as the mere pretense of a target for tobacco-juice: an army of wire-woven waste-baskets jammed with the detritus of inchoate legislation ; an army of desks whereof the chief office was the upholding of an army of boots, over the tops of which an army of politicians could insolently disregard their business and defy order and public decency. Such was the Illinois legislature *in those days.*

Our friend had been elected as an independent, so there was a desperate effort made by each of the party caucuses to rope him into its fold. His first tactical error was the announcement that he would not go into either caucus ; this united them all against him. He should have encouraged each to hope on, hope ever, for his final adherence. The only thing opposing party caucuses *can* agree on is a common war against a common enemy.

He was consulted, *pro forma*, as to what committees he would like to be appointed to.

"I 'd be willin' t' serve on Agriculture 'n' Drainage, ef I c'd also hev a show on Appropriations 'n' Bankin' 'n' Currency. I 'm told them 's th' ones that controls legislation 'baout 's heavy 's any."

He listened eagerly as the committees were announced. All the leading ones passed without "Prouder of Spring" on their lists. At last "Library" was reached, and Zury caught the sound of his name, also of a half-suppressed titter following it. But the worst was to come. "Geology and Science," "Chairman: Prouder of Spring," was greeted with an irrepressible roar. This committee was the butt of boorish jokers. To turn a matter to ridicule the favorite expedient was to have it referred to the Committee on Geology and Science. Suppose some tobacco-hater offered a resolution looking to the enforcement of the rule against smoking during the sessions. Instantly from all sides arose the cry, "Refer to Committee on Geology and Science!" "Geology and Science!" "Geology and Science!" Resolution of inquiry as to alleged attempt to bribe a member. "Geology and Science!" Resolution forbidding members to accept or use railroad or steamboat passes. "Geology and Science!" Inquiry as to what articles have been supplied to members and charged under head of stationery. "Geology and Science." Bill to regulate the elective franchise and secure purity in elections. "Geology and Science."

Luckily the hard-headed Zury could stand ridicule and persecution better than most men. His face fell into its cut-stone shape and he bided his time. His sorest trial came when he first thought it incumbent on him to address the House. He knew what he wanted to say, in a general way, and pondered over it long and hard. How he longed for even an hour with the accomplished Anne Sparrow McVey! He would have risked a trip to Springville but she had let him know distinctly enough that he would not be received. Besides, was he, a full-grown man, ready to acknowledge that he could not hoe his row without her help? Scarcely.

His old good luck deserted him in these novel circumstances, and he met with a disaster; thus. Remembering the kind of drill or training he had enjoyed under Anne's guidance, he tried to imitate it, by actual practice of his proposed speech. In the supposed solitude of some woods within easy walk of the Capitol, he went over the whole matter, aloud, alone.

"Mr. Speaker: A resolution inquirin' what articles hev ben furnished to members as stationery, hez ben referred to th' C'mitty on Geology and Science. Naow I dunno 's givin' a name to a c'mitty putts any fence 'raound such c'mitty, ner any fetters on its actions. Th' c'mitty, sence I hed th' honor t' be made its chairman, hain't hed no geology ner no science referred tew it. It 's time ain't no ways took up with th' baowels o' th' yearth, ner the course o' scientific l'arnin' in th' mind o' mankind. Therefore th' said c'mitty hez acted on th' said res'lution regardin' stationery." And so forth.

Now it so happens that apparent solitude is not always real solitude. By an unfortunate chance some one heard the rehearsal of Zury's maiden effort and told it to some of his legislative brethren. His enemies — that is to say nine-tenths of the whole assembly — laughed at the tale and lay in wait for the unlucky Prouder of Spring.

After organization was complete and an order of business agreed upon for every day in the week, the "call of committees" had its place in the calendar, and in course of events the Committee on Geology and Science was called upon and its chairman arose. To his astonishment and embarrasment, Zury found himself greeted with loud and long-continued applause.

"Mr. Speaker:" (more and longer applause.) "A resolution inquirin' what articles hev ben furnished to members," (again stamping and claping resound and interrupt:) "and charged to stationery account."

Vociferous demonstrations of ironical approval here put an end to all proceedings, and continue until a member arises, presumably to restore order. Catching the speaker's eye he begins.

"Mr. Speaker: I dunno 's givin' a name tew a c'mitty putts any fence 'raound sech c'mitty. Jes' look at it wunst. Fancy aour respected C'mitty on Geology 'n' Science a pursuin' its researches intew geology 'n' science, inside a pen, surraounded by a legle fence, eight-rail, stake-'n'-rider, hawg-tight, bull-strong, 'n' stud-hoss high."

Roars of laughter here broke in and continued until it seemed to poor Zury as if it would never stop, though he bravely kept his feet.

Another member jumped up and caught the speaker's eye, and the House paused to listen.

"Mr. Speaker: The C'mitty on Geology 'n' Science, sence th' onnable member from Spring became its chairman, hain't hed no geology ner no science referred tew it, consekently it hain't hed no 'casion t' c'rect the baowels o' th' yarth with cathartic pills, salts 'n' senna, calomel 'n' jollop, ner otherwise. Th' operations of Nature hev hed t' go on withaout." (More shouts, howls, and shrieks of laughter.) "Ner yet hev I heerd that the said c'mitty hez ben called upon t' teach th' scientific world haow t' scient."

Zury now gave in and sat down, and the assembly finished its frolic by recommitting the resolution, with power to the committee to send for paregoric, opodeldoc, and syrup of squills; all to be charged to stationery account.

Three or four of the better class of members took occasion to greet Zury kindly, and urge him not to take to heart the boys' joking.

"Who — me? I hain't no idee o' taking noth'n' t' heart, ner a-carin' one soumarkee what the' sez er dooz. The whelps! I'll fetch 'em t' book. The' got t' go on the record, right on that very p'int — the stationery steal."

But he was very much mortified. No check he had ever met with had been so humiliating. He had one comfort — Anne did not see the defeat, and would probably never hear of it, as such scenes did not get "spread upon the records," nor were they, in those days of imperfect journalism, set forth in the public prints.

The next time his committee was called, he rose calmly, waited in perfect composure and stood unmoved until the ironical applause died away.

"Mr. Speaker: The C'mitty on Geology and Science directs me t' report progress on the resolution referred to it inquirin' regardin' the disposition of th' stationery appropriation."

Here the storm broke out afresh and continued until its instigators were weary and sought for some more effectual way to "squelch" the irrepressible member from Spring, who stood there in an attitude which said plainly, "I can stand it as long as you can, and a little longer." Then one Gunnitt, a burly giant (slightly exhilarated with whiskey) came quietly behind Zury, and lifting high one of the wire-work waste-baskets, half full of scraps of paper, inverted it and jammed it down over the head of the would-be reformer.

Instantly Zury seized him by the throat. In another moment he had him down on his back in the aisle, and was pounding the floor with his head until it seemed as if both floor and skull must be broken. Men dragged Zury off in time to save Gunnitt's life, though the blood streamed from his nose and mouth as he was helped away.

Zury borrowed a pin from one of the rescuers to repair his collar which they had broken in pulling him back, then stepped to his place and raised his voice again in the now quiet hall.

"Mr. Speaker: I move for a vote of censure on the member from Spring Caounty, and I move that that matter be referred TO THE C'MITTY ON GEOLOGY AND SCIENCE!"

The reference was carried by acclamation which resolved itself into wild cheers for the committee's indomitable chairman. Then Zury once more took the floor.

"Mr. Speaker: Th' C'mitty on Geology and Science—But before I proceed with that c'mitty's report, I desire to accommodate any other gentleman who may want to suppress that report."

Thereupon he took his own waste-basket and set it out conspicuously in the aisle.

"Thar. Any member who wants t' try it on, kin have th' extinguisher right handy."

A new roar of applause greeted this liberal offer.

"Th' c'mitty d'recks me t' report progress on this h'yer resolution, and requests further time on it, and also paower t' send fer persons 'n' papers."

A few voted with him, not enough to carry his motion. Nor did a sufficient number join him even to have the yeas and nays ordered, whereby members would have been forced to express themselves *by name*, pro and con. The subject was dropped: but no further stealage from the stationery fund occurred for many a year. The cause triumphed though its advocate was defeated.

It was inevitable that the "personal difficulty" between Prouder and Gunnitt should be settled in some way. A duel was out of the question, because, as is well known, dueling in Illinois was stopped at once and forever very early in the State's history, when the survivor of a fatal duel was tried, convicted, and, in spite of tremendous efforts for his pardon, actually hanged by the neck until he was dead.

In a day or two some of Gunnitt's friends called on Zury with a view to patch up a peace.

"Wal, gentlemen, I 've heered all yew 've hed t' say, 'n' I 'gree with ye so fur 's this: I think the' ought t' be an apology passed. So I 'm quite ready t' step right 'raound with ye, ef brother Gunnitt will see me; 'n' we kin settle it up then 'n' thar."

There could be no possible objection to this reasonable offer, and they were all soon in Gunnitt's room at the ——— Hotel. The sufferer received them with an unmistakable expression of astonishment in his sadly blackened eyes. Zury took the initiative.

"Brother Gunnitt, I 've told yer friends h'yer that I think apologies should be passed regardin' aour little fraycus; 'n' I 've come right 'raound t' see ye, 'n' tell ye I don't bear no malice; 'n' pervidin' ye 'll jes' 'llaow ye 're sorry ye 'ttacted me th' way ye did, why we 'll shake han's on it, 'n' let bygones be bygones."

The others were taken aback by this unexpected turn. They hastened to protest that they had understood that the member from Spring was to apologize to the member from Bourbon.

"Naow gentlemen, ye 're a workin' agin yer friend's best interests, 'n' I 'll prove it tew ye. Fer me t' 'pologize 'd be t' own up th't I wuz th' aggressor. Naow haow would it sound, daown t' Bourbon, t' 'llaow th't Bourbon's representative hed ben attacted by a man o' my size, an' arter bein' laid up a day er tew, had accepted an apology fer th' attack? I put it to brother Gunnitt himself, ef it war n't th' fack th't he 'ttacted me, 'n' ef it won't look better, tew hum, th't he did so, 'n' arterwards 'pologized handsome."

Gunnitt and his emissaries here retired for consultation, and soon returned quite of Zury's mind.

"Brother Gunnitt authorizes us to say that the aggression was by him, and was unprovoked, and that he regrets having been led, in a moment of excitement, to act as he did toward brother Prouder, regardin' whom he cherishes sentiments of distinguished consideration."

"O. K., gentlemen. I 'm willin' t' fergive 'n' ferget, 'n' h'yer 's my hand on it!"

This happy solution gave both amusement and satisfaction, and was buzzed about legislative circles with great gusto.[1]

[1] The wit of the session seized upon it and told Gunnitt that his baptismal name ought to have been Uriah Benton: — U. B. Gunnitt would then have told the story, as well as named the hero of it. This jest took so well that he cast about for other names to pun upon; and finding a doorkeeper named Ender, who was hard of hearing, he dubbed him one of Illinois' great deaf enders. Thenceforth he was regarded as a professional joker;

Zury's career from the start was a vanishing illusion. The whole power of the body was vested in the "hold-over" members — men who had enjoyed the training of a previous session. They cut out the work, and when cut out, the rest could either do it or leave it alone. They perceived that they could do nothing else. And it is almost an axiom that an independent, a man without a party following, can never effect any object, however praiseworthy, unless it be as a "balance of power."

He soon observed another element of power and leadership. A quiet, knowing, self-possessed, respectable individual would come on the scene, greeting him as an old friend.

"Prouder of Spring, I believe! I am glad to see you. You may remember my name: I had the pleasure of sending you a pass over our road. I am attorney for the —— and ——, and want the privilege of laying a little matter before you which *we* think will benefit the public, at the same time that it may relieve us from some hardships we 've been laboring under."

Shrewd indeed is the man who is not influenced, in spite of himself, by these well-prepared, plausible advocates — "the lobby."

No need to follow Zury through his term. He did not try any more "speechifying," for he soon

fun was expected from him whenever he opened his mouth; laughter greeted his most serious words; and as a result his political career was ruined. So do men deal with fun-makers; they prize them, praise them, enjoy them, and desert them. Humor is a fatal gift in a working community.

learned that in a legislature, oratory is absolute delusion and humbug. Nobody is convinced by it except the constituents at home; and the only effect of it, even on them, is a conviction that their representative is "some pumpkins — kin hold his own with th' best on 'em." When the the member from Buncombe County "orates," he is talking for Buncombe, and it is in Buncombe only that he seeks and finds his audience.

Zury put it thus: —

"A member o' th' legislatur, he kin either talk er work — he can't dew both. It ollers reminds me of a steamboat th't useter run on Spring River. The' culled her the "Pooserpomponnuk," 'n' her name kivered her side from stem to starn. She hed a mighty small biler 'n' a mighty big whistle; 'n' when she run her engine she could n't blow her whistle; 'n' quick 's she opened her whistle-valve, her engine stopped, kerchunk!"

So he became what is known as a "working member;" attended strictly to business in his committees, on the floor and outside, and so acquired the enviable reputation of a man not prone to "shooting off his mouth."

The official treatment of a member not within the clique of party leaders, old legislators, etc., is in itself mere insolence. Prouder of Spring rises in his place, knowing himself to be "in order" and possessed of as good a claim to the floor as any member on it.

"Mr. Speaker!"

Mr. Speaker looks to the right, to the left, down

at the clerk's desk, or anywhere except at the person addressing him, who stands impatiently awaiting the coveted recognition, "The member from Spring." Meanwhile the letter-writing and reading, the chatter, the laughing, the clapping of hands for the pages' attendance goes on like mad, just as if this were "high change" in an open mart.

"Mr. Speaker."

Again the wandering regard takes in the whole horizon except the point whence the words come. At last Mr. Speaker seems to be looking directly at Zury; when lo, a voice from a seat behind him breaks the silence.

"Mr. Speaker."

"The member from Massac," promptly responds the speaker; and the member from Spring subsides. He has no remedy. The presiding officer reckons humanity by number, not by weight. The strongest man is he who has the dominant party to back him; the next strongest is he who has the subdominant; the weakest, he who has so much strength, virtue, and courage that he stands alone.

"I say, Crumbacker, why can't you never see ner hear me? I'm a goin' t' buy a stepladder and a speakin' trumpet, but what I'll be recognized!"

"Oh, Prouder — this morning you mean? I was sorry, and I owe you an apology; but you see it was fixed that Whacker was to speak, and I'd fallen in with it; so what could I do? No danger but what you'll be heard! I've known that ever since you got away with Gunnitt of Bourbon! Some men I might hesitate to set back for fear of squelching 'em; but not you, Prouder, not you!"

"Wal, 'nough said on that head; naow I want to fix it fer my turn."

"Let's see; how would Saturday suit you?"

"O. K. Make it Saturday." And Mr. Speaker makes an entry in his pocket diary.

It was not for some days that Zury learned that it had also been "fixed" to adjourn from Friday to Monday.

At last came the day long agreed upon for final adjournment. The closing session is an elastic occasion. Though the day is appointed by joint resolution, and therefore absolutely binding on both branches of the legislature, yet a session begun on that day is still that day's session, no matter how long past midnight it may endure.

The hour of opening arrives. The speaker raps the House to order, and the chaplain puts up his little prayer. Half a dozen members stand devoutly during the prayer; the rest hurry to their desks, their hands crowded with the pet measures which they have failed to carry during the earlier part of the session. Each is resolved to "put through" one or more during these closing hours, and awaits the signal gun.

"Amen."

Instantly it is as if bedlam had broken loose in Pandemonium. The pool is troubled: the man who dips in first hopes to be healed. The intentness of all baffles the purpose of each. Hour after hour the uproar goes on. Both houses are in session, so that half-completed bills may be sent from one to the other, and the governor occupies his room near by to sign them as they are sent to him, wanting only his approval to become law.

Now the lieutenant-governor (chairman of the upper house) and the speaker of the lower house have everything in their own hands. They rush things through in the hubbub, no one fully knowing what they are about, and no one responsible for most of what is done. More measures are passed than have been enacted in all the rest of the session.

Toward the close, perhaps in broad daylight of the following morning, members lose their hopes of securing attention to their personal purposes, and turn their efforts toward the stoppage of all action. Some one picks up an envelope of loose papers and shies it over the heads of all before him. It scatters its contents as it flies, and finally lands, perhaps on the speaker's desk or behind it. Then the air is full of missiles; pamphlets, newspapers, reports, fall like snow-flakes. At last, for some occult reason, all is hushed in a moment. Some member (not of the speaker's party) moves a vote of thanks to the speaker for his able, impartial, and gentlemanly conduct as their presiding officer; and it is carried nem. con. Then Mr. Speaker returns *his* thanks in well-chosen words, for the invariable courtesy which has made his task a pleasure, and the gentlemanly deportment which has done honor to each of the members of this House; and the House ceases to exist.

At the close of his first term, Prouder of Spring naturally found it necessary to stop at Springville on his way home. He had called at the warehouse occasionally, but had never spoken to Anne. Now he thought it full time to break the embargo; so with unaccustomed and becoming diffidence he presented himself at Anne's desk. She received him graciously. Time had softened her resentment — what there ever was of it — and besides, her reserve seemed no longer necessary. "Out of sight, out of mind." Any too warm interest in him which she might have suspected in her lonely heart, arising from the thought of the great use she had been to him, and he to her, had cooled and disappeared so completely that she doubted its ever having existed.

"Good morning, Mis McVey. My two years is up, I guess?"

"Yes, indeed! It ought to be by this time. At any rate I am glad to see you. What kind of time have you had in the legislature?"

"Wal, kinder mixed. I guess they must have found me out, as the boy said."

"Found you out?"

"Yes; found out that though they elected you to go, it was only me that got thar after all."

"Oh, pshaw! You were elected, because you ought to be; and you went because you were elected; and I suppose you had all the success you deserved."

"Yes, that's the trouble; just that much and no more."

"Were n't you successful?"

"Wal, that remains to be proved. The jury 's got the evidence and they 've got to give the verdict."

"What jury."

"Why, th' electors o' Spring Caounty. If they send me agin, next term, it 'll look like I was, anyhaow, half-way successful."

"I fancy you had a very satisfactory experience. Otherwise you would n't care to go back."

"Oh, ye see, its this-a-way. Politics is like sheep-ticks, hard to get shet of when once they 've got a holt. A politician 's like the circusman's 'fabled Pollypethicus, that can't live on land and dies in the water.' If he has done well, he wants a reëlection as an indorsement; an' if he 's made a blame fool of himself he wants it *bad*, as a vindication."

"And you want to go back — how?"

"I guess I want to go back *bad*, if anyway."

"Well, I hope you 'll succeed."

"'Fraid I can't git t' have your help this time. Mary she don't leave home any more. Got some kind of a falling sickness — first thing she knows she don't know nothing, and has to be picked up."

"I heard she had had some bad turns."

"Yes — worst kind. I wish she 'd get well or — something; jest for her own sake. Because you see she can't bear to see anybody, nor to have anybody see her. Cur'ous, too — she never used t' be so praoud. Looks 's though sickness had made her kind o' — simple."

"I 'm very sorry to hear it!"

"Oh, it makes it *bad!*"

Then, after a little pause, he added, "Ye know ye owe me the continuation of the wall-paper story yet."

"Dear me! How a few indiscreet words may lead to a life-time of remorse!"

"Remorse? Wal, ef you repent and make restitution your remorse will be cured!"

"Will it? I never tried that remedy. Well, I'll surely keep my promise before I die."

"O. K. You 're a woman of your word; so all I 've got to do is to be sure 'n' outlive you." (Another pause.) "I don't s'pose you 'd care to — make another trip to Wayback."

"No. Phil is a fireman, now, and only at home every other night. I could n't leave Meg alone the nights he 's away."

"She might go along."

"That would leave an empty house the nights he spends at home. No. I must give up all thoughts of repeating that delightful experience. But I shall never forget it."

She heaved a little sigh, and both were silent for a while.

"Wal! So it goes!" And with a cordial hand-shake they parted. He went straight to the partners and opened the subject of Anne's salary, as if he had just had a most serious conference with her on that matter. The direct consequence of the talk was an important and welcome advance, whereof she received the first intimation on the following day when Zury was gone home. She had enough presence of mind to suppress the surprise she felt, and receive their remarks on the matter with dignified reserve.

"You must n't blame us, Mrs. McVey. If you had spoke of the matter we would have tried to have made it satisfactory. But you could n't expect us to open up the subject, now could you?"

"Well, perhaps not."

"We will try to make it so you don't lose nothing by the delay. The advance we name is really larger than we should feel called upon to pay, if it was n't, as Mr. Prouder remarked, somewhat your due from being delayed till now."

"Very well. It is all right now, at any rate."

"Perfectly satisfactory?"

"Perfectly."

How her heart glowed as she walked home and gave her children the good news! But she did not mention Mr. Prouder's agency in the matter.

Zury was reëlected. He found his campaign unexpectedly easy. It was not words this time that prevailed, although with words he was much better supplied than of old. It was his "record" in the legislature. What part of his record? About a minute of it — that minute when he did not really know what he was doing; when the hall was resounding with the eloquent thuds of Gunnitt's head on the floor of the aisle.

CHAPTER XXII.

MAN PROPOSES; WOMAN DISPOSES.

"Good-day, Mis McVey! Inkin' up the big books same as ever, I see!"

"Yes, they are not worth much until I have ornamented them with my pen-and-ink sketches. How did you leave Mrs. Prouder?"

"Oh, least said soonest mended. Ye would n't believe it, but I've had to git another woman to look out for things, besides S'manthy 'n' Alphy! For takin' care o' the house an' feedin' the hands they were O. K., but when it came to pickin' up Flory — mebby jest when the hands was a-feedin' —! Ye knows he ain't the build to pick up as ye would a box o' matches!"

"Her illness has not made her thin?"

"N-o-o-ot a bit of it! I told 'em all to keep it a secret about the additional help — not to let on to Flory what was the trouble. She don't seem to suspicion nothin' about it. It would hurt her feelin's."

"I should think she would be gratified to feel that you took such tender care of her."

"Nary! She 'd jest fret herself to death to think o' bein' no more use in the world. She was always right on it fer work, accordin' to her powers. But laws! None of the three daughters was ever a touch to their mother."

"Such a worker?"

"*I* believe yer! When o' man Peddicomb come to his land, shortly after we come to ours, she was wuth more onto th' place than what he was. *She* — why she was one of these 'come gals' kind of women. An' I don't expect ye know what that means, neither."

"Oh, yes. I learned that story when I lived there." (She did not mention that it formed one of the "sketches" she had jotted down in that school-house winter.) "I guess she did n't live long at that rate!"

"No, but she did more work than some women do in twice the time."

"Perhaps she'd have lived longer if she had n't done so much."

"Like enough. But that's the kind of a wife for a poor farmer to start in with. Peddicomb would n't never have kept his three-quarter sections if it had n't a ben for her."

"All the same I don't think the game was worth the candle."

"Game?"

"Yes, I mean that the outcome did n't pay for the sacrifice."

"Fine farm, the Peddicomb farm is."

"Yes, a fine farm, in another man's hands. Her own life sacrificed, one daughter dead, another a hopeless invalid, and another, with her child, a poor dependent."

"Dunno but ye 're right." And Zury pondered on the new thoughts thus suggested.

"Poor Flora! And now you have to be away, too!"

"Yes; this is my last session, though."

"All your ambition gratified now?"

"Oh, yes. I got my indorsement by my re-election."

"And now you wish you had n't?"

"Not exactly; you know I 'm one of the hold-overs now, so it 's my turn t' impose on the green members!"

"That suits you, I 'm sure!"

"Well, partially. But I 've got no party to back me."

"So your hands are tied?"

"Not entirely, there 's a United States senator to be elected this session, an' my vote will elect him; the balance things is teterin' on jest now!"

"I should think that would give you all you chose to ask."

"It would — in promises — only for one thing: my vote ain't for sale."

"Dear me! You make my head swim with your contradictions! It 's like the old story of Hans in luck, everything is met and offset by something just the contrary!"

"The way of the world. Give an' take. Loss an' gain. Nothin' ain't never quite so good nor quite so bad as you look for it to be."

"Who are going to be the prominent candidates for senator?"

"Oh, of course Blue on the Whig side, an' Green on the Democratic side."

"Which do you prefer?"

"I don't give a cent to choose between 'em! Party backs both of 'em. Either one would promise to make me judge of the Supreme Court of the United States, if I'd vote for him! Yes, an' if he had the power he'd give me the appointment, too; 'n' me jest as fit for it as Satan's back parlor is for a powder-house!"

"How shall you vote?"

"Oh, for a man I think fit, who has n't offered me anything, directly or indirectly, and who would n't put me in a place I was not fit for, not if I could make him president. Same time, he might help me politically. I'm not naming the man."

"Not even to me?"

"Well" — smiling — "that is different, of course." And he took a pencil from her hand, wrote a name on a bit of paper, showed it to her, and then tore it to fragments. "I'll write to you all about it when the time comes."

Anne flushed and smiled in gratification at the confidence, then, as one of the ubiquitous race of reporters who had been standing near, awaiting his opportunity, approached them with "interview" legible in his eye, she gave Zury her hand and he bade her good-bye and walked off with the intruder.

She was sadly cut down at seeing in next day's "Springville Bugle" a paragraph to the effect that "our member" had passed through town the day before, and had shown himself remarkably close-mouthed on the senatorial question, but the Bugle, with its customary enterprise, had ascertained, from a reliable source, that the first choice of Prouder of Spring would be Judge Grey.

"Well! What a fool I was! He went straight from me and gave the name to that reporter!"

Zury, likewise, was dreadfully taken aback at the sight of that same paragraph.

"How she fooled me! Or I fooled myself! She went right off an' told th' fust feller that asked her! Mebby him 'n' her was fast friends a'ready!" And anguish marked Zury for its own.

The election of senator is the first business of the legislature having it in charge. On the very day when the contest began, the news came that Mrs. Prouder had died, with the suddenness incident to her disease. The gravity of the legislative crisis made it improper for Zury to be absent from the capital, so the funeral took place without him. A will was found, duly executed years before, whereby the simple creature had devised all her property to her husband, never even mentioning poor Semantha or Alpha. To Zury this seemed all right; to the rest of the world, all wrong; to the disinherited mother and daughter, quite natural. They never expected anything.

"But yet," said Semantha, "ef she *hed* a saw fit t' a left me that thar quarter it mought a ben th't Abner he'd a come back 'n' lived wi' me agin. But th' Lord's will be done!" And she cried a little at the thought of the happiness she so narrowly missed — the joy of welcoming the return of a worthless, faithless vagabond who had robbed her and deserted her once and would have done it again if he had had a chance. But, as folks had always said, "S'manthy's put her foot in the fire — now she 's got t' walk on the blister."

For many days the legislative journal showed (and shows) the monotonous story. "The two houses met in joint session for the election of senator. Number of votes cast, 160. Necessary to a choice, 81. Ballot: Blue, 78, Green, 77, Grey 5. Meanwhile an outside observer would have been as puzzled with the aspect of things at the capital as men are in trying to make head or tail of the flying, crawling, humming, buzzing, of a hive of bees at swarming-time. At last came the crowning act. The simple words, "Blue 79, Grey 81," settled the business. Zury had made a United States senator, and could subside into his natural insignificance as soon as might be.

He and Anne met once or twice during the session, always with the coolest of bows on both sides. But with the close of the session Zury concluded that he could not afford to remain estranged any longer. Soon after the adjournment, during one of Phil's customary absences, the ex-member from Spring called on Anne once more, this time at the cottage. Anne was surprised, grew a little pale, but managed to receive him with dignified composure. Years seemed to have left him almost unchanged. Somewhat older, and smoothed by contact with the world, yet strong, sharp and egotistical as of old. With public life his address had become more assuming, — less considerate. She observed a slight change in his speech: it was not clear as of old; he seemed as if talking with his mouth full. Then, too, he had become somewhat oratorical, circumlocutory, and prone to speak of present company in the third person, as if it were "Mr. Speaker! The onnable member from Pike"; etc. His English was in a transition state. With attention he could express himself reasonably well, and this attention he habitually gave when talking with Anne and other educated persons. But with his old associates his dialect was as uncouth as ever. Then too, when he had been talking carefully for a while, he was apt to grow interested and forgetful, and slip back to the old ways.

After the usual commonplaces, Anne said, —

"I see you elected your candidate to the Senate."

"Yes; Grey got in. So it did n't make any difference after all."

"What did n't make any difference?"

"Why, your tellin' his name to that reporter."

"My telling his name!" (She flamed up and gave him a withering look.) "I never mentioned the matter to a living soul. *Your* telling his name you mean — after imparting it to me as a dead secret!"

"I never peeped it to no man, not till I saw the hull thing in the Springville Bugle."

"What can it mean?"

"Did you never see the feller again?"

"Never; — only he came and stood near the railing after you went away. I was afraid he wanted to ask me what you said, so I turned my back and went on with my writing." Then after a pause, "Those scraps of paper!"

"The scraps of the paper I wrote the name on, and then tore up!"

The case was clear. The enterprising scribe had picked them up and pieced them together. Again Zury and Anne had been angry at each other for months because of — nothing.

"Well," said Zury. "I expect we both of us was fooled. Now tell me how the Widow McVey has prospered: her and hers."

"I 'm well, Mr. Prouder, with more blessings than I deserve, I dare say."

"Sho now! I would n't relish to hear anybody say that except the Widow McVey herself."

"Of course we all have our ups and downs in the world."

"*To* be sure. This a probationary state of trial." (In a cheery, consolatory voice, but with a glance at the weed on his hat.) "I too am bereaved. Mis Prouder, she was called shortly after I saw you last."

"I had heard of it. Poor Flora!"

"Well, it was a blessed deliverance for her, the way she was." (Just then Margaret entered.) "Why, who 's this? Margaret?"

"Yes. Margaret, this is our very old and good friend, Mr. Prouder."

"How d' ye do Mr. Prouder? I began to think I should never set eyes on you: to doubt if there was any such person."

"Well, Margaret. I saw you once when you did n't see me. Now I am mighty glad to meet you. You don't favor your mother much, do you?"

"No, I do not." (A sigh.)

"Never you mind. Beauty 's only skin deep, and sometimes not that. You could scrape it off some of these Springville gals with a hoe, an' then they 'd have to run home and paint up again before their best friends would know them from a side of sole-leather."

"Well, my Margaret never painted nor powdered her face *yet*."

"No, I should say not, nor her hair neither. If she did, it would n't be jest that shade, now would it?"

"Oh yes, if she wanted to please her mother, there would never be a mite of difference." (To herself: "You horrid old idiot!")

"*If* it was her mother she wanted to please. That 's a pretty big *if*."

"Well, or her brother either."

"But now suppose it was some other gal's brother she wanted to please."

"But I don't. I would n't care if no other girl in the world had a brother, so long as I could keep mine."

"That 's right my gal! That 's the way to fetch 'em — let on you don't want 'em."

"It does n't seem to work that way in my case. They don't 'come a runnin',' as folks say."

"Never you mind. Ye ain't so old as your mother *yet*, and she ain't a bit too old to take notice."

Both the women laughed at this — Anne rather nervously, for she began to perceive that perhaps she had a problem coming up to be solved.

Even as Zury was talking he was making a mental inventory of the pretty and simple surroundings, so different from the coarse, bare space and plenty of his own farm-house.

"That table-spread reminds me of purple 'n' fine linen; the tents of Kedar and curtains of Solomon. How much might that have cost, Mis McVey?"

"Two dollars."

"Gee Whillikin's! Two dollars!"

"Yes, you see we only bought the stuff and fringe and tassels; Margaret and I worked the centre and corners." She said this with gentle pride and some softening of the heart toward Zury because she thought his surprise arose from the cheapness of the fine gay bit of color. In fact he was only thinking, "two dollars for one table-spread!"

"Find it pretty lonesome?"

"Lonesome? No, never! Oh, you mean Phil's being away. Yes; that is hard, but he comes home every other day."

"Ah, yah! There it is! I've no children t' go or t' come — t' leave or t' find."

A long pause followed this; then, when Margaret left the room to prepare supper, —

"Mis McVey, I may be wrong, and I'm liable to stand corrected if I am; but it does seem to me as if Providence had fore-ordained you and me to travel together the rest of our journey through the vale."

"Oh, Mr. Prouder! I never could think of marrying again."

"Well, I 've been thinkin' of it for a long time — at least the best part of — some months." (He corrected himself so as not to overlap the time of his widowhood.)

"I never thought of it at all; and I don't want to think of it."

"I know; that 's what the widows all say. At least, so I 'm told. But I guess they 're pretty liable to think better of it when they do bring their minds to it."

"Well, then, I 'm different from the rest."

"We 've been acquainted a long time; ye 've known me pretty well, 'n' I 've known you pretty well."

Anne was silent, and bent over her work.

"Ye see ye 'd never come to want, it ain't likely."

She thought to herself, "I should probably never come to stop wanting so long as you held the purse-strings."

"Ye know that children of the widow inherit the widow's share in this state, accordin' to th' statoots in such case made an' provided."

"There is n't any statute to prevent a man's leaving his money as he pleases."

"Oh, ye need n't fear my willin' my property away from my own — step-children."

"I was n't thinking of that. I was thinking that you might leave Phil and Margaret whatever you chose, without — my marrying you."

"Oh, as to that, there 's a new theological college of my persuasion jest startin' at the State capital that 's got big hopes of me. I expect them pious men of God 's prayin' already for my life — for the lengthenin' of it until I devise and bequeath, and-so-forth-and-so-forth; and then the Lord's will be done — and mine probated and executed."

Anne sewed on steadily, thinking of the possibility of Margaret's going through the world as an heiress instead of a dear, dependent old maid.

"This is going to be a tremenjous country in the next generation or two, or three. Such glories as the Queen of Sheba never dreamed of, and did n't see at Solomon's court neither. A man or a woman that starts in with a hundred thousand when I drop it, will be cuttin' a broad swath before he dies, and his children broader yet to the third and fourth generation. Somehow, I like to think of Philip — your son — just *spreadin'* himself, after you and I are dead and gone, backed by — well, maybe a *million* of money!"

"Perhaps it would be the ruin of him, and be all lost and worse than lost in his own lifetime."

"Mebbe, mebbe; but in *your* children's case it

ain't likely. Though come to think, Johnny McVey war n't no great shakes as a provider."

She flushed angrily at this coarse thrust; but only answered, —

"Phil is not a fool, nor a spendthrift. *Nor yet a miser!*"

"Phil won't have to be mean. I guess I've been mean enough for two generations! And Margaret, give her a hundred thousand, and the fellers would be swarmin' about that red head of hers, like skeeters 'round a torch!"

Anne sighed and worked on in silence.

"I've watched Phil ever since he was knee-high to a duck. Watched him when you did n't know it; nor he neither."

"Well?"

"Well, he suits me. Yes; Phil McVey *suits* me!" He could not have told her, if he had tried, how well Phil "suited" him; how he doted on him; how the thought of Phil filled his lonely heart with a yearning even rivaling the regard he felt for Phil's mother. But she guessed it, and said gently, —

"I don't wonder!"

Zury gazed at her with admiration.

"You do look splendid!"

She almost looked up to see if he meant it.

"For a woman of your age."

Then she was glad she had n't.

"Which, of course, is not old by any means."

Smoothing her work on her lap, and glancing up with a softer look, she said, —

"You hold your age well, too."

"Who, me? Yes; I could work twenty-five hours a day, same as ever, if I had to; but I don't. I 've good enough help — same time it would suit me to have a smart feller like Phil to look after the property whilst I was seein' the world — me and the rest of the family. Huntin' for the island and the rest of the old wall-paper story, you know."

"Phil is a great machinist. He would n't go on a farm."

"Go where he was sent, I guess." (The old hard look.) "That 's if he knows which side his bread 's buttered on."

"Phil has no call to do what does n't suit him, for the sake of you or your money!" said Anne, firing up hotly in defense of her son.

"He could n't expect nothing for nothing, could he? Could you? Could I? My money 's there, and there it will stay until I tell it to budge, or till I die and leave it."

Anne's tongue was just going to retort, "Have I or mine ever asked you for any money?" But her woman's wit thrust into her hand a missile worth a quiverful of such blunt arrows as that.

"By the way, you got your hundred dollars all right, did n't you?"

Even Zury, the hardened, felt the sting of this cut. He dropped his hat and picked it up again; grew fiery red and stammered, —

"Oh, yes — and that reminds me — I did n't want *you* to pay me that money, Mis McVey."

"And the interest. You got that too, did you?"

"Certainly, certainly! See here; that was all a mistake arisin' out of Johnny's going to Californy and dyin' so sudden."

"Because I knew that they stopped it out of my wages at the store — but you never sent me the canceled note."

"Of course I did n't; because I did n't consider it *no* way settled. The money and the note both belongs to you, and I guess I've got 'em both in my pocket for you now. Ye-es; — here's the note."

Ann took the old scrap of paper, worn to rags and soiled almost to illegibility, and after glancing without a sigh at the words, "John Endicott McVey," signed at the foot, in a hand pretentious and feeble, she quietly lighted a match and burned the paper to ashes, as if saying, "Now we are square, and I think we will stay so!"

"As I was sayin', I never meant to have you to pay for your husband's horse. It ain't the law in this state for a widow woman to pay her husband's debts out of her own money. When I took the note I did n't allow to have that triflin' McVey ridin' off my live stock for nothing. That was all."

He proceeded to count out a hundred dollars (from the same old plethoric pocket-book which had held the note, and which had almost grown to be a part of his being), and handed them to Anne.

Anne held the bank-bills a moment, and then gave them back to him, saying, — "The money 's not mine. I paid John's debt voluntarily and you received it. Now, if you feel that it does not properly belong to you, just add the interest — I see you have not thought of that — and give it to Semantha. I hear that she and Alpha are as poor as ever."

Another hard hit!

"Oh, don't be a mite afraid about them! I 'm goin' to take care of them, of course. Not with your money, neither! I 'll tell you — this money is yours by rights, but money is powerful scarce jest now; s'pose I was to keep it for you; mebbe somethin' 'll turn up to change the circumstances of both of us, as I was saying. Oh, Margaret! The Princess has dropped in, has she, t' see the Queen? Now, Margaret, I was jest about to pay your mother an old balance, and she agreed with me it was jest as safe with me as with her, so let that pass. But I know young gals want money sometimes as well as the rest of us, so look here!" Then he began again handling over the filthy rags that mean so much to us all. He ran over the hundreds and fifties without difficulty — even the twenties did not did not detain him long. The tens he passed slowly by; one of the fives he almost pulled out; but, finally, he offered her the smallest and raggedest bill he had!

"There, my gal! See what you can buy with that against I come next time!"

Margaret put her knuckles on her hips and replied, —

"Oh dear, no, Mr. Prouder! I could n't think of it! I have no earthly use for the money. Phil gives me more than I want all the time."

"Take it, Margaret, take it!" He spoke pettishly in his haste to get through with a painful operation — as one might address a dentist who hesitated after the forceps had taken hold. Meg looked at her mother, who nodded contemptuously, with a look that boded ill for Zury's success in the object of his visit.

So Meg took the bill, stuffed it loose in her pocket in a manner which cut the donor to the quick, and announced tea. Snowy raised biscuits, golden butter, limpid honey, lumpy cream, cold ham, preserves, cake, blushing squash-pie, glittering glass and charming china, made Prouder's face beam and his mouth water when he followed mother and daughter into the tea-room.

"Sakes alive! Is this the way the Princess takes care of the Queen and the Prime Minister from Wayback?"

Anne glowed with pride of her daughter, and to think of the possibility of *her* being the means of making that daughter and her absent son "wealthy people." Or of her declining such a magnificent possibility.

Mr. Prouder was not quite so brilliant as usual for a while after they sat down. He helped the ladies with his old-time gayety, but sobered down when he proceeded to feed himself. He spread his biscuit and essayed to bite it; failed and took it down to his plate where he cut it into bits;

mumbled it in silence for a while; then took a drink of tea and spoke these ever memorable words: —

"I 've stood this thing jest as long as I 'm goin' to."

Whereupon he whipped out of his mouth a partial set of false teeth, rolled them in his bandanna, and stuffed them in his pocket.

"There now! Zury Praouder ain't any dentist's fool if he has got a gilt sign, and guarantees a fit! A fit! I'd like t' guarantee him a fit! And I 'll give him fits when I catch him, too! Dog-gone him!"

Whereupon Anne said, —

"What remarkably pleasant weather we 've been having!"

But she *thought*, —

"Oh dear, it can *not* be my duty to marry Zury Prouder! It is n't — it is n't — it is n't — it is n't! So there, now! That 's off my mind!"

"Mr. Prouder, what more can I help you to?"

"I thank you, Margaret. I would n't choose any more. I 've supped hearty."

So the repast came to an end and was cleared away, the two women washing the dishes on the tea-table, after the pleasant fashion of our ancestresses. There was the table-tub with its shining hoops, the little mop of cotton twine, the red-embroidered towel of snowy linen, and, prettiest of all, the shiny, pink-tipped fingers, glowing with the work.

Anne's new resolve freed her from the burden

of uncertainty, and her spirits, which had been perceptibly lower while she was laboring over an unsolved problem, took a great rebound.

"Why don't you ask me for the conclusion of the wall-paper story?"

"Oh, *to* be sure. I was comin' to that. S'pose you read it out now!"

"Well, I have n't *quite* finished it yet."

"Not altogether? Well, read what you 've got ready, why not?"

"Oh, to tell the truth, I have n't *quite* — begun it, either!"

"Not struck a lick at it! In all these years!"

"I 've almost begun it. There 's plenty of time."

"How do you know about time? Got your life insured?"

"Oh, springtime is past; and I always noticed that, if I lived through the spring, I was safe for the rest of the year!"

"Ah, I see. Good enough! Well, for a fact, you do look this minute as though Death himself would n't never darse't to touch you."

"Look as if I could scare him away?"

"Look as though you could coax him away. Do what you had a min' ter with him!"

"Well! That 's nice! But there 's another thing. Having passed my word, I *can't* die until I 've written that story out."

"If I thought that, I 'd say 'Don't you touch it! Never!' The world could n't go on without Anne McVey."

"Nonsense! Her death would n't make a ripple in the flood. Only two hearts would bleed." And she looked lovingly at Meg, whose eyes suddenly filled with tears.

"Make it three, make it three, and I 'm agreed," said Zury, with unusual seriousness.

"There! In a minute we shall all be crying over imaginary woes. Let 's talk of other things. You have n't begun to tell me about Wayback yet. They have n't disturbed the old school-house, I suppose."

"Oh yes, improved it until you 'd hardly know it. Every bench a back, every desk a drawer. The old logs are about all there is left of what you used to see."

"I 'd like to lay my cheek against those old logs, before I die."

"I guess the logs could stand it if you could. But the folks! Oh, *you* 've got right smart to answer for. Stuck up till you can't rest! You made them gals so toploftical that common, low-down farmer's boys war n't good enough for 'em, and they all like' ter died old maids! Old man Anstey, he 's built him a house. Reekie, you know she married the preacher, Masten. War n't he a mighty smart customer! Better, too, if anything, after you gave him a settin' down. Gifted in *dis*course, fervent at the Throne and happy at funerals. Conference took to takin' notice of Masten, and he clum and clum: last place I heard of him he was at Galeny, with the best follerin' in Jo Daviess County. I saw 'em when I was up to Galeny a spell ago. I was up there lookin' into lead-mining property a little; did n't buy, dunno 's I will and dunno *but* I will. It 's owing to how the cat jumps. Well, as I was sayin', I called on Eureky in Galeny; and, sakes alive! you 'd oughter see the style they put on! Hired gal to wait on table jest as though it was a hotel!"

"Family, I suppose?"

"Oh yes. Eureky 's got a daughter most as big as you. Named fer you, too, like most of the oldest gals of your old scholars. And ha-an'some! Yum-yum! Stand from under when *she* begins to take notice!"

Anne's gayety was sympathetic and catching. Not only did she shine, but she made poor Zury feel as if he had never been so brilliant in his life, and, all the while, he was becoming more and more satisfied that he had at last "struck his gait" as they say of trotters, and that his life would be happier in its remaining years than he had ever dreamed of its being in his youth. Anne saw his happiness, his confident hope, and his ardent admiration. She even let it go on and on with a certain enjoyment that was not quite blameless, but wholly womanly.

One thing troubled Zury. Anne never let Margaret leave her for a moment. How could he demand the hand and heart of the mother while the daughter was present? Or how get the daughter out of the way? Time was flying, he must depart in a little while.

"Might the Prime Minister from Wayback make so bold as to ask the Princess of Springville t' get him a drink of water?"

"Oh, surely Margaret, let's have a pitcherful. You draw some fresh, while I get the ice."

"Oh mother, you sit still and I'll" —

"Do as I bid you, my dear."

This was said with that "shine" of the eyes that serves as a masonic sign between women, and at once establishes a secret understanding, and an offensive and defensive alliance. Margaret knew in an instant that, for some occult reason, she was not to leave her mother alone with Mr. Prouder.

When no further excuse for delay was possible, the poor fellow took his leave, with one last effort.

"Well, I must be travelin'. Would n't it be accordin' to Jefferson's manual if the Queen was to escort the Prime Minister jest a short ways towards home?"

"With pleasure. Come Margaret, where are our things?"

Zury began to lose confidence. They walked a little way down the rural street, flecked and streaked with moonlight and shadows, and then back to the widow's gate; the stream of talk becoming more and more attenuated as embarrassment and consciousness of cross-purposes increased.

"Mis McVey, might I have a half a minute alone with you?"

"Oh, I can't have any secrets from my daughter."

"Well, then, the matter I started in on when I first come 'round this afternoon — is that all right?"

"All right? Yes; all right, just as I said to you when you first mentioned it."

"What you said then was all wrong as I understood it."

"No; it was all right. I guess it will stand. I meant what I said, and I mean it yet."

The poor fellow aged at heart as he listened. A lump rose in his throat that made his good-bye inaudible. He tottered a little in his lonely walk to the hotel. Never till now had he known how dear to him was this unrecognized plan and purpose of his life; and never till now had he felt the weakness of wealth as a means of happiness. He took out the fat pocket-book, full of money and promissory notes and securities, and tried to re-awaken the spell which it ought to exercise over his sinking spirit. Vain, vain, vain! There was no joy in it at that moment. He even threw it down and trod on it!

"Ye beastly varmint! It's you that's ruined me! It's you that's made me such a —— that she can't bear me, rich as I am! And she's right, too! Zury Praouder, ye miserable cuss, — ye've even got a hundred dollars an' more of her money in there, and ye know it; an' ye tried to give it to her, and ye could n't; ye nigger slave!"

Then tears came — though not to his relief: the hot, bitter tears of age that come from such a deep place that they scald the heart-strings as they start. They sprang from his eyes and ran down his nose and dripped off on the pocket-book as he picked it up.

As he laid his weary head on his pillow that night he groaned aloud: —

"Oh mother! mother!" His anguish took him away back to the helplessness of childhood.

How did Anne and Meg fare on the same occasion?

"Mother! *What* does it all mean?"

"My blessed girl! Come and strengthen your mother! There — put your dear curly head in the old place, and tell me you don't want to be rich."

"Rich, mother? I *am* rich! Nothing could make me poor while you live on the earth, except to see you unhappy!"

"You are sure you don't want a hundred thousand dollars?"

"I'd like to give it to you, for your very own! I have no other use for it."

"I've had it offered to you and Phil, and I refused for both."

"Did that man offer to give it to us?"

"Yes; not exactly to give it, but to trade it, — he to have me while he lives and give it to you when he dies!"

"Ugh!"

The English alphabet is not provided with vowels and consonants which can express the sound that accompanied Meg's shudder of repulsion and disgust as she hugged her mother more closely and strenuously. Suddenly she thrust her away to arm's length and looked at her with something as near to indignation as those gentle eyes could express.

"Mother! he spoke of this when he first came, and yet you treated him civilly all the rest of the time! I would n't have thought it of you!"

The young woman disapproved strongly of her mother from that moment onward — until it came time to "kiss good-night," then she broke down and magnanimously forgave her for having even tolerated the idea of making her children rich by a sacrifice of herself. If she had not forgiven her, — if they had gone to sleep having any alien thoughts between them, — it would have been the first, last, and only time in all their lives.

CHAPTER XXIII.

A NIGHTMARE: ALSO A HORSE-SHED.

POOR Zury Prouder could not shake off his troubles so easily as could Anne and Margaret forget theirs. They slept and woke as gay as larks, he a prey to disappointment and mortification. These fiends sat at his bed-head, and though they could not retard his usual prompt falling asleep, they could and did hasten his waking up. After a very short slumber, with the first gleam of consciousness — such a glimmering as would ordinarily have only added zest to his later rest — came their sharp, sneering voices and startled him broad awake.

"Ho, Zury! You Zury Prouder! The lady would n't have ye, would n't she? No; not at no price! Well, who but an old fool like you would ever think she 'd so much as look at yer shadow! She a lady, born and bred, and a scholar, and you a — !"

The poor fellow groaned and turned over, shaking his shaggy head in a vain effort to repel the pestiferous voices.

"You, Zury! Don't go to sleep again! We wanter talk to ye! Thought ye was rich enough to buy up any poor widow-woman on th' footstool, did ye? He-he! Not Anne McVey! Better go fer one of your own kind next time — low-down trash like yerself — ye poor ignor'nt old miser! Mortgage-sharp! Land-shark! Owin' her money ye could n't pay even when ye got it out t' hand over to her!"

He groaned again and buried his face in the pillow, shutting his ears with his hands.

"Oh no, Zury, it war n't no dream about her givin' ye the mitten. She did it, an' she meant it, too; an' if she had n't, it would have been *her* that was the fool instead of *you!* Ye 'd starve her to death, body and soul! Rich are ye? Oh, yes, — mebbe. Awful rich! *You* can't buy no two-dollar table-spread! *You* can't have no supper-table that looks like a picture. *You* can't have no women folks that looks and talks and acts like ladies! No sirree! She spends as much money in a year as you can make in a week; and that 'd break your poor old miserly heart, ye old skinflint, ye know it would!

"Them children of hern — what would they have been if *you*'d had the rearin' of 'em? The gal, she 'd have been about like Alphy! Your own dead wife's own niece — not half as edicated nor half as nice dressed as poor old man Anstey's gals! An' him 'eenamost a pauper; an' you the richest man in Spring County; an' the meanest on Goddlemighty's green earth! And look once at Semanthy! Your own sister-in-law! Slaved for ye all these years, and now ye got her dead sister's property in your hands; and she nothin' to show for all but poor-house feed an' scarecrow clothes for her and her daughter! Ye had n't oughter let Anne McVey set eyes on them in their dirt and rags! It gave ye clean away! That 's the kind of a sweet-scented prospeck ye held out to her!"

Another helpless groan.

"That boy, Phil: think ye 'd know him for the fine feller he is if you 'd had a chance to bring him up in your ways? You and him would a been forever chasin' the same sixpence 'round the country, an' you usially ketchin' it first! Oh, he 'd be a sweet-scented young gum-tree, compared to what he is now, if he 'd been in your care instead of hers!"

"Oh Lordy, Lordy!"

"Made a good speech, did n't ye, when *she* told ye what to say! Got ye into the legislature that speech did. And then ye thought ye 'd try a quarrel with her! Boomin' success that quarrel was, was n't it? Did n't take her long to learn ye your place."

"Oh there, there: lemme rest!"

"How d' ye come out when ye tried to make a speech on your own hook? Chairman of Geology and Science made another boomin' success, did n't he?"

"I took down Gunnitt, anyhow!"

"Ya-as, jest what you 're fit for! What any brute beast could have done if he 'd been big enough!"

"And ye thought, ye old fool, that a natur'

like hers could be bought with *money!* Sho! She don't want you ner your money. Her kind of goods won't swap for your kind of currency. Ye ain't her kind of a man: no, and won't never be, not at *your* age! Ye lost yer chance when ye did n't run away to sea ner yet to the Soul-sleepers' college. An' then again — ye traded her off for a farm! Acted the dog, an' traded her off for another farm!"

"Well, well!" said Zury aloud, as he finally rebelled against his persecutors, sat up in bed, and stared into the darkness. Then he groped about, found his clothes, and, carrying his boots in his hands to avoid arousing attention, finally got out into the star-lit streets. By habit his steps led him to the neighborhood of the store where Anne worked; then by intention he walked out to where her cottage stood — so neat, so simple, so humble, so like others about it, and yet so different to him!

The stillness was awful. But even this was better than the torturing thoughts that had hounded him as he lay awake, for the first time in his life. As he wandered aimlessly about, in search of the mental rest that comes from bodily weariness, he heard a train approaching on the railway, catching its first murmurs while it was yet a long way off. He strolled toward the station and watched its arrival, and the dispersal of the few tired, cross, and sleepy travelers. Among them was a poor woman with a whimpering child at her side and a wailing one in her arms, which she jogged up and down with a ceaseless, weary motion.

"Are ye shoor?" he heard her say in a despairing tone and a fine brogue to the station-master.

"Sure 's shootin'! No sech a man hain't be'n raound a-askin' fer nobody sence I come on at six last night."

"Oh dare! What 'll I do at all, at all?"

"Better go somewher's till mornin'. Then mebbe ye kin find him — if he 's in taown 'n' t' work at his trade, ye 'll find him."

"Sorra the place have I got t' go to!"

"Wal, ye kin git t' stay in th' waitin'-room." So he unlocked the door which he had closed for the night, and lighted a most malodorous lamp, evidently lately blown out; and the helpless, lonesome, disappointed soul bestowed her poor bundles as well as she could, and then went on trying to still the baby with the same fruitless waving and shaking motion.

"Oh marmy, marmy," called the other from where she had seated him on the bundles.

"Shut up! I ain't got nothin fer yez! "Shut up I tell ye!" And the wail descended to a whine, but never ceased.

Zury thought to himself, "Them folks is havin' a hard time tew." And he smiled grimly at the community of misery, albeit its causes were so diverse.

As he turned away, he saw the glimmer of a lantern, carried by one of the train-hands who had just arrived — evidently the fireman, going home after housing his engine. Zury followed listlessly, observing that the youth walked toward the

McVey cottage. No need to keep in sight; the boy's whistle was a guide. Could it be Phil? He walked along, unobserved, and saw the other take all the turns that led to the "sweet, sweet home" of Anne and her children. Yes—he turned in at the gate and knocked gently at the door, which was opened almost instantly by a tall, white-robed figure: evidently some one had been cheerfully and hopefully awaiting his accustomed coming, for a laugh and a kiss were audible in the moment that intervened before the door closed.

This was not calculated to calm Zury's perturbed soul. He walked again toward the station. As he walked his grim bedside foes suddenly spoke again.

"Oho, Zury! If you were such a feller as the widder McVey 'd ought to marry, that thar poor woman would n't be left alone and friendless with her babes."

"'T ain't none o' my business," said Zury aloud in reply.

"No, Zury, you 're mighty right, it ain't none o' yer business! That 's because ye ain't *her* kind of a man. Ef you was Anne's kind of a man,—like her son Phil, for instance,—it 'd be your business, fast enough!"

"What business has the woman got travelin' about alone, like a blamed tramp, anyhow?"

"Same business ye 've got yourself mebbe,—'cause she can't help it, no more 'n yew can."

"I can help it. I can go right home to th' old farm t'-morrer!"

"Then y' ain't so excusable as she is, ye old fool. What ye trampin' round h'yer for?"

Still Zury neared the station, and at last he peeped in — no change in the distressed group, except that the baby was being quieted by nursing, and the older child made more noisy by beating.

"Oho, Zury, rich Zury, richest ma-an in Spring County, an' th' meanest, ye' could n't pay a cent to help that lonesome critter, not to save your life!"

"Ye're a liar! I could! But I don't wanter!"

"Phil could, poor as he is! *He* would n't be abed and asleep now, not if he'd a heard the smallest hoot of them cryin' children! But you could n't! No sirree! It'd cost ye a hull doller, mebbe! Much 's your corn-crop has growed since we woke ye up 'n' started ye out."

"I tell ye ye're a liar! I *kin* — and what's more I will."

He set his teeth firmly and walked into the doleful room.

"What's the matter, sonny?"

The boy stopped crying and held his peace.

"Be ye hungry?" Still the little fellow sat speechless, startled out of his misery by this large and terrible new-comer.

"Tell the gintleman, Mike. Spake up now like a man, an' tell the gintleman ye did n't have hardly a bite the day."

"Oh well, see h'yer, this won't never do — stayin' h'yer like this. Come along o' me — I'll find ye a place to lay down and suth'n' another to eat, anyhow; an' then ye can find your old man in the morning!"

"The Lard reward ye sorr—if ye'd do that same!" said the poor creature eagerly, and after two or three efforts she rose with such alacrity as the heavy baby allowed, jerked the long-suffering boy off her baggage, and seized upon it with her disengaged hand. Zury took it from her, in spite of her protests, and would have led the boy also, except for that youth's preference for his accustomed support—the dirty end of his mother's dragging shawl.

As they emerged from the station and faced the east the pale dawn greeted them, and it grew into an almost rosy light before they got to the tavern. There they found the "all-night clerk."

"Hello, Mr. Prouder! Thought you was abed an' asleep in number seven!"

"Had to go to the train to meet a man. H'yer's a woman and a couple o' children—no place to go, an' nothin' to eat. I s'pose ye won't charge 'em much for bed an' breakfast?"

"Oh no, we're used to it. I'll give 'em a place to lop down in, and all they want to eat."

"Well, I may's well pay ye naow for 'em—How much?"

"Not a cent, Mr. Prouder. Fust place, we do that same thing, at the same rate, pretty nearly every day, when we ain't drove ner crowded. Next place, we'd do it for you, anyhow, and mighty welcome, too! Come along, mom. Come along, Patsy! Here 's my midnight lunch, enough for three, I have n't scarcely touched it — coffee, cold sausages, pie, bread — one thing another. There, go into the porter's room, he 's gone to bed up-stairs, since the train came in — you eat first, and then lay down on the cot, and lock the door and sleep as long as you like."

The sun was peeping over the horizon, as Zury pulled down his blind and lay down once more to piece out his night's rest. The troublesome fiends were gone, or silenced. He felt as if perhaps there *was* some doubt as to his not being "Anne's kind of a man" — maybe so — if it was always as cheap to be decently kind as he had found it so far, — but then that looked as though he had not learned anything after all — he wished the clerk had taken his dollar: never mind, he 'd give it to the woman in the morning. And the clerk said the tavern was doing this kind of thing every day! By this time he was asleep as sound as poor little Mike down stairs.

When wakefulness returned it brought new consciousness of pain and disappointment, but also new courage and hope. Naturally enough, the poor wayfaring family was a comforting thought and occupation for his mind. When he came out from breakfast, they were already wandering about in front of the tavern, making futile and feeble efforts to find the husband and father — the missing link whereon hung their slender chance of not dropping into the poorhouse. Its slenderness did not much trouble their simple, trustful souls; almost incapable of hope or fear. Zury kept to his intention: at least he gave them — *some* money.

Finding that they were still without the needful clew, he led them to "the store." There he provided them with a good stock of coarse food — without expense to himself — and getting hold of the name of a man who might be the missing link, he volunteered to go in quest of him. Anne had seen him bring them in and soon found time to question them. When she learned that he had befriended them, when she heard the poor creature's florid and effusive expressions of thankfulness for his small and cheap beneficence, it brought a glow of pleased surprise to her heart. She learned, too, the time of night at which he had picked them up; and she guessed that he had slept but little. Could it have been on her account?

Zury soon returned with the husband and father; and as he stood contemplating the family reunion with a smile — rather grim, though also quite benevolent, Anne went to him and said with her own frankness, —

"Mr. Prouder, I've been talking with that poor creature, and — I don't know when I've been more pleased, delighted I may say" (she wanted to say "surprised"), "than I was to hear of your kind-heartedness, and your — liberality!"

He looked at her with a sadness in his eyes that quite touched her, and said something about not having done anything to speak of.

"But you 've done everything! You were just the right man in the right place at the right time, and did the right thing. As the ministers say, Providence must have picked you out as an instrument for the succor of the helpless!"

"They do say Providence can work with pretty poor tools."

"Poor tools! It would be the first task you were ever found to be a poor hand at, if you were to turn into a philanthropist and did n't do it well!"

His look softened, but he kept on his unaccustomed silence.

"Perhaps you 've been hiding an unknown quality of benevolence all these years, and now it is just coming out!"

"Mebbe so — mebbe so — but I guess not. I expect I 'm a hard, knotty old stick."

She returned to her desk, truly grieved that she could not comfort or console him; and the regret haunted her all day — and longer.

As for him, he spent the drive homeward, and the days and weeks that followed, in a strange train of thought. Dim glimmerings of new aspirations animated him: new views of life, not quite adopted, but at least contemplated as being among the possibilities, in this world or some other.

Within two or three months, strange rumors begin to shake the firmament in Wayback. Let us listen to the news.

As good a place as any in the world to catch the sense of a community like this is the "horse-shed" that is provided near every meeting-house and court-house. More politics are talked, and more opinions formed, changed, and confirmed in the horse-shed than in any other one locality in the township; so much so, that "horse-shedding" has become a verb in the vernacular. Many a lawyer has accounted to his client for an adverse verdict, by such expressions as this:—

"Oh, that feller, 'n' his lawyer, 'n' their friends has be'n a *hoss-sheddin'* them jurymen! Yes, sir-ree, the' hev, 'n' I know it! The facts was with us, the law was with us, the bench was with us, 'n' the bar was with us; but facts 'n' law, 'n' bench 'n' bar, is all fools to a hoss-shed! It 'll lay over 'em every time!"

Well, on a certain summer Sunday afternoon, the Wayback meeting-house was baking hot, the minister was perspiring, and pouring forth perfervid eloquence — coatless, vestless, collar-less and cravat-less — and there was no wind blowing but his; so, of course, the horses out in the cool, untroubled shade needed a *great deal* of attention. No farmer was quite willing to intrust his team to the other fellows out there — unless he happened to be sitting very near the pulpit and very far from the door. The best seats in the house — those you come to first as you enter — were consequently all emptied soon after "firstly," by their occupants' sliding out to attend to the teams in the horse-shed.

"Wal, pards," — in a hesitating, tentative

voice as making a suggestion too startling to be lightly ventured upon,—"d' ye know—Zury Praouder he 's a-goin' off some?"

"He never wuz to hum no gre't. Dunno 's he 's away more 'n usial."

"Away thunder! He 's on the daownhill! He 's a-gittin' old—I don't say dotin'. He 's a-losin' his grip!"

"What! Zury?" In chorus, with dissenting variations.

"Wal, naow jest hol' on till I tell ye what I 've heern tell. You know when his o' woman died she left her things 'thaout no word, 'n' her sister S'manthy that 's lived thar fer ever 'n' ever with her growin' gal, she kinder wanted 'em, 'n' she dropped hints raoun' 'mongst her own folks 't they 'd oughter chip in 'n' make up a little puss 'n' buy 'em offen Zury fer her."

"Thasso-thasso," said one of the hearers who had been applied to, and would have liked to go on and detail his reasons for not "chipping in," but was headed off by the more interesting subject.

"That ain't neither h'yer ner thar—'t warn't done 'n' the matter drapped; 'n' some 'llaowed th't Zury he 'd auction 'em off; 'n' some 'llaowed he 'd keep 'em fer his third, 'n' so 't went on. Wal, wha' d' ye think I 've heerd? 'N' I know it's so, tew!" (Here his voice sank into an awestruck whisper that drew all heads nearer to his wonder-uttering lips.) "A week ago this blessed day, when S'manthy wuz a clearin' off the breakf's', at half-past six in the mornin', Zury he upped 'n' told her she c'd hev her sister's things!"

A moment's pause here occurred, a silence broken by expressions of amazement and disbelief.

"Wal, ye kin b'lieve it er not, — this is a free kedntry, — but either it 's a fact er else S'manthy 's a liar er a looney, one o' th' six! She told Mis Bromwell on it 's soon 's she c'd git over thar, 'n' Mis Bromwell told my wife, 'n' my wife told me, so ye git it cheap 's I did. S'manthy says she was so flabbergasted for a minute she did n' know what *tew* dew — ye might a knocked her daown with a stick o' wood! Zury he jest went aout 'n' set daown on th' door-stone, 'n' S'manthy she went 'n' leaned agin the door-post 'n' told him — 's well 's she could fer a-cryin' 's she wuz — 't her frien's war n't a-goin' t' dew noth'n' in the way o' buyin' on 'em in fer her, 's fur 's she c'd see; 'n' Zury he 'llaowed he c'd keep up his eend o' the double-tree 'n' pay his debts 'thaout his sellin' his wife's clo's. 'N' so it went. 'N' what 's more, she 's to meetin' this mornin' with one o' Mis Praouder's gaounds on!"

"Thasso! Fust time she 's be'n t' meetin' in a coon's age!"

"Dew that, er don't it — look like Zury 's a-breakin' up?"

A sad silence, as in contemplation of the wreck of a strong mind, brooded over the group; a stillness broken only by the rustling of the trees, and the stamping of the fly-bothered horses, and the sonorous shouts audible through the open windows of the meeting-house, where the poor preacher was showing his determination and his ability to keep some of his hearers awake at all hazards and at any expense.

"Looks like dotin' sure enough."

"Naow look a-h'yer, pards, till *I* tell ye a leetle on the same side. Storekeeper he 's a-owin' Zury some rent, of course, — mebby a matter of twelve dollars, — 'n' this week Zury he upped 'n' told him haow S'manthy's gal, Alphy, she 's a-gittin' ready t' marry, 'n' storekeeper he wuz t' let her git up t' the vally o' the back rent, 'n' he 'd settle it with S'manthy!"

"Wal! *wal!* WAL! Looks like soff'n'n' o' the brain 'n Zury! Tho' come t' think it 'd be only soff'n'n' o' the heart in some folks! But when a man as hain't *got* no heart starts in t' act so 'course it 's his brain that 's the matter."

"Wal; who 'll we git fer supervisor, 'n' 'ssessor, 'n' school d'rector?" So the conversation drifted away from the setting to the rising star. But before long it was recalled to the old theme, Zury, who was still, as for a generation back, the most interesting topic in that horse-shed.

"But look a-h'yer men! Zury a-givin' away his wife's clo's looks as though he did n't 'llaow t' marry agin!"

"Yes — or else 't he 'llaowed t' marry some gal them clo's would n't fit, 'n' 't would n't have 'em 's a gift!"

"Why anybody 'd a bet ten t' one Zury 'd a married agin afore this time — that is, ef he 'd ever a took time enough t' 'tend tew it!"

"'T don't take long fer a man like Zury. All he 's got t' dew is t' jest wink at any gal in Spring Caounty, 'n' she 'll have her bunnit on 'n' be on the road t' the Squire's 'fore he kin wink t' other eye."

"The' wuz a talk one spell 't Zury wuz a-goin fur the widder McVey t' Springville — her 't kep' school here in this very school-haouse one spell."

"She wuz chain-lightnin' then! Dunno but what she is now. That wuz a matter o' fifteen or twenty years ago, but I guess she ain't no slaouch even naow. Did n't look so when she wuz h'yer jest 'fore Zury got 'lected t' th' legislatur. But, then, that 's all past 'n' gone. If he 'd a had any idee in his mind o' that kind he 'd a upped 'n' done it quick 's his wife died."

"Wal, hit er miss, the' dew say 's how jest after his wife died Zury he upped 'n' got him a new suit, 'n' some new teeth, 'n' went off daown t' Springville, whar she lives, 'n' whar she 's a-clerkin' fer the store whar he gits his wholesale truck."

"Oh sugar! Zury ain't no man t' up 'n' marry no ol' widder! Strappin' gal baout nineteen 'd be more 'n' Zury's line th'n any ol' widder!"

"Wal, some Smart Aleck, daown t' th' Wayback store, he upped 'n' tackled Zury 'baout the widder McVey when he got back; 'n' Zury he took him by the collar with one hand 'n' by the ear with t' other, 'n' led him aoutside 'n' said a few words t' the feller 'd never tell what they wuz fr'm that day t' this."

"Pr'aps the widow she would n't hev him!"

"What! Not have Zury Praouder!" This proposition was such a blatant absurdity that it broke up the conclave, assisted by the fact that the closing hymn marked the time for hitching up and driving round.

From these hints it may be seen that Zury's powerful mind, set for many a year in certain ways, is under stress of some yet more powerful influence, and as it seems to be bending its course in a way which we, who love him, highly approve of, let us go back to the place whither his thoughts turn, in season and out, with any excuse or none.

Now it happens that in Springville, at the McVey cottage, he is again almost forgotten. A new, long, incurable grief has smitten the little household. Phil has left them! The pride and joy of those two gentle women's hearts has quitted the maternal roof to seek promotion in his chosen profession. On the little Springville railway he could only be a fireman, perhaps for years to come; on the greater Chicago and Galena road he mounts the foot-board at once, a full-fledged engine-driver. He is to have charge of the "Pioneer," the first engine ever run out of Chicago. They could not blame him — they could only mourn for him. While he was with them, praise and blame were always mixed; admiration of his powers was tempered by disapproval of his unruliness; and wonder at his mechanical progress and prowess was somewhat balanced by regret that he did not take more polish in an intellectual and social way. But now that he was far away every virtue was exaggerated and every fault forgotten; so that a stranger, on hearing Anne and Meg expatiate on the boy's great goodness and good greatness, would have wondered in what part of the Kosmos such paragons keep hidden, that they are never visible to the common eye — always chance to be in the very place you are not acquainted with — and what is more, on meeting Phil they would never recognize him from the portrait painted for him by motherly and sisterly love.

Well, for good or ill, he is gone. The winter of discontent reigns in the cottage with more than usual gloom. And out of doors it is autumn, late autumn, and the "pinch of the year" is approaching with all its accustomed ferocity. The daily walks to and from store and school are turned from pleasure to pain, and the cottage interior takes on a loneliness that is appalling.

"Mother, just see how self-forgetting Phil is! He always speaks of *our* unhappiness, never of his own! 'You will be so lonesome,' he writes; when we have each other, and he has nobody at all! Yet he pretends never to think of it in that way."

"Yes — yes" — (musingly) "but the fact is, Meg, that is truth, not affectation. He does not suffer as we do."

"Now, mother!"

"At your age I might have thought he was pining for his home-women; but now I know better. It's better so. No man who is ever going to come to anything is ruled by family affection."

"It 'll never be so with me!" And she clung to her mother with an almost painful intensity.

"Perhaps not. But Phil would say, 'business before pleasure' — and even that is a deception, for in fact business is his highest pleasure."

"Would n't he love to be here holding our hands in his this minute?"

"Yes; for just about a minute. But he 'd love better to be driving the Pioneer's snow-plow at full speed through a blinding snow-drift; as he wrote in his last of having done."

"He seemed to enjoy it, in spite of the awful danger; any wheel leaving the track would have meant death or maiming, he said."

"He enjoyed it all the more on that account."

"Dear, dear! What a difference between men and women! Yet I like him all the better for the difference."

"Yes, and he likes us all the better. What man likes a mannish woman; or what woman does n't detest a womanish man! Every boy that is ever going to be worth his salt, has to be weaned twice; once as a child and the second time as a man. Both times it comes hard — hard — the first time on the child, and the second on the mother."

"But if the mother has a daughter that will *never* be weaned again" —

"Then she is a happy, blessed mother." (No stage directions are here needed to indicate the by-play.)

Phil's letters were not many nor fluent. Sons

are so cruel! Oh, if they only knew or could know, before it is too late, what pains they inflict and what joys they withhold! From these treasured missives the loving folks he had left behind learned that he had made new friends. Of one family, named Sanders, he wrote with some freedom at first; mentioning among other things that Mrs. Sanders was the prettiest married woman he had ever seen. Later he went to board with them, and after this he quite dropped that subject, and even some express questions asked in Meg's return letters elicited no sort of response.

But of another family he wrote longest and oftenest. These were the Mastens. Masten was the young Methodist minister whose acquaintance we made at Wayback, who married Eureka Anstey and, in the rotatory process peculiar to his church, found himself at Galena with (as Prouder had expressed it) "the largest following in Jo Daviess County." The reader may remember that Zury also suggested a remarkable degree of personal attractiveness in the eldest daughter of the Masten flock; one named for Anne McVey.

From what Phil wrote, Anne and Meg concluded that Annie Masten was quite as lovely as they had heard she was; and partly from what he said, and partly from what he refrained from saying, they further concluded that his heart was more touched by her charms than he cared to tell.

CHAPTER XXIV.

A LONG SLEIGH-RIDE.

MANY, many leagues of snowy prairie lie between Galena on the north and Springville and Wayback in the centre, of the huge State of Illinois, whereof the most northern point touches the latitude of Boston, and the most southern the latitude of Richmond, Virginia. On those pale plains the snow flies (or flew in those days) over whole degrees of latitude and longitude without an impediment; and the wind sweeps (or swept) with no obstruction save the snow. You could scarcely say the wind howled — that would indicate that it met with some obstacle around which it eddied and of which it complained. It simply sped along swift and silent, as in mid-sky.

But in the more southern region of Springville, the snow was some two weeks later than up at Galena, and during those two weeks things happened which were most interesting to some of our *dramatis personæ*, and which may deserve some attention from the reader.

Anne's refusal of Zury Prouder was, as we have seen, a rude shock which let him know what he ought to have learned far earlier in life — that he was not nearly the masterful man he had always thought himself, but in reality a very narrow, ignorant, ill-bred, and unwise person, seeking for happiness where only a mean, unworthy, and temporary gratification can be found. Money-making, as an end and not a means of life, is like climbing a chimney that grows narrower toward the top; one reaches a place where he can get neither up nor down, and is enveloped in dirt and darkness till he dies. Zury did not say this to himself in words, but his ennui and loneliness said it to him daily and hourly.

The same old yearning led him to the same old expedient — a sight of his second idol, Phil. For this blessing he actually made the great journey to Galena, far away in the northwest.

In the Springville house, Anne and Margaret solaced their sadness with bright dreams — impossible of realization — called up by a warm invitation they had received from the Mastens to come to Galena for a long visit. But alas, as has been said, the way is long, and no railroad would help them, except some forty miles or so of the Galena and Chicago Union, to reach which took weary days of overland travel.

Zury Prouder had never called on them after the memorable afternoon and evening tea and talk we have read about in a former chapter. He felt that the answer was meant to be final; and also, in his secret soul, he thought that it was the proper reply for a woman like Anne to give to a man like himself.

Months had passed since Phil left Springville

for Chicago; and, during this time, things had grown more humdrum than ever. Margaret's indignation at the step-fatherhood and benefaction proposed by Zury to her mother had become moderated, as the strongest emotions are by Time, the Eater of Things.

On a certain early winter day, behold Zury once more at the well-remembered white gate. He had privately passed it before, but lacked the hardihood to enter. Now he hoped, by putting on a courage he did not feel, he might carry through a call successfully. He would, at least, settle for himself the question whether he was a coward or not.

"Good evenin', Mis McVey! How is the Queen of Springville? *And* the Princess; how is she?"

Both ladies were well: Anne smiling, though embarrassed; Margaret grave and self-possessed. It may be remarked that an offer of marriage very rarely puts a widow into a lasting and vindictive rage, though that same widow's grown-up daughter is apt to consider it a personal insult.

"I was passin', an' jest drop't in, promiscuous-like."

"Glad to see you, Mr. Prouder. Lay off your top-coat. Why did n't you come in in time for tea?"

Margaret could scarcely believe her ears. But then — mother knew best.

"Well, I dunno, I dunno." (He wished now that he had come in months sooner.) "Ye know I'm a pretty busy man. Have to keep up my end o' the double-tree. Must n't quite lose my reputation as the — as a man of business."

"Have you been very well?"

"Who, me? Well, so as to be able to lean upon my elbow and take my medicine." (This with a chuckle in view of his invariable health.)

"What 's the news over at Wayback?"

"News? Why the' ain't none. Stock 's gen-er'ly good an' fat for winter. Ground hain't been froze hard enough to git inter the field an' gather corn to speak of. But the farmers' boys will soon be thrashin' their arms and blowin' their fingers in the corn-fields. Dunno 's you know it, but huskin' and wagenin' corn 's the all-firedest coldest job th't ever was given out since Adam was a babe."

"It must be! Very little exercise — just walking along and taking hold of one bitter-cold ear after another, and stripping off those icy husks! But I never thought of it."

"Of course ye did n't! Why should ye? Ye 'd leave some of them little white fingers of yours behind ye on the ground before ye got to the end of the second row!"

"I 'd stop before my fingers froze off! Or run in the house and get my mittens."

"And have th' ole man after ye with th' halter-strap? And all the women-folks laughin' at ye! Ye can't do no job of work in a corn-field with mittens on!"

"How are the Ansteys?"

"Well, now ye speak of it, o' man Anstey has been kinder ailin' like, — jest downcy, not bedfast,

— but o' woman Anstey, she 's been *good* and sick!"

"Poor things! How in the world do they get along?"

"Oh, they ain't bad off. Th' neighbors drop round and feed 'em their medicine. The young-uns, they 've come along. Bijah, he 's marr'd and fetched his woman home — right peart of a gal, too, when she 's able to get round to work, which ain't very often, seein' she 's got three of her own and on her fourth a'ready. Silas, he 's doin' the heft of the work on the place besides what Bijah does."

"And brother Bromwell?"

"Oh, Omri Bromwell, *he 's* a-gittin' pretty near once through. May last a spell yet, though. Had to joke him a leetle last time I saw him. Says I, 'Brother Omri, how old are you anyway?' Says he, 'Nigh onto seventy-six.' Says I, 'Seventy-six! Sho! ye hold your age well! I sh'd have thought ye was a hunderd!' But would ye have believed it, th' old man did n't like it! Gettin' childish, and dotin' a leetle!"

"Well, I should n't have liked it myself!"

"You! Sakes alive; it would be a bold man would say you held your age well! Ye hain't got no age to hold! Which is mother an' which is daughter, anyhow? Hain't ye lost count some way? Got changed in yer cradles or something?"

"You *shan't* call my daughter older than I am!" And the two women gently embraced each other.

"'T ain't that she 's older than you; it 's you that are younger than she is! That 's where it is. But sho! That 's neither here nor there. Age and youth 's all one, an' we 're noth'n' but poor worms in th' sight of th' Almighty."

When Zury had been frivolous he liked to "even up his averages" by an extra pious sentiment.

"My son writes me that he saw you in Galena."

"Who, Phil? Did he write that, though? There now!" (This with a glowing and gratified smile.) "I was comin' to that. Mighty powers, ain't he chain lightnin'?"

Zury's eyes danced and his cheek glowed with an admiration which he was powerless fully to express. He went on for a full hour to detail what he had observed in his watching of Phil on a certain day when he had made his acquaintance on the "Pioneer," and on other occasions. The two women listened spell-bound, both for the sake of the subject, and the rude, grotesque, picturesque force of the plain man's diction. If Zury had had the wisdom of the serpent, and had begun his ill-starred courtship with such an hour's talk as this, no widowed mother in the state could have hoped to withstand his eloquence and refuse his suit.

"But here I am, like an old dromedary, talkin' ye to death an' never sayin' what I came a-purpose to say. It 's this: I 've got to team it up to Galeny as soon as the snow flies. Now you two jest put on your bonnets an' go along."

"Oh — Mr. Prouder — you take my breath away!"

"Well, a week's ride against a north wind 'll be liable to give it back to ye."

"It would change your journey altogether. If you went alone you 'd take a single cutter."

"Why, bless your simple soul! A single cutter 'd never get there! The hoss could n't travel on the divide; he 'd have to go either in the nigh hoss-track or the off hoss-track, an' then where 'd your runners be? Unless ye had one of these lop-sided nut-shells, an' that would n't begin to stand the wear an' tear. Never you mind me. I know which side my bread 's buttered on!"

"Well, it 's no use. I could n't either take the store books along, or keep them while I was gone; nor expect to pick up my job again when I got back. Much obliged to you all the same! It 's the kindest offer I ever had in my life."

"Not by *one* that I know of. Now, as to the store job, jest leave that to me. They 're tryin' to sell me a big bill of goods, and I 've got 'em down to bottom figgers so far, an' was goin' to close the whack in the mornin' anyway. Now, I 'll go to th' old man and tell him I 'll do it, if he 'll have them books took care of whilst you 're gone, and kept for ye when ye git back. See? 'T won't cost him a cent 'cause he 'll make the junior pardner do the work."

"Oh, Meg! To see Phil at home! And Eureka! And my pretty namesake!"

"Mother! don't you dare to think of letting the chance slip by!"

Three happy hearts in Springville that night! Three happy hearts in Galena when the letter came detailing the plan! Which was the most utterly joyful, — the yearning mother, the tender daughter and sister, the son, who had a double gain to hope for, in seeing his beloved women, and showing them off to Annie Masten? Or was it, after all, the contriver and author of the whole scheme of affection and delight, Usury Prouder? The hard man, to whom love was so rare, benevolence such an unaccustomed luxury, and the exercise of power and patronage such a soul-satisfying happiness!

"When the snow flies." This means a great deal to the dwellers in the country, where weather of all kinds, especially bitter weather, has an importance which city-people can scarcely conceive of. In due time the snow flew, and later the snow lay on the ground, even down in the latitude of Springville. Starting with fair sleighing, they were pretty sure of finding it improve as they journeyed north. Zury took his best team, which is saying not a little. He also took seventeen fine crocks of butter, stowed where it would be in nobody's way but his own. (Butter was worth at the lead mines exactly double what it was at Wayback.) Robes and rugs, peltries and blankets, made the women absolutely insensible to cold, while Zury sat up, brave and gay, with no outside wraps except his shaggy coat, cap, gloves, and boots, looking like a very good representation of a middle-aged Santa Claus.

They were not to go by the sleigh further than the nearest point on the railroad. There they would meet some of those whom they had come so far to see, and go on by freight-train to Galena. This arrangement was admirably made (under Zury's directions) and the very day for the meeting fixed by means of a letter which, traveling night and day by mail, reached Galena in half the time it must take them to get there.

Prouder was a fine traveling-companion. He could talk, could listen, could be silent, and endure silence in others. The relationship of fellow-traveler is a most trying one, as many a bridal-trip has shown. The time is apt to come when it would be a relief for the weary wanderers to meet a friend, "or even an enemy," as Punch says. Now Zury seemed ready, at a moment's notice, with his best thoughts, looks, words, and actions, at each and every hour of the twenty-four. The impression he made upon Anne and her daughter improved daily; but alas, truth must be told! Anxious as he was to please, careful as he was to behave himself as much like "highflyers" as his observation and memory enabled him to do, still, what was bred in the bone would not come out of the flesh, and he failed signally: though it was but in one point and by a hair's-breadth, yet it was a failure. This was the nature of it. He carried a fine, large handkerchief, and flourished it expressively; yea, and blew mighty blasts thereon, like Wouter Van Twiller; but, unhappily, he used it economically! Instead of making it his main reliance, he treated it as a reserve or auxiliary force! A sad and fatal error.

Stopping at noons and nights, sometimes at a city, oftener at a village tavern, but oftenest at some roadside farmhouse, they made nearly fifty miles a day; piecing out the short days by an occasional spin in the moonlight when roads and weather favored. They reached the railroad on the day before that set for their meeting with their Galena friends; and on the morrow, by the first train, came Phil and Sam Sanders, his fireman, bringing Mrs. Masten (Anne's old scholar) and her daughter Annie. What a union and re-union!

Eureka had developed into a typical parson's wife: dutiful, motherly, tactful, and *somewhat* pious; albeit perceptibly less church-y than of old, through a certain disillusionment that comes from being behind the scenes and knowing all the ropes, from flies to traps, from pulpit-lungs to organ-bellows. Annie Masten was all their fancy had painted her, and more.

Prouder started early toward Galena, with his sleigh. Then, after dinner, all the rest took the "Way-freight-train" for the same point. Anne and Margaret had sometimes ridden in a "caboose," or freight-conductor's car, when Phil was a fireman, but to the others it was a new experience.

The caboose is always the rear car of the freight-train. It is usually a long, empty box-car, with great sliding doors, open to the floor, in the middle of each side, and a door at each end. A red-hot stove, sitting in a box of sand, and braced to the floor on all sides, keeps it warm in winter. The whole length of the sides, except where the doors are, is occupied with long, narrow boxes for fuel and tools, cushioned over to serve as seats and beds for the train-hands. A jagged bit of looking-glass is always tacked up near some window; and the walls are covered with time-cards and regulations for running trains, with here and there a picture of a fine horse, or a red-cheeked beauty, or a war-hero, or some other work of art which brakeman or conductor has deemed worthy of a place in his rude picture gallery.

These free and simple surroundings, together with the low speed, and the liberty to wander here and there and look out at sides and ends, make a ride on a freight-train more like a picnic than an ordinary and orderly journey.

Before the train started Annie said, —

"Why, Sam; where 's Phil?"

"Oh, he 's aout ahead talkin' to Jack Dougherty, the engineer; mos' likely tellin' him t' start 'n' stop kinder easy, so 's not t' jerk you women folks out o' the rear door every time he gives her steam t' go ahead."

"Why, is n't he going to ride with us?"

"Oh yes — never fear, he 'll be back."

"What a long train!" said Annie, who was looking out.

"'Baout twenty cars. See Phil away ahead thar, 'long side the engine? Thar! Dougherty 's whistled 'off brakes;' now look out, she 's a-startin'! Ketch a holt of the side o' the door, like that; *so*." And they started.

"Why, Phil 's left!" cried Annie. "We 're off, and he 's standing there yet!"

"Oh, he 's jest a-waiting for us to come along."

"But we are going faster and faster all the time!"

"That don't faze Phil, not a mite; twelve mile an hour gittin' on, or twenty mile an hour gittin' off suits Phil 's well 's anything else."

In a minute or two the open door flashed past Phil as he stood, and Sam leaned out to see him "make it." Phil only nipped his cigar a little more firmly between his teeth, grasped the hand-rail as it passed, swung himself on the rear step, and — went on smoking.

"See?" said Sam. "He did n't never think noth'n' abaout it; jest lighted on the platform like a green-head on a yearling colt. Why — wha — what 's the matter?"

This to Annie, who was sitting on a bench and leaning back against the wall, her face colorless, lips open, lower eyelids relaxed, hands hanging at her sides; in short, as Sam said, "lookin' 's though she did n't take no interest in things. Did n't keer whether school kep' er not!"

"Oh, nothing," said she, recovering herself with a deep breath; and then she rose and steadied herself by the side of the car till she reached the little mirror, by help of which she re-arranged her pretty hat, disordered by its heedless contact with the wall when she sat down so suddenly.

"Phil!" said Meg, calling him at the back door, "come in here this minute! Did n't you promise mother and me you 'd never take any needless risks?"

"Risks?"

"Yes, risks! You just got on to this car going at full speed."

"Well, if I 'd gone slow I should n't have got on."

"Nonsense! You know what I mean! You got on when the car was going at full speed!"

"I held it back all I could, the minute I got hold of it, but I could n't make it go any slower."

"You 'll be killed, getting on cars in motion in that way!"

"See here, Meg; gettin' on cars in motion never killed a man yet. It 's gettin' under 'em that hurts! If you ever catch me doin' that you may scold."

"Well, when you are killed I hope you 'll be satisfied!"

"I expect to be, perfectly. And if I am not, I promise you I won't complain."

"Who is that young man writing in a book balanced on his left arm?" asked Meg of Sam Sanders a few minutes later. "I don't see how he can write, staggering about so!"

"Oh, that 's the corn-doctor. I 'll interdooce ye tew him in a minute, soon 's he gits threw enterin' his way-bills."

"The corn-doctor!"

"Oh yes — but *yew* hain't no need t' be afeared on him; yer hat 's chalked, good."

"My hat?" And the bewildered young woman raised her hand to the "chalked" article.

Annie soon explained to her that in Sam's vocabulary a "corn-doctor" meant a conductor, and a "chalked hat" meant a free pass.

Then Phil and his mother had a long, long talk, while Margaret and Annie learned all they could about railroading from the caboose point of view. The two girls "foregathered" amazingly. Each seemed to have been all her life looking for somebody just like the other — never found till now. They fell in love with each other, and each secretly wished they might never part more.

Phil could n't help wondering why his mother did n't begin at once talking about Annie Masten, and keep on the same subject for the rest of the day. Yet he could not start the topic himself. His mother, meanwhile, did not have to ask him about Annie; she knew it all beforehand by motherly instinct.

Toward the middle of the afternoon the engineer gave the signal he and Phil had agreed upon to announce that Prouder and his team were in sight; and all went to the doors and windows, and made the car gay with fluttering handkerchiefs and waving hats. Prouder put his horses at a gallop, and kept within hearing distance for almost a minute, while Phil, at his mother's request, shouted, —

"They say they owe all this to you!"

Prouder lifted his hat, and, as he pulled up his panting team, asked himself with a cool, critical expression, —

"Lessee, lessee; o' man Zury, did ye or did n't ye ever hear sweeter music 'n' that in' all yer born days?"

His thoughts wandered back to the voices of his dead sister and his dead boys, and his heart grew so soft that he had to shake himself together with an effort and say: "Zury! Look aout! Mebbe ye 're dotin'! Ye know there 's no fool like an old fool!"

CHAPTER XXV.

AMARI ALIQUID.

As has been often said, the happiest states of life furnish poorest materials for the story-teller. "Blessed is a land without mountains, a people without a history, and a life without events." "No news is good news" in family life. When Phil was away on his engine, his loving women simply looked forward to his return, and that return, when it came, paid them for their waiting.

Zury Prouder had bought a "lead-hill," and he and Phil were preparing to open one or more lead mines and their accompanying works as soon as the spring should open. *Then* Phil would leave the railroad, and begin to become a solid, prosperous business man, with unlimited capital to back him! Happy dreams for his mother, and Meg, and — perhaps some others.

There were two sprigs of bitterness in Anne's cup — one the ever-present consciousness of the near approach of a new parting; the other a sprout from seed unconsciously sown by loquacious Sam Sanders.

The coming departure was a common grief.

Said the minister, sonorous and splendid, —

"Mrs. McVey, your stay with us is like the

shadow of a great rock in a weary land. Eureka's spirit feels your influence like the balm of Gilead. In her girlhood it was the chiefest blessing bestowed on her by a kind Providence; and now in her — maturity — it once more sheds peace and happiness upon her, and at the same time on us all."

"Now, father!" protested Annie, in expostulatory tones; "you talk as if you were officiating at somebody's funeral, and praising the influence of the dear departed!"

"Annie, my daughter! There is nobody else who dares to talk to your father as you do!" Eureka said deprecatingly.

"Well, mother, he must have somebody to take him down. The rest of his congregation — you among them — just *grovel* at father's feet! My business is to go on saying to him, 'Alexander, thou too art mortal,' to keep him from getting spoiled by the worship of foolish females."

"Well, my daughter, I suppose it is good for me. A prophet is not without honor save in his own country. As Saint Paul says, no 'chastisement is for the present joyous, but grievous, but after it yieldeth the peaceable fruits of righteousness to them that are exercised thereby.' Now I thought you would be a staff to my declining years!" The good man smiled on his lovely daughter in a way that showed he loved her none the less for her chiding.

"So I am, father! Your staff, — of course, — your rod and your staff. You know rods and staves have various uses: they guide folks when held in the hand, and also when laid over the back."

"I'm afraid he did not keep one handy when you were growing up, Annie," said Meg.

"No, that's true! They don't grow on the prairie. He spared the rod and spoiled the child."

"Well, not exactly spoiled her. Only kept her down to a reasonable degree of angelical-ness — so her wings should n't sprout before their time."

"No, Mrs. McVey, I insist that I am spoiled. If I had been properly treated I should be like the dear woman I am named for."

"Well, my love, it's not too late. You can be brought under wholesome discipline yet. But wait till next week. Wait till we are gone back to Springville. Be just as you are, till then."

"Now, now!" cried Annie, clapping her hands to her ears, "I will *not* hear of your going! I am spoiled enough to have my own way about that."

"Why, my dear, we must go sometime, and we ought to have gone before."

"I see you are talking, but I cannot hear a word."

"Oh well, then," said Phil, "we'll change the subject."

"Then I'll open my ears again," responded the thoughtless girl, taking down her hands. "Why, what are you all laughing at me for?"

"Oho, Miss Pretense! If your ears were shut, how did you know what Phil said?"

"Oh, well, you see — I knew Phil would n't talk about that horrid subject; so when I saw him open his lips I just — listened a leetle bit."

"Ya-as," put in Sam Sanders, "I 'bserve that whenever Phil speaks yer ears are tight open!"

All laughed at this highly personal remark, and as Annie blushed a good deal and seemed mortified, Sam hastened to qualify it: —

"Oh, I did n't mean *yew* particular, Miss Masten. All the women are the same way. Thar 's Dolly, naow; n' matter if the rest is all talkin' theirselves blind, it don't take more 'n a whisper fr'm Phil fer her t' ketch right on tew."

Now it was Phil's turn to look foolish, and a sudden awkwardness fell on all the group, which Anne silently noticed and wondered at.

Said Zury, "I don't see no call for ye to hurry off so sudden. Don't go on my account. My time 's well spent on the lead-mine hill, an' my team in the tavern livery is earnin' their keep an' more too."

"Oh, surely. We won't go on anybody's account but our own," said Anne, "and only on our own because we must sacrifice the delights of Galena to the duties of Springville."

As soon as she could have a talk with Sam alone, she suddenly asked him, "Who 's Dolly, Mr. Sanders?"

"Why, Dolly Sanders — my brother Jim's old woman."

"Old woman? I thought she was — rather young."

"Young? So she is. She thinks she 's awful young, though I guess she 's old enough to vote, an' would n't tear under the wing. But ye know we call every man's wife his 'Old Woman' — jest for short, like."

"Oh, I see! Well, tell me about Dolly."

"Why, what abaout her?"

"Well, is she pretty?"

"Pretty? Oh, she 'll pass in a craowd!" (This with a series of winks of each eye in rapid alternation. Then, straightening his face:) "But she can't hold a candle t' Annie Masten! No, not a blowd-out candle with the wick pinched short off!"

"Oh, I see," said Mrs. McVey, somewhat relieved.

Then Sam, wishing to be polite, and to express friendly sentiments, must needs "shoot off his mouth" some more, and of course "put his foot in it."

"We 'll all be awful sorry t' have ye go! Any mother o' Phil McVey's would always be welcome 'mongst them that knows him. The women folks 'll jest cry their eyes out — all that is, unless mebbe it 's Dolly."

"Why, what difference can it make to her — away off in Chicago?"

"Oh, no difference at all! Of course — not a mite! Phil ain't nothin' t' Dolly but a kind o' sort of a brother; 'n' livin' in th' house 's he dooz, 'n' Jim away on th' road jest when Phil's to hum — 'n' theayters, 'n' concerts, 'n' one thing another."

Anne felt a strange sinking of the heart — an actual physical tension, as if some of the "involuntary muscles" had contracted spontaneously and unnaturally. One watching her would have seen that the blood left her face, the lines deepened, and she looked older than she ever had looked in her life. Motherly anxiety, womanly jealousy, friendly alarm on Annie Masten's account — all seemed to seize on this little hook of uncertainty and raise themselves to dreadful proportions. Luckily, dull Sam observed nothing, and soon took his leave.

"Philip, my son. What did Sam mean by what he said about Dolly?"

"Oh, Sam 's a born fool! Don't pay any attention to what he says!" said Phil, evidently disturbed.

"No, but I 'll pay attention to what you say; if you 'll only be frank with your mother and tell her truly all about it."

"All about it? There is nothing to tell," responded the youth, surly and guarded to a degree that added to Anne's distress.

"Are you — attentive to her?"

"I board with her, and pay her my board." ("So he is not going to tell me he ever took her to the theatre.")

"Is that all, dear?"

"Of course it is! What more should there be?"

"There should not be anything — but there might be."

"Well, mother, there is n't."

He answered, truly enough, to the letter; for certain attentions he had bestowed on Dolly had lately ceased. His thoughts were now full of Annie Masten — and of his mother and sister. If Anne had asked him about the past, he would have had to tell her a very different story, or keep silent — or "lie like a gentleman" as the phrase is where a man tells a falsehood to shield a woman from having her name unfortunately linked with his. But Anne did not know this. She had got a glimpse of the past and guessed nothing of any change — any difference between past and present.

His mother moved her chair close to Phil's, and drew his head to her shoulder with an inexpressible tenderness. But even as she did so, she perceived that it was a man she had to deal with — not her baby any longer. He was a separate person — not part of herself, now.

"Oh, my son! Don't you love your mother?"

"Now, mother! What have I ever done or left undone that you should ask such a question as that?"

"I don't know, Phil. I want you to tell me. And you refuse!" Here she broke down and cried helplessly.

Then Phil kissed her and took her in his arms in his turn, caressing and trying to comfort and reassure her.

"Mother dear, I never stay in Chicago a minute when I can be with you, and when I am there I only long for the time when I can get back to

Galena. There is no woman there who holds any place in my heart or my thoughts, compared with — you all. Now *don't* be foolish! *Do* trust me!"

She did the best she could. But it seemed to her that she had always been dreading just such a horrible failing in her son's life as Sam had hinted at, — and Phil had not satisfactorily denied it, even now.

During the remainder of their stay, Phil redoubled his efforts to make them all happy — Anne especially, and she got over her alarm in some measure. No one could resist his efforts to please, and his mother, when with him, felt as if it was impossible that his frank gayety and his undisguised admiration for her beautiful namesake, Annie Masten, could cover — anything unworthy.

On the following Sunday Anne said to Eureka and her daughter, —

"Now, my dears, I think we may as well fix on Tuesday as 'the day of wrath, the dreadful day' when Meg and I must go away!"

"Mrs. McVey," said Eureka, solemnly, "as I always say to mamma in such cases, I am like cold dumplings."

"Cold dumplings, dear? Do you mean your heart is heavy?"

"No. I simply mean that I disagree with mamma. Now I disagree with you! Suppose we should die, some day! How sorry we should be to have cut short this greatest joy of our lives!"

"My darling, joys are like grapevines — all the better for pruning. Tuesday let it be. Don't make my duty harder by opposing it. It is hard enough already."

A few tears came to her eyes. Annie answered by other tears but did not argue further.

So the parting came. Zury set off on a Monday morning, and on Wednesday the mother and daughter went on Phil's train to the "jumping off place," where the absolute good-byes must be spoken. The train slowed up — stopped — they alighted, Phil was kissing them and saying "Good-bye mother, good-bye Meg; for just a little while," and he was back on his engine and the train was off again! Before they knew that the dreadful time of trial had arrived, it came, was here, was past. The long pain had begun again!

The drive to Springville was prosperous, though not by a great deal as gay as the drive northward. Beside the distress of separation, a serious depression seized Mrs. McVey, — dark, cloudy visions wherein were mingled Phil, and Dolly, and Annie, and herself, and Meg; all in inextricable turmoil and confusion.

As Zury said, "We slid up hill, and now we have to climb down!" He would often create a diversion in her sadness; usually by long and graphic details of the work Phil was to undertake for him in the spring on the Red Hill, at which time Mrs. McVey and Meg were to move to Galena and keep house for him.

"Mind ye keep a room fer o' man Prouder, too, 'cause he 'll be there or thereabouts; on hand, like a sore thumb!"

Mrs. McVey's low spirits were such that Zury's tact, small though it was, sufficed to show him that this was no time to renew his suit for her heart and hand. Perhaps, too, he would be restrained by an unconscious chivalry from doing so at the very moment when she felt herself under deep obligations to him for a great and precious service.

Anne, on her part, was sorely troubled in conscience, from time to time, by the thought that she was not rendering "value received" for the faithful and devoted attentions of her elderly admirer; especially his kind considerateness in not now urging the suit which it would seem so hard and cruel and ungrateful in her to refuse. She made heroic efforts to behave herself as she knew he would like to have her — to talk, to smile, to listen, to sympathize; and, of course, the effort to please him increased her liking for him.

Once when they were driving alone up a long hill, Margaret having alighted to secure a little of the exercise her strong muscles demanded, Anne opened the subject: —

"How selfish my low spirits make me! Here I don't say a word to you for hours together, Mr. Prouder!"

"Sorry ye ain't happy. But if *you* can stand bein' down on your luck, surely *we* oughter be able to stand it to let you take your time an' get over it your own way!"

"Oh, you 're spoiling me! You 're too good to me; taking all this trouble, and I wrapped up in my own gloomy fancies! I ought to be trying all the time to amuse you and interest you, and raise *your* spirits, never minding my own, good or bad!"

He answered, after a moment's pause, in a tone which was either fatherly or loverly, whichever you pleased, low and soft.

"Why, Anne Sparrow McVey, don't ye *know* ye ain't no call to do *anything* to please me? Not a thing? Jest bein' yourself, an' settin' there where I can see ye, an' sayin' a word I can hear when ye feel like it" —

Here his voice failed, and he leaned back and touched her shoulder. She took the hand, pulled off the loose coarse glove, and laid the knuckles, wrinkled and gray as they were, gently against her cheek; and then he took it back and kissed off the tear she had left on it.

When Meg got in again at the top of the hill, all flushed and refreshed, she cried, —

"Why, see! Mr. Prouder, you 've dropped your glove! Or did you do it on purpose to signify that you wanted to give me the mitten?"

"Thasso-thasso! Wal! How did that glove get down in the bottom of the sleigh to be sure!" And he pretended to pull it on with his teeth, but in reality was kissing the tear-spot once more, whereat Anne smiled to herself.

So they got back to Springville and to work again; the last a real blessing, as may well be imagined. Anne's book-keeping had been kept up for her, after a fashion; that is, the daily entries had been made, and only the occasional tasks left to await her return; monthly statements, trial balances and so forth. Her evenings for a month (with the able help Meg could give her) she felt were well spent in catching up and making atonement for the splendid month of idleness. Yet the intrusive cloud of melancholy kept hovering near.

"Shall I ever see my boy again?"

"Why not, mother?"

"Oh, I don't know, daughter; but shall I?"

"Very well, if you don't know why not, I'll take upon myself to answer. There is *no* reason why you should n't see your boy again — more times than you 've got fingers and toes, and hairs on your head besides! And you will! Now are you satisfied?"

"Oh, my darling, it 's a comfort to hear you say so, though I know you don't know any more about it than I do."

"Mother! Either you are sick, or you are *jealous!*"

"Jealous?"

"Yes, jealous of Annie Masten! You know you 'll see Phil McVey again, but you 're afraid he 'll be some other woman's boy and not yours any more. So you 're jealous!"

"No, no, Margaret! I am not such a hateful old woman as you try to make out."

"Well, what is it then? I declare, you make me nervous, too; you 're so unreasonable and so unlike yourself!"

"I should be delighted, or try to be, if Phil were to marry Annie. But if he is going to, why did n't he say a single word to his mother about it?"

"Because he is n't ready. When spring comes and he leaves the road and becomes a man and his own master, you 'll see!"

"Oh, dear! Will spring ever come to all of us, alive and well?"

"'Seed-time and harvest, and cold and heat, and summer and winter, and day and night, shall not cease.'"

"No, my child; but for me and my children they will all cease. I only hope they will pass away from me first — if that is not selfish. It is the natural order of things; and oh, if things will only follow in their natural order for me!"

"Mother, mother, *mother*, what shall I do with you if you are so naughty! 'Go read yer book,' as Mrs. Anstey used to say. I should be deeply grieved to be compelled to apply pankypank to my maternal parent and send her to bed in the day-time; but there is a point beyond which forbearance ceases to be a virtue!"

"Well, well, my love; I don't want to make you unhappy. I suppose I am a foolish, doting old woman, verging on my second childhood before I 'm fairly out of my first."

Then followed, of course, some family rites and ceremonies, oblations and genuflexions, wherein the old relations of mother and daughter were reversed; the younger being the comforter and the elder the comforted; or trying hard to "make believe" that she was.

On the day of their arrival once more at their little home, Prouder had left them and their trunk safely in the house, and started off to make perhaps half the journey from Springville to Wayback before night. He made a short matter of his farewell, for a variety of reasons. Their thanks were a burden to him, feeling as he did that he was the obliged party after all; and then, he wanted to make it gay, so as not to leave any additional sadness on poor Anne's spirit; and lastly, he could not trust himself to say much — bravado was his only escape from making a fool of himself, he thought.

But before he got a mile out of town he gave way. Could he bear it? That vacant seat behind him, where those two women had sat in his company for many days — the very straw their feet had broken and tumbled, still in the sleigh — and he there alone! Alone! Alone! He stopped the team, got out and got some snow to cool his eyes and forehead; then he got in again and started forward at a slow walk. He came to a turn in the road from which the town would be visible to him for the last time; rose in his place to give a farewell look; sat down again, and — turned the horses about and drove back to the hotel in time for supper.

What *could* he say to excuse his sudden reappearance at the widow's house? Well, he'd think of that on the way up. But on the way up he could n't think of anything; not a word. He leaned on the gate and watched the light behind the curtains for a long, long time, trying to distinguish between the shadows cast on them, so as to guess which was mother and which was daughter. At last common sense prevailed. He said to himself, —

"Zury, do you want to be here this evenin' an' no other nights to speak of? Or do ye wanter let 'em alone to-night with a chance to be with 'em day an' night for weeks, months, an' years? Take your choice, ol' man, right here an' right now! Ef she ever marries ye, it 'll be because ye 're Zury Prouder, an' not a driv'lin' ol' dotard! Ye dog-gone triflin' ol' fool — what ye doin' here anyway, a hangin' 'round a woman's house this time o' night, leanin' against her fence like a sick kitten to a hot brick? Get aout an' go home an' mind yer business! Then come an' see her like a man when she begins to think it 's high time for ye to show up!"

So he walked firmly back to the hotel; and early next day drove rapidly off to his own place without even a look behind him.

Not many days later, he stopped at the Ansteys on the way to Wayback. The old man was in arrears on his mortgage interest, as usual; and seeing Zury alight and tie his horse, left the bedside of his sick wife, and hurried to the gate to take the anticipated hard talk on money-matters, beyond her hearing, where it might have gone hard with her.

"Wal, brother Anstey! Haow 's th' o' woman!"

"Wal, she don't gain none." Then, hastily,

seeing that Zury was for pushing by him into the house, "I expect I know what ye 're after, Zury, 'n' maybe we mought 's well talk aoutside h'yer, whar th' o' woman won't be worried."

"'Course ye know what I come fer, 'n' th' o' woman wants t' know tew! Ain't I jes' ben up 'n' seen yer darter, 'n' yer gran'-childern; 'n 'nex' time er tew I come daown mebbe I 'll hev some stories t' tell ye 'baout yer great-gran's tew!"

How admirable he was in that sick chamber during the next hour! How his talk flowed in an even, distinct, familiar key, comforting and inspiring those two dull old parents! He gave them subjects of thought, and hope, and comfort, and even laughter, that made a new interest in their life, which could not die except with life itself.

He did not know he was doing anything particularly kind, nor did he do his kindness with intention. It was an impulse he would have had in him at any part of his life; but in his earlier, harder, more active days, such impulses were usually overslaughed, crushed, and killed by the stronger preoccupations of the greed of gain, and the ceaseless craving to "make every edge cut," whether of money, or property, or time. But now the husk was peeling off.

Old Anstey followed him to the gate to talk about the defaulted interest, which he did at a length no reader would tolerate, though Zury listened patiently. At last the latter said, —

"Brother Anstey, don't ye know what 's the matter with yer place 'n' allers hez be'n? Ye hain't kep' enough live stawk. Ye sol' yer craps instead o' feedin' 'em. Naow, ye see, h'yer 't is agin this year; yew 'n' yer boys 's got ter kill yerselves a-getherin', 'n' a-deliverin', 'n' a-sellin' yer stuff, jest when th' don't nobody wanter buy, not at no price!"

"Wal, but Zury, what's a man t' dew? I hain't no stawk, ner no money t' buy stawk; 'n' I hed t' mortgage my crap t' git money t' pay yer interest las' time, 'n' keep my fam'ly a-goin'— med'cine 'n' one thing another!"

Prouder smiled a grim smile and answered,—

"*I*'d a foun' some way t' git some stawk ontew the place in the las' twenty-five years! I'd a kep' every sow-pig th't was littered, n' matter ef I'd a had t' eat ther tails 'n' ears off whilst the' wuz a-breedin'! But that ain't nuther h'yer ner thar. I'm a-goin' t' take up that crap mortgage 'n' hold it fer ye, 'n' put in enough more cash t' hawg this place fer all it 'll carry; 'n' you 'n' the boys 's got t' feed 'em till spring, 'n'—then we 'll see!"

Old Anstey opened the gate and went out to where the other sat on his horse, impatient to do his kindness and be off to escape gratitude. Anstey went up close, without saying anything, till he had laid one hand on the horse's mane and the other on the rider's knee. Then he said,—

"Zury! D'ye mean it?"

"Noth'n' shorter!"

The old man broke down and cried with joy and relief; said he,—

"I thought this year was goin' t' take my wife 'n' my farm! God forgive me — I thought so! I 've conned over how mebbe Bijah 'n' his fam'ly could git t' work fer yew, 'n' Silas fer some o' th' neighbors; 'n' mebbe Reekie she could take the youngest t' Galeny, after th' ole mother 'd gone t' the grave 'n' th' ole dad t' the poorhaouse! I did! But naow — the day I see enough hawgs rootin' raound th' place t' eat up the crap instead o' sellin on it, I 'll say there is a God in Israel — 'n' Zury Praouder 's his minister. I will!"

"Sho! S'pose I 'm a-goin' t' see all the money you 've put inter this place, 'n' all the money I 've put in, lost fer want of a turn o' my hand? No, sirree! Th' ain't a-goin' t' be no foreclosin' morgidges h'yer! I 'm a-goin' to stawk up this place ontel I git my money outer it, — every dollar, principal 'n' interest! That 's what kind of a hairpin I am!"

And so disguising his benevolent scheme under the mask of a far-seeing selfishness, he galloped away, and as he went he asked himself, —

"Would she be pleased ef she knew 'baout that little stroke o' business? Would she? Would she?"

His heart glowed with the unspoken answer. Later he added, —

"Her Phil's wife's gran'f'ther in the poorhouse! *My* Phil's children's great gran'f'ther in the poorhouse! Mebbe-mebbe! But not while I 'm between him 'n' it!"

CHAPTER XXVI.

ANOTHER PROPOSAL AND ANOTHER ANSWER.

TIME, the voracious, swallows and digests griefs as well as joys. It is an unromantic fact, but a fact nevertheless, that every minute of separation tends toward indifference, the first as well as the last. It seemed to Anne and Meg that the longer they were parted from Phil, the more they loved him; but it was not so. The seeming, in such cases, is a false one. Rationally considered the matter is only a simple sum in proportion. When the mother and sister had been separated from Phil for a month, alienation, or consolation, or forgetfulness, or whatever name you give to time's kindly healing agency, had already begun. One is a proportionate part of a hundred in time, as well as in everything else; in heart matters as well as in mathematics.

The first evening when Zury Prouder presented himself at the McVey door found both mother and daughter very glad to see him.

"Well, well! It does seem kinder natural to see you two chummin' together so peaceable-like!"

"If you'd wanted to be really and truly friendly, you'd have come in time for tea! But you 're too proud to be wasting your time on two lone, lorn women!"

"Oh, I could n't well git 'round. Besides, I knew my name was n't in the pot."

"There's always enough in the pot for one more, when that one's a friend like you! We'd have gone hungry gladly for the pleasure of seeing you eat."

"'T would n't have been my pleasure to eat, and you hungry. But, come to think, I did have a ham left over, and it's out in the sleigh now. If ye don't mind eatin' a Wayback ham, to taste like old times, I'll fetch it in."

"Surely we'll eat it! Double pleasure it'll be, too! In the first place, it will be a tip-top ham if it came from the Prouder farm; and secondly, it 'll taste all the sweeter, knowing who gave it."

Zury flushed with pleasure as he went out for his simple gift, and wished it were a barrel-full.

"Dear, dear, Meg! To think of Zury Prouder's giving anything away for nothing!"

"You take care it turns out to be for nothing, mother. I'm getting scared!"

The widow only gave a little blushful laugh, which was n't quite gone when Zury got back.

"Oh, what a picture of a ham! That color is just like the finest coffee, made with rich cream!"

"Well! Sometimes ham's jest as good meat as Goddlemighty lets grow. More times it ain't only middlin'. It's all owin' to how ye cure 'em. The hawg always does his part all right; it's us poor humans that comes short of our part. I've got the boss receet for a dry pickle, but then ye don't get jest the finishin' touch unless ye 've got fresh-cut green hickory chips to smoke 'em with."

"I can smell the green hickory smoke in this, this minute."

"'Course ye can! All-fired sweet smell it is, too. The hickory bark in a woods-fire" — (here he checked himself.) "As I was sayin', my teams 'll be over for stuff from the store, and I can jest as well send ye a cord or two of hickory. Dry 'll suit ye best here, bein' ye hain't any hams to smoke."

"Oh, you 'll take so much care of us you 'll make us tender-footed! We shall forget our old lesson of how to get on by ourselves!"

"Well, ye might do worse th'n that, tew!"

"Now sit down, and tell us all about Wayback. How is Mrs. Anstey?"

"Best thing I can do is to repeat what o' man Anstey said to me as I passed his house this morning. 'Zury,' said he, 'it 's nip 'n' tuck with th' o' woman. Some days nip 'n' some days tuck. One spell kinder chipper, 'n' then agin downcy. Ef she kin live till spring, she may git well, but ef not, then I hain't much hope.' Now you ladies can make what you please out of that."

Meg could not help laughing, but Anne said, —

"Oh, if it were n't dear old Mrs. Anstey, I might laugh at the idea of giving up hope if she dies before spring!"

"Wal, I kept my face straight. I saw what he meant — that he had n't much hope of her living till spring."

"She's a dear old soul; whether she lives or dies I love her. How is brother Bromwell?"

"Omri Bromwell, he'll live to bury us all yet, you see 'f he don't! He ain't never a-goin' to die — he'll jest dry up and blow away."

"How's that little niece of your wife's that lives at your house?"

"Oh, Alphy, she's growed up, as a matter of course; an' *she's* beginnin' to take notice, too. Lived to my place ever since, and I heard she'd made a barrel of soft soap and bespoke one of my next litter of pups, so I s'pose she allows to marry, come spring."

"Is that a sign? When a girl makes a barrel of soap and gets a dog?"

"Yes, Margaret. Preparations for house-keepin', ye see. *You* hain't made no soap nor bespoke no dog yet, I don't expect?"

"No, nor I don't mean to! No such luck!"

"Oh, don't you get discouraged, not a mite. Me and Phil'll try an' provide the soap agin you pick out the feller."

"You need n't hurry."

"Speakin' of Phil, I shall be travelin' up north again, soon's the roads get settled. Anythin' ye want to send?"

"Oh yes, lots o' things. I've got a pair of mittens knit for him."

"See ye don't give no mittens to no feller except yer brother!"

"I'll never have the chance."

"Can't most always tell! The' say red hair's comin' in fashion."

"Is that so! Yes, I've heard something of that kind, and I only wish it would hurry and come true!"

"Oh, ye do, do ye? Ye own up at last! First time I ever heard ye let on ye was a woman!"

"To be sure! Just as soon as red hair comes in fashion, do you know what I'm going to do?"

"Marry the President, I s'pose. Yo'll surely be entitled to!"

"Wrong for once! I'm going to cut mine all off and sell it!"

"You, sho! How much'll ye take for it?"

"Ten dollars."

"And let the buyer do what he has a mind to with it?"

"Just exactly."

"It's a whack! Here's your ten dollars — the hair's mine — now ye keep it jest where it is, an' mind ye take good care of my hair!" And he selected a nice, *clean* ten-dollar-bill and thrust it at her.

"Nonsense! I take it all back! My hair isn't for sale."

They had quite a little scuffle, he trying to force the bill upon her, and she persistently and deftly returning it into some one or other of his numerous pockets as fast as he could get rid of it.

"Oh, ye think ye're mighty strong, don't ye? Now look here!" And he grasped her two elbows from behind and lifted her clear off the ground.

"Oh-set-me-down-set-me-down! I give in!"

"You 're a witness, Mis McVey."

"Yes," cried Anne, much amused.

"The hair 's mine, to dew what I have a mind to with."

"Yes, yes! Oh yes, set me down."

"Very well, then," and he set her down and planted a kiss right in the thickest part of his new purchase.

"Mercy, my! Is that the way men do, mother?"

"I 'm afraid they do, my dear, when they get a good chance."

"You bet they do, Margaret! Only usially they 're younger, as ye 'll find out when ye get older!"

"Never! I 'll never sell my red hair except to a gray-haired man!"

"Glad ye liked the trade so much ye don't want any change."

Meg laughed, and soon left the room to attend to household matters or re-arrange her ruffled plumage.

"Oh, Mr. Prouder," said Anne, "I have something to send Phil by you — some advice. I wish Phil would n't go back to the Sanderses to live."

"What 's the matter with Dolly Sanders?"

"Nothing in the world. But I don't like her, and I think she does n't like Annie Masten."

"Ever hear of her sayin' anythin' about her?"

"Nothing that I know of, good or bad."

"Hmm-hmm-hmm — lessee, lessee. Did Dolly know Phil before she married Jim Sanders?"

"No."

"How long 's she known him?"

"Only since Phil went up to Chicago."

"Hmm-hmm-hmm! Jesso-jesso. Well, a woman like you usially jumps right, even ef she *does* jump in the dark. I 've got to carry up a pup to Dolly that I promised her, an' I'll see how the land lays."

"I can't see why there should be any trouble about it. Just let him stay away."

"Wal, now, ye know as well as I do that there *is* some trouble about it, er else ye would n't be askin' me to 'tend to it for ye. Ye 'd jest write Phil yourself what ye want."

"Well, of course, I 'm not on the ground, as you will be."

"'Course Jim Sanders don't allow to keep up that establishment alone!"

"Then let Dolly find some other mother's son to board there, and let my son alone."

"Mobbe she hain't got all the lettin' alone t' dew."

Anne's forefinger tapped on her teeth nervously in the old "puzzlementary gesture," her foot beating on the carpet, but she did not reply.

"Phil ain't a feller to let women alone much."

Still the silence and the small tapping boot-toe.

"Well, I 'll see about it. One way strikes me might work. I 'm cal'latin' to have right smart of work done at the railroad shops in Galeny, an' the foreman there, him an' me is thicker 'n three-in-a-bed. Now he might work it so that Phil's engine sh'd run into Chicago days an' double back nights, an' then lay over twenty-four hours. Day on an' day off, ye see. Mighty convenient fer me, too, 'cause after Phil got to bed of a mornin' he could n't sleep much longer than noon, and then him an' me can put in th' afternoon on the hill."

"Oh, that would be splendid! You are the best planner in the world, I do believe!"

"Ye would n't mind his spendin' his evenin's at the preacher's?"

"No," replied Anne, with one of those little jealous sighs.

"Oh, he 'd learn lots of theology at the preacher's! Predestination an' free-will, savin' grace, original sin, an' etarnal love — specially love — what he would n't know in a month ain't worth knowin'!"

"I suppose he 'd learn fast."

"'Baout love? Larn an' teach. It would be in a line where he 's pretty well edicated already, if I 'm a judge! Fact is, I guess he was born so — though I do' know where he could have inherited it from! Some is born so — some ain't. I did n't never think I 'd oughter have been, nor wish I had been, until now."

"Oh, you mean" —

"Yes, that 's jest what I do mean! I know I 'm old to be thinkin' of such things, but I shan't never be any younger. And if I do think of 'em it 's your fault, not mine. No other woman don't never put 'em into my head — nor never will."

Anne knitted on in silence and made no sign to the yearning eyes of her old lover. When he spoke again his voice sounded thin and far away with the dry tension in his throat.

"Don't ye go to send me off again, Miss McVey — don't do it! It 'most killed me before. Young folks can turn from one thing to another, but old folks — I know I'm rough, and ignor'nt, and no gentleman, and all that; but I hain't forgot how to learn, and I 'm so fixed in this world's goods that I don't need to do anythin' else for the little time I 've got to stay — and your word shall be law to me and mine — I 'll only go my own way until I see ye don't like it, and then I 'll go your way until I can make ye think my way 's better — if it is, which ain't likely."

Tears began running down Anne's cheeks, but Zury's eyes were too dim to see them.

"I don't say nothin' about the money — only all ye want shall be yours without havin' to ask for it. And I 'll try never to save another cent, not if I can help it. I 'll make what I can with Phil, but not by skimpin' and parin' and jewin'. Not if I can help it. Though it 'll be hard fer a hand that 's always been used to doin' *so*" (he made a motion as if picking up a handful of grain) "to learn to turn round and do *so*" (and he loosed the phantom grain and let it drop). But I can do it! I can do it! I never failed in anythin' I undertook yet, — only one, — and I don't give that one up! Had I better, Miss McVey? Anne, *had* I better?"

Anne had laid down her knitting, and sat covering her wet eyes with her hand. After two or three minutes she said, —

"We'll see after we get up to Phil's new home on the Red Hill — if we ever get there."

"Oh, thank the Lord for all his mercies, and all that is within me bless the Lord!"

Zury spoke once more in his natural voice: the tension in his throat was gone as if by magic. He rose as he spoke and went gently over to where Anne sat, and bending down kissed her hair, just as he had kissed her daughter's. It was silky yet, and only paled with gray; red hair is apt to be so instead of streaked and silvered as black hair becomes.

If she had been younger she would have raised her face to his. If he had been younger he would have bent down his face to hers, but, being elderly folks, they discreetly parted without any further visible tenderness. Zury went his way out into the darkness and Anne hastened to find Margaret. The poor girl was crying as if her heart would break.

"Oh, mother, mother!"

This was all she could say, but it spoke volumes for the bruised soul, chilled away from the natural joys and loves and sympathies of her age and sex, and now threatened with separation from the one love which she had fondly thought would be to her, through life, a full equivalent for all she must forego of human hopes and blessedness. It seemed somewhat as if a mother-bird should push away from the parental nest a poor fledgling which had come into the world with only one wing! It must fall to the ground and die alone at the foot of the tree while all its happy kind were flying high and free, and the mother had filled the nest with others.

"My sweet daughter! Come rest in my arms once more — *so*. Now what was it Ruth said to Naomi?"

"'Entreat me not to leave thee, nor to return from following after thee.'"

"Well, my daughter; 'Whither thou goest, I will go.' Now, you say the next."

"'Where thou lodgest I will lodge.'"

"'Thy people shall be my people.'"

"'And thy God, my God.'"

"Now, darling, listen to your mother while she vows a vow. 'The Lord do so to me and more also, if aught but death part me and thee.'"

And so they went to bed and to sleep. Margaret slept with her mother that night so that they could keep their hands clasped in sleep as of old.

Prouder did not stagger on his way back to the hotel, as once before on the same road; or if he did, it was not with despair, but rather with the intoxication of hope.

At the warehouse, three days later, Anne found two letters; one from Phil, which she, of course, opened first; though the long business-like envelope of the other was rather alluring. Phil's news was fresh, bright, gay, like himself; and what was better, it breathed *goodness*, and steady devotion to his best self — and to "the Mastens."

Now, what could be in the other? Zury's rugged handwriting — that was unmistakable. A letter and a printed something.

The latter was a certificate for two hundred shares ($100 each) of stock in the Springville Gas Company, issued to Usury Prouder, and indorsed by him to Anne McVey. The letter read: —

WAYBACK, ILL., *January* 21, 185-

MRS. ANNE McVEY, — I hand you inclosed 200 shares of S. G. C. stock. This stock pays regular ten per cent. in cash, and ten per cent. more or less in stock to represent new extensions laid out and paid for from the surplus earnings. I hope you will find it a good investment, and remain, Yours respectfully,

U. PROUDER.

Anne laughed and blushed, and nearly cried at the striking evidence of the power of her elderly charms. Here she was, "fair-and-forty" at least, but there must be something about her such as, in her girlhood, she had fondly hoped to possess — some quality that might take hold of a strong man with a strength to which his strength would be but child's-play!

She erased the indorsement and mailed the shares back to their owner, with a letter not quite as formal and business-like as his, but still somewhat in the same line.

SPRINGVILLE, ILL., *January* 23, 185–.

USURY PROUDER, Esq.

DEAR SIR, — I did not intend, when I talked with you last night, to indicate a final purpose to purchase the kind of stock received by your letter of to-day. I was glad to hear from you, and hope to see you soon, when we will talk over the matter and others of interest that may arise. Meanwhile, I beg leave to return the certificate you inclosed, and hope it may continue as profitable an investment in the future as in the past.

Yours very truly,

ANNE S. MCVEY.

Then, fearing that Zury would not "read between the lines," she added a postscript.

P. S. — As to the other matters we spoke of, I am still of the same mind. Please call when convenient. A. S. MCV.

As Anne feared, Zury was dreadfully taken aback at seeing the inclosure fall out of her letter when he opened it — his gift rejected — perhaps his lady turned against him! But a great sigh of relief and gladness swelled his heart when he read the letter and postscript. Now, once more he wrote to Anne, and re-inclosed the much indorsed and much traveled gas-stock.

WAYBACK, *January* 25, 185–.

DEAR MADAM, — I know my own mind for sure, and that it will never change. You don't know it for sure — therefore I hope you will not refuse me to make the arrangement I have decided to make. I return the papers, and, live or die, I never want to see them again.

Your obedient servant,

U. PROUDER.

This was carrying persistency too far; but how to check it without needless pain to the poor rich man? Well, she must use all her tact.

SPRINGVILLE, *January* 27, 185–.

DEAR MR. PROUDER,—As you perhaps know, or will some day find out, I have a terrible temper, and one that is hard to control when aroused. Do not disturb it by sending back this stock any more. I have no present use for it; and if any future occasion should arise, *then* I will put my temper in my pocket — and the shares, too.

Now, to turn to a subject we shall not disagree about, — when are you coming to see us?

Yours very truly,

ANNE S. MCVEY.

"Gee-whillikins! Ain't she a woman for gettin' a man down, and keepin' him down!" But, even as he said this, he chuckled with delight at her masterful ways, and enjoyed his feeling of entire helplessness before her. To talk with her by letter was so delightful that he almost dreaded to see her again, for fear he should wake up from a dream, or in some other way come to grief.

But he ventured into the effulgence of the cottage, after a while, and was only moderately sobered and set back when Anne reminded him that she had as yet promised nothing save that they would *see* when they all got together at Galena — if they ever did.

"Wal, jest as you say. But ye can't prevent me I'm kinder lookin' out for ye a leetle — s'posin in case I was to be taken — I'm li'ble t' die any day 's well 's other folks — or suth'n' else sh'd befall to keep things from turnin' out as I'm hopin'."

"Oh, you may look out all you like, only you must not *do* a thing — not a thing — in that direction. It would seem like a yoke on my neck; and whenever I feel *that*, it will be time for me to lie down and die!"

"Oh, there ain't no fear of you not keepin' your independence! I mistrust the trouble 'll be for me to keep mine; or get it back, I should say, for I'm blamed if it ain't clean gone now!"

"Well, you must get it back if you want to please me. We must both be independent, all our lives."

"How d' ye mean — independent?"

"Oh, I hardly know how to explain it. One reason why we have hitherto got on so well, — *usually*, — is that neither has had any power or authority over the other; neither has had to ask the other for money or for anything else. And that is the way it must go on. Don't you think so?"

Zury was a little crestfallen and did not reply.

"You see, after you got tired of me, it would make me angry to have to ask you for — anything. And such a temper as I have!"

"Ya-as — I know all abaout that, and I respect ye for it tew. But when I want to make ye independent regardin' money, ye wun't hear nothin' of it!"

"Well, it's too soon! As I have before said, we'll see when we get up to the Red Hill."

So the very next day the crafty Zury went to the bank and deposited in the vault the certificate of Gas Company Stock, indorsed again to Anne, inclosed in a sealed envelope, marked, "This to be opened by the cashier in case I die before reclaiming it. U. Prouder."

Time flies, with a hop-skip-and-jump, between this chapter and the next: things occur which belong to another story rather than this; but there comes no change in the strong man's unwearied docility and devotion, or in the beloved woman's gradually thawing reserve; and her growing gratitude, esteem, affection, love.

CHAPTER XXVII.

A LAST LOOK AT THE PROUDER FARM.

We picked up our homespun thread at the Prouder section: we followed it in its windings, knots, and twists to the school, the woods-fire, the riot, the stump, the polls, the machine-shop, the mines, and many scenes beside. Now, a whole generation later (well on in "the Fifties"), it leads us back to the very place we started from.

Usually it is a sad thing to see old friends again, after long years have changed them beyond recognition. But sometimes that which is uncouth and sordid in youth is lovely in age. This happens oftener in a frontier locality of these days than at any other place of earth or age of time. It has happened to the Prouder homestead. When we first saw it, it was the abode of toil and hardship — poor in money, comfort, grace, gayety, leisure, cultivation, refinement, liberality. Now (though so many years later, yet still in the same man's lifetime) all these things have grown and clustered about it like flowers and fruits about a lonely rock. Nature's prodigal soil and man's prodigal labor have worked (like coral insects) to make a lovely island where was before a pathless waste.

We will begin with the oldest object visible on the place — the log-house, so hastily yet solidly built by Ephraim and his son, as a shelter into which they might unload the few "sticks of furniture" they had wagoned all the way from Pennsylvania in their "prairie schooner," and which served as the first living-place for the builders' family.

"The "clapboard" roof, or its scanty remains, have disappeared. A professional English thatcher, who had settled in the neighborhood, has covered the hovel with a regular old-world thatch; a thing of soft outlines and overhanging eaves. What a dignity the tumble-down shanty at once took on when this classic top-finish was put on it! It was as when the Lord Chancellor's time-honored powdered wig is donned by a common-place barrister; at once he becomes, in looks at least, the worthy successor of the long line of jurists who have occupied the woolsack, — of Bacon, Lyndhurst, Eldon. The log-shanty was a hovel no longer, but a croft, a grange, a farmstead — a thing to draw in pencil, to paint in oil, to photograph. Moss and flowers, and patches of thrifty greenery, planted themselves in all the places where they could add to its beauty and show themselves off to the best advantage — the vain things!

Then, the roof being thus made far better than it had ever been in its best days, the walls were made far worse in a house-builder's view: the "chinking" was completely removed (it had already largely removed itself), and the free air and light of heaven thus allowed unobstructed ingress and egress; so that the structure was thenceforth a cool and shady summer-house; a nesting-place for pigeons and swallows, and the favorite play-house for dogs, cats, and other household pets.

The "girdled forty" next behind has given place to "the best orchard in all Illinois," and a kitchen garden has been added which serves as a supply to the residents of this farm, and as an educator to all the other farms and their owners, showing them what variety of good eatables is available to the granger in lieu of the everlasting "pork 'n' taters" of the pioneer.

But what has come over the later board palace that used to be so hopelessly hideous? It is still there; but so hidden in its own improvements as to be utterly unrecognizable. Its whole south side is occupied by a greenhouse and hot-house glorious to behold, opening out on a flower-garden worthy of it; all showing by inherent signs that they are the delight of some ladylike soul, aided by a gentlemanlike purse.

The side of the house that looks toward the forest has burgeoned out into a kitchen and laundry, fit to make the housework of the family almost a delight instead of a hardship, supplemented as they are by a tall wind-mill and high tanks, which keep the house supplied with water both hard and soft. At a little distance, half buried in the lawn, stands a gas-house—still quite a novelty in country places.

But the "feature" of the mansion is an eighteen-feet-wide piazza that runs entirely around the remaining two sides of the old square structure; in some places latticed for climbing plants, and elsewhere open for sun and air; connected with the interior rooms by great glazed doors opening to the floor, instead of windows; in short, the coolest, warmest, most breezy, most sheltered place that ever a favored child was turned loose into to be happy in.

Now to give the finishing-touch to the whole picture; the final chord to the sonata; the key-stone to the arch; the crown to the work; the signature to the indenture; the moral to the tale, and the point to the moral.

On the great porch hangs a hammock, deeply depressed by a short, solid weight in its middle. At one extremity of the heavy bundle may be observed a mass of fiery red curly hair; at the other, a pair of stout little legs almost equally red — and curly. Above and around the sleeper hangs, in gauzy folds, a mosquito netting, stretched over an umbrella-like frame, suspended by a cord that passes over a pulley in the ceiling and comes down to a fastening within convenient reach.

As we look, there occurs a stirring in the precious little bundle: arms and legs seem to resume accustomed activity after unaccustomed quiet. At the first sound, a matronly figure steps quickly and gracefully out from one of the open doors, goes to the fastened cord and pulls the mosquito net up to the roof. By this time two fat hands have grasped the sides of the hammock, and a handsome, blue-eyed boy-face is raised with difficulty above the edge.

"I ront my poppa."

"Here's mamma. Does n't Willie want his mamma?"

"No. I ront my poppa."

"Papa is gone out on the farm."

"Gone yidin'?"

"Yes. Shall mamma take Willie up?"

"Yidin' on P'ince?"

"Yes; riding on Prince. But mamma is here."

"I ront t' go yidin' on P'ince."

"Papa will take you when he comes home. Now, does n't Willie want to come with mamma?"

"No."

"Does n't Willie love his dear mamma?"

"No. I ront my sisty Med."

"Sister Meg is in Springville."

"At the bid house?"

"Yes; at the big brick house. Now come and play with mamma."

"I ront—tumbody."

"There is n't anybody else, my darling."

"Yes; is too! Tumbody else."

"No, my blessing; just papa and mamma, and Sister Meg and Willie. There ought to be somebody else, but there is n't."

"What 'oo tyin' for?"

"I 'm crying because there is n't anybody else. Now come and kiss poor mamma!"

"No. I ront Sep."

"Well, Willie shall have dear old Shep." She whistled clear and shrill, and lo, lumbering along with awkward alacrity, comes a ludicrously exact reproduction of the pristine Shep — he of chapter first. All things else have changed since we first saw them, because they have endured: he alone is the same, because he has died repeatedly. Individuals alter, but types are perennial.

Shep is the patient, docile, and long-suffering attendant on his young master. He seems to recognize the fact that to play with the boy is his most valid excuse for existence. The mother leaves the two playmates and returns to her book; and soon there is a long row of blocks, wheeled rabbits, Noah's ark, tail-less and head-less animals, and other heterogeneous accessories, tied by a string to the collar of the dog, and being dragged about the piazza in large curves; the boy leading the locomotive power, and adding to his duties as engine-driver the more onerous task of making the "choo-choo-choo" and the long "hoooooot" as the train approaches its stations.

Now the sound of an approaching wagon is heard; not a rattle of wheels by any means, but the slow, creaking noise of a farm-vehicle moved by horses more accustomed to drag the laboring plow than to turn the festive wheel.

"Why, of all people in the world, here come the Ansteys! Jule! Jule! Run and take care of Uncle Anstey's team. Drive up to the step-blocks, Uncle Anstey. There, that's right!" And as snowy-headed Jule took the horses by the bridles with needless care, Anne helped the old, old woman out and down, and kissed her heartily, while the old man drove on to look for his beloved Zury.

"Wal, wal! The Lord bless 'n' presarve ye, Anne Praouder! I did n' never 'llaow t' git s' fur f'm home agin — not till I 'm carr'd feet-foremost. But I 'd heered sech wonders 'baout ye, 'n' yer haouse, 't I 'llaowed I 'd jes' try 'n' ketch a glimpse o' heaven on th' yarth, in case I should n't never git t' see it nowher's else."

"Heaven! You! Well, I tell you, Aunty Anstey, I never want to go there if it 's a kind of place where your kind of folks are n't wanted! But how well you look. Here, sit down and rest."

"Ya-as: a feller he come along by th' haouse 'n' had s'm stuff 't he as't a dollar a bottle fer; 'n' seein' it come so high I knowed it must be good; 'n' he jest called fer a spune 'n' gimme a dose right then 'n' thar — did n' tax me a cent fur it. 'N' then I 'xplained tew him 's haow I wuz a pledged total abstainer, 'n' could n't take no sperrits, not t' save my life; 'n' he larfed, 'n' 'llowed th' war n't no sperits in this, only jest enough t' cut the sensual iles of the rewts it wuz made of; 'n' arter I tuk the fust swaller he did n't have t' wait five minutes by th' sun afore he hed his dollar 'n' I hed a bottle. It 's t' be took afore eatin' 'n' arter eatin', 'n' afore sleepin' 'n' arter sleepin', 'n' wunst-in-a-while between-times. I fetched it along in case ye sh'd be anyways ailin' — yew er the babe — 'n' sh'd like t' try it."

The old soul produced a large, dark, square, high-shouldered, suspicious looking bottle, and drew the cork; whereupon a strong smell of alcohol pervaded all that part of Spring County. Anne studied the label, and made a pretense of committing to memory the name and address, but declined to take a dose on the spur of the moment, or to administer one to her little one.

"Ain't ther' noth'n' the matter on him, 't a dose *mought* knock?"

"Not a thing in the world! He 's just perfection, body and soul!"

"Wal, he dew look pootty peart. Still, ye can't tell b't what the' *mought* be suth'n' jes' a-comin' on th't this 'd knock ef took in time. Thet 's th' gret thing — t' take remedies in time. Lemme jes' look at his tongue. Come h'yar, sonny, 'n' see yer ol' gran'-mom fer a spell!"

Thereupon the train started for the most distant corner of the veranda, turning round an unusually short curve with a suddenness that laid Noah's Ark, rabbit, two horses, and an elephant, flat on their sides, in which condition they were compelled to make the rest of the trip, by the urgent necessity of escaping from the old lady.

"Oh, Mrs. Anstey, you don't know how well he is! And so bright! And so loving! Why, it was only a week ago last Friday, about this time in the afternoon, or a little earlier, when he woke up from his afternoon nap, he kissed me without my asking him to!"

"Dew tell! I wanter know!" The old woman spoke with civil hypocrisy, for she could in no wise comprehend or sympathize with such sentimental ecstasy. Thereupon Anne went on at great length, expatiating on the glories and beauties of the new miracle of humanity — a theme older and more wonderful than that commonly known as "the old, old story."

"Naow Mis Sparrer — McVey — Praouder, I should say — ef ye 'll gimme a spune I 'll jes' take a spunefle, 'n' I want yer t' show me some o' them things I heerd tell on. Th' dew say 's haow ye jes' hev t' go t' th' wall 'n' turn a handle, 'n' th' hot water 'll pour aout; 'n' turn another, 'n' th' col' water 'll pour aout; 'n' turn another 'n' th' rume 'll heat up afore ye kin say Jack Robison; 'n' turn another 'n' ye hev a light 'thaout no lamp ner candle."

"Surely, Aunty! I 'll show them all to you." And she went to the wall and pulled a bell-rope.

"Wha' 'd ye dew then? Did ye turn a handle then?"

"No. I just pulled this, and it has a wire that reaches one of the bells in the kitchen — there 's a whole line of bells, one marked 'parlor' and one marked 'door' and so on. This one is marked 'porch' — and here comes Sarah. Sarah, bring a tablespoon, please, for Mrs. Anstey."

"Lawzee suz, and sakes alive! That thar gal 'll dew anythin' ye tell her tew, I s'pose! Ef ye wuz t' tell her t' git right daown on her han's 'n' knees 'n' scrub the floor, I s'pose she 'd jes' up 'n' dew it! No relation o' yourn, nuther, is she?"

"No relation that I know of; but indeed she would do anything I asked her, — and gladly, too! Why she scrubs this floor every day without any telling, if it needs it! She is very fond of me — and I am of her. All I fear is that she 'll marry soon, and I shall lose her; and all the reason why she does n't, is simply that she hates to leave me."

"Sakes alive! Haowdy, Sarey, haowdy!" (shaking hands as she takes the spoon.) "I 'm pleased t' make yer 'quaintance. I 'm ol' Mis Anstey 't lives daown in th' bottom timber. Mebbe ye heerd tell o' me. Be ye pootty peart?"

The smiling Sarah confessed that she was quite well.

"Naow, Sarey, ef you 'll jes' wait a half a minute I 'll give ye the spune agin." And the old woman poured out her dose with trembling hands, and at the same time poured forth praises of the medicine — which also breathed out its own charms loudly on the circumambient air.

"'N' Sarey, ef ye 'd like t' try a dose on it ye 're heartily welcome! Ye dunno whut it mought cure ye of — er keep ye fr'm hevin'."

Sarah gratefully declined and departed with the spoon, while Anne carefully shut the lattice gates designed to keep the youngest scion of the Prouder race from rolling down the steps. Then they began the tour of the house, the good old soul's spirits being raised and her tongue loosened by her "medicine."

First the drawing-room.

"Oh naow, Anne Praouder, yew jes' git aout! Ef thar ain't yew 'n' Zury a-hanging agin the wall jes' like the 'd ben a lynchin' — only the gold frames! Ha-ans'm! Yum-yum —! Ye 'd better believe it! Wal, of all and of all! I'd jes' love t' set h'yer all day 'n' look at ye, ye pootty creeter!" and she caressed Anne's hand affectionately. "Jes' look at the eyes on 'em! They mus' be fixed so 's t' turn raound somehaow — ther' looks jes' follers me wherever I go! *An'* the books! Hev yew read all them books? No wonder ye 're so all-fired smart!"

"Now look over there in the corner by the window, Aunt Anstey. That 's Mr. Prouder's desk; look at the little picture hanging above it."

"Fer the land's sake, the picter ye did of the ol' log-shanty 'n' the new frame haouse when ye wuz a-boardin' raound! Don't it look old-timey though? I s'pose ye keep that t' remind Zury haow humble he started aout! Wal, it 's all turned aout fer th' best, thank the Lord! But them wuz pootty measly times!"

"No, he thinks more of that than of any other picture we have in the house, and he *says* it 's because those were the blessed days when he first met Anne Sparrow!"

"Dooz, dooz he? Wal, I 'm glad he hez the sense t' recognize his chiefest heavenly marcy! He wuz a pootty poor speciment in them days, 'n' would a be 'n so yet ef it had n't a be 'n fer yew!"

Next came the bath-room, for the "handles"

that governed the hot and cold water had taken the strongest hold on the imagination of the old household care-taker.

"There, Aunty, just turn that one, and you 'll see how it works."

"I 'm a leetle afeared — ye know I ain't uster sech things — haow much shell I turn it? — thar! Sakes alive see it come, see it come, see it come! 'N' pours right daown inter th' tub! No waitin' till some arternoon when ye 've got time. No well-sweep, ner yit a windlass, ner yit a pump; 'n' no carr'in th' bucket, 'n' fillin' th' kittle, 'n' choppin' s'm wood, 'n' startin' th' fire, 'n' waitin' till it biles, 'n' then huntin' th' holder, 'n' takin' on it off, 'n' pourin' it in th' wash-tub, 'n' then — cleanin' yerself 'n' throwin' th' slops aouter winder."

"No! You just take your bath and then pull this chain; see? All the water runs down the drain-pipe into the garden-pit."

"Wal, I thank the Lord I lived t' see this day!"

Then the glories of the spacious, well-appointed kitchen, with its clean, leisurely maids, were duly honored. Then the bed-rooms, palatial in the visitor's eyes. Then the gas was turned on and lighted, and the heating apparatus shown off. Then the green-house and garden furnished new occasion for exclamations of delight. But, last of all, the old woman wanted to see once more the hot and cold water pour out of "holes in the wall" — that appealed most strongly of all to her love of the wonderful.

"When matches fust come in, I thought it wuz a merikle t' jest scrape a little cold stick 'n' hev a fire right off. Then when a guerryotyper come along 'n' tuk my ol' man so it seemed 's though he 'd jes' looked in th' glass 'n' th' image hed struck in 'n' stuck thar — thet wuz another. Then the railroad come along. But this beats 'em all. Ye jus' turn th' handle, so-fashion, 'n' thar ye be! Yes — I thank the Lord!"

"I tell you what, Mrs. Anstey, you must come and stay with me, and then you shall get to know all these things."

"Oh, it 's enough fer me t' see 'em all 'thaout a-usin' on em! I don't wonder Sarey don't wanter quit sech a place! I sh'd think ye could n't dog her away! If I wuz her no man could n't persuade me t' marry him 'n' go; no, ner come within forty rows of apple-trees of it, nuther! Not if he wuz as rich as Julius Cæsar!"

At another time she did make the proposed visit, and took her first "tub." Anne knocked at the door to ask if she had everything she needed; and she replied: "I 've got in, at last; 'n' I feel jest like I wuz a-floatin' in th' claouds o' heaven!"

When old Anstey left his wife with Anne, he drove forward to have some talk with Zury. His mare (aet. twenty), with the discretion born of years of reflection, allowed her end of the double-tree to lie back as far as it would go; whence it arose that her single-tree was almost worn in two by the wheel. At the same time her mate "the colt" (aet. twelve), in all the enthusiasm of youth, pressed forward regardless of her expostulatory bites, and was always a yard in advance of his mother.

Zury was at the "bottom field," a patch adjoining the river, known throughout the region as a marvel of unfailing fertility. Those bottoms are of Nile-like formation and productiveness. Whatever drought prevails, there is always "corn in Egypt." The only drawback is that every two or three years the river rises and carries away fences, sheds, stacks, and all other adjuncts of farming from all the "bottom fields," excepting of course those appertaining to the Prouder farm, where there are no loose properties allowed; the fences and sheds being held up by stakes set deep in the ground below the yielding surface.

"Wal, Uncle Anstey! That can't never be you, can it?"

"Ya-as; it's me yet awhile Zury. Not fer long though—not fer long."

"Oh, you sho!" rejoined the younger man, pressing his horse close to the wagon and leaning forward for the accustomed hand-shake. "You're good t' bury me yet! I ollers 'llowed fer ye t' be one o' my bearers."

"Wal, not hardly, Zury. I'm workin' on borry'd time—twelve years on borry'd time last March."

"Borry'd time?"

"Ya-as; I used up my three-score-'n'-ten more ner twelve years ago: be'n a livin' 'aout some other feller's leavin's sence that."

"Oh, I see! Wal, the' 's a plenty o' fellers

drunk 'emselves t' death, 'n' fooled away the'r health th' way yew never did, t' leave years 'n' years a-layin' 'raound loose — more 'n you 'n' me 'll ever need."

"Thasso-thasso, friend Rice! But yew look likely t' to use up a big slew on 'em, Zury! Never seen a man grow young th' way yew be'n a dewin'! Sakes alive! Mus' be suth'n th' same way ol' Solomon wuz kep' alive, 'cordin' t' th' Scripters! He-he-he!"

"Wal, wal; if happiness can do a man good, I'd oughter be pootty healthy. All th't heart can wish! Makes me tremble sometimes when I think how any changes mus' be fer the wuss! All th't heart can wish!"

"Glad on it, Zury. Glad ye don't want into Congress ner noth'n'."

"Why, ef I thought Anne would care to have me go: what is there about political matters jest now, anyhow?"

"Wal, t' tell ye the truth, Zury, 'course lots on us 'll work fer ye 's long 's ye say th' word. But I don't give ye no spesh'l incouridgement."

"Why, what 's the matter?"

"Wal, it 's this-a-way." (Here the old man became visibly embarrassed.) "Th' fellers suspish'n ye, 'n' yer wife tew, fr'm some things the' 've observed, of bein' — mind the' don't all lean that-a-way, but some dooz — 'n' I ain't no ways pards with them as dooz — ner I wun't go fer t' name them as dooz, fer mebbe they 'm a-actin' up t' the'r lights, 'n' I kin disagree with 'em 'thaout a-blamin' on 'em — fer who am I th't I sh'd set up fer t' jedge 'em" —

Here the old man paused as if loath to break the awful charge to the man against whom it was harbored, perhaps with cruel injustice.

"Out with it, Uncle Anstey! I 've got to stand it I suppose. And I can stand it if they can. But let 'em look out before they whisper a word agin Anne — agin my wife! The man don't walk the footstool who can do that and not be sorry for it! Him that tries it on must take the consequences!"

As he spoke his face darkened and hardened in drawn level lines till it looked like a mask of Vengeance carved in Scotch granite. This look was accompanied by one that spoke an old pain, regret, mortification, shame, remorse.

"Oh, the' don't blame yew no more 'n her, ner her no more 'n yew, on'y she bein' a woman, 'n' comin' fr'm Bosting; the' c'nsider that an excuse. 'N' then, as t' the consekences, th' hoss-shedders don't scare wuth a cent. *Yew* know *that!*"

"Any man th't reaches his hand towards her; he better consider consequences! They 'll foller him! He wun't get shet of 'em this side o' kingdom come!"

"The fellers, ner the'r wives nuther, don't give a continental fer no consekences; a-sayin' whut the' think 's so!"

"Wal, out with it; wha' 'd they 'llow?"

"'Course ye wun't harbor no hard feelin's agin me fer a-bringin' on it t' yer knowledge?"

"Nary a mite."

"I mebbe wrong, but I 'm a doin' on it fer th' best. I'm a doin' 's I 'd be done by. Ef folks wuz t' git up 'n' talk agin' me 'n' my ol' woman the' way the' dooz agin yew 'n' yewrs—though I don't expect the' 'd ever pick on us fer anythin' that-a-way"— And he laughed uneasily.

"No; not likely."

"But ef so be the' should, why I 'd take it t' be th' part of a ol' friend t' up 'n' aout with it—spit it right aout, hit er miss."

"Yes, yes," groaned Zury. "Do it! Say it! Spit it out! I expect I can stand it."

"Wal, ef ye will hev it, h'yer goes,—

"THE' 'LLAOW YE 'RE A-PUTTIN' ON SCOLLOPS."

He paused to observe the crushing effect of this awful indictment; almost the most hopelessly fatal that can be found against any Western political aspirant. Treason, arson, homicide,—even horse-stealing could scarcely be worse! Great was his consternation at Zury's way of receiving the deadly blow. The accused smiled, grinned, chuckled, laughed, and even roared with amusement and relief. In all their long acquaintance Anstey had never seen his strong, cool friend in such a transport of merriment. It may be doubted if any one had—if Zury himself could look back on another such outburst.

"Whut tickles ye, Zury? Whut's the matter? Be ye crazy, er whut? Be ye perpared t' deny whut the' say, 'n' prove it on 'em?"

"Deny what they say? That 's owin' t' what

the' dew say. Ye hain't told me yet. What's the specifications?"

"Why, fer one thing, the' 'llaow ye don't ollers talk country-fashion. When ye pass th' time o' day er what not with yer ol' neighbors; why then it saounds pootty much th' same 's ever; but when ye talk t' strangers — conf'rence delegates, city-folks a visitin' yer wife, er what not; why then ye kind o' clip yer wurds like stuck-up Eastern folks, 'n' 'ffected Europian furriners th't plain English ain't good enough fer."

"They do, do they? Wal, what else do they charge?"

"Wal, the' 'llaow 't whut with sarvints, 'n' stablemen 'n' one thing another, ye 've both got so 's ye can't wait on yerselves no more. Naow, thet ther hoss ye 're a ridin' on — his coat 'd dew fer a lookin'-glass a gal c'd see her freckles in — 'n' his tail 's banged square off like th' butt of a wheat-sheaf. I don't expect ye 've laid a curry-comb on him yerself this blessed day!"

"Guess not! Ye want me t' break old Jule's heart?"

"Wal, ef th' Allwise hed a wanted hosses' tails to a looked like that, could n't he a made 'em growed so?"

"Like enough. I expect he can do most anything Jule can do."

"'Course he kin! 'N' more tew, ef ye come t' that!"

"Should n't wonder. What more do they charge agin me?"

"Oh, it 'pears t' them 's though ye don't take no more stock in common folks like them — don't care fer the'r 'pinions, ner fer the'r votes — don't condescend t' lay aout t' please low-down trash like yer old constitooents. The' ain't never no hayseed in yer ha'r, ner parara mud on yer butes. Ye're ollers fixed up fine — stan'-up collar 'n' straps t' yer pants: 'n the' dew say — mebbe its a lie — ye putt on a clean biled shirt every day!"

"Sho now! Do they say that?"

"The' jest dew! I tol' 'm it wuz a campaign lie; but the' 'llaowed th' women folks hed caounted th' wash a hangin' on th' clo's-lines."

"Why did n't ye tell 'em mebbe th' shirts wuz Jule's?"

"Oh, 't would n't dew no good — anybody kin see Jule's hickory wunst a month."

"Anything else, for the land's sake?"

"Wal, naow ye speak on it, the wust comes last. That thar ha'r on yer upper lip!"

"Some fellers finds fault with that who pass remarks on old Prince's banged tail?"

"Wal, yes; its the giner'l talk o' th' hoss-shed."

"Would ye advise me to shave it off, Uncle?"

"Ef it wuz mine, I'd hev it off so quick it'd make yer head swim!"

"Now, look here, Uncle Anstey, jest give the hoss-shed my compliments, and tell 'em that if the Allwise had wanted my lip shaved, he could a shaved it, jest as easy as rollin' off a log."

"Oh, th' ain't nobody a denyin' thet, 's I know of."

"And tell 'em that jest as soon as they let their beards grow the way the Allwise starts 'em, I'll let old Prince's tail do the same."

"Oh, the' wun't never dew it!"

"And tell 'em that I know some medders where hayseed 'll do a heap sight better than it will in my hair, though it won't raise a crop of votes."

"Hayseed fer a crap of oats?"

"Votes I said. And tell 'em I'll see all their shirts, and them in 'em, biled to rags before I'll consult 'em about the bilin' of mine."

Anstey shook his head in regretful disapproval.

"And tell 'em that when I go to Washington, I'm goin' to make believe I'm sent by a constuency of clean, prosperous, hard-working, common-sense American citizens; not by a lot of jimpson-weed galoots!"

"Oh, wal; ye wun't never go!"

Anstey now changed the subject. Pushing his foot down into the dark, powdery mould (too soft and fine to be turned in furrows), he said,—

"Meller as an ash-heap, ain't it? Lessee, haow long is it ye be'n a-crappin' this h'yer bottom t' corn?"

"Twenty-two years, without a halt or a failure, excepting three seasons, when the flood swept it too late to replant. Call it ten acres, and throw off the odd year, this little patch has given me full thirteen thousand bushels of corn, besides what the deer have eaten. See that good white oak there? I hung up a buck on that tree when it was a sapling; first deer I ever shot. It was before sun-up, one winter morning, when I was niggering logs to fence our first piece up on the prairie—father's it was then."

"It 'll make a good saw-cut when ye want one."

"Yes; I 'd a had it to mill last year, only Anne happened round here on horseback, and I told her about the deer hanging on the sapling, and she begged for its life for the sake of old lang syne!"

"Women is cur'us critters!"

"About as near right as God can make 'em!"

"*I* b'lieve ye!"

Then they started slowly toward home, Zury checking the impatient Prince to keep pace with the Anstey team — that ingenious steed securing his desired additional action by ambling sidewise wherever the road was wide enough.

"Dunno as I told ye about our goin' travelin' shortly."

"I want ter know! Clar away up t' Galeny agin?"

"Further than that."

"Wha — whut, not to Bosting!"

"To Boston and further yet. Clean across the Atlantic Ocean."

Anstey brought his ever ready team to a full stop while he gazed, open-mouthed, at the speaker.

"Yes, Uncle; c'mittee of the whole has decided by a unanimous vote that Europe can't go on any longer without being seen. Ayes one; that 's my wife. Nays none. Absent or not voting two; that 's me and the baby."

This stunning news produced such consernation that the silence of their progress became almost oppressive. The elastic prairie-roads gave no sound; only the squeak of the old rattle-trap wagon broke the stillness. It seemed to be complaining of its labors, continued too far into decrepit age — so much that it attracted Zury's notice.

"The old scrap-heap is gettin' shaky, like the rest of us, ain't she, Uncle."

"What? This wagin? Oh, she 's pootty fair of a wagin yit awhile. Last me threw, I guess, 'n' carry me to th' ber'rin'-graoun'."

"Tell ye what, old man, I 've been botherin' my head about how to collect my rent from the wagon-maker that 's workin' in that blacksmith shop of mine. I 've seen the day when it would have come near keepin' me awake nights — that doubtful debt — near to a hundred dollars. That day is past, thank God; but still I don't wan't to lose it altogether. Here 's the shop-lot now."

As they pulled up at the door he called out, —

"Hello, Jinks, how goes it?"

"Haowdy, haowdy, Zury! O' man Anstey, I hope I see ye!"

"Oh, I 'm peart, I thankee."

"Wal, Jinks, how be ye fixed?"

"Same 's ever, Zury. Hain't sol' m' wagin yit. Thar she stan's — put up at odd times, by days' works — she 's 's good as the' make 'em. Wuth a hunderd 'n' twenty ef she 's wuth a dime."

"Could n't turn her in on the rent and call it square?"

"Wal, gimme a *leetle* more rope, 'n' ef I don't make th' riffle some other way, I'll take ye up."

"Tell ye what I'll do: if ye'll take me up now, I'll throw in this old one and call quits."

"Done! I kin git my change aouten that when I've fixed her up 'n' give her a coat o' paint."

Here an unexpected obstacle cropped up. Old Anstey "got up on his ear."

> "On his pale cheek the flush of rage
> O'ercame the ashen hue of age.
> Fierce he broke forth" —

"Who's a-dickerin' away my property 'thaout my consent?"

He drove off in a huff and a hurry, using the spare ends of his lines in a way that took his horses by surprise. Age and poverty had not quelled the independence of the pioneer.

It was with the utmost difficulty that Zury, riding after him, could get speech with him.

"Naow Zury, ye see th' fellers is mighty right 'baout yer bein' away offen yer ol' time manners! When ye wuz a-makin' 'n' a-savin', same 's th' rest on us, ye would n't a never a gone t' a made free with no man's wagin — no, not ef he wuz twice't as old 'n' poor 's I be."

"Oh, see here, Uncle! I did n't mean anything out of the way."

"Wha' 'd ye do it fer, then?"

"Oh, my foot slipped. My intentions were all O. K., being to benefit you, and get my rent out of that ornery skeezicks at the same time." Zury said this with perfect good humor, amused with the spirit of his ancient friend.

"I don't give a continental whut yer intentions wuz! 'N' as fer benefits, we ain't none on us Spring Caounty men 'raound a askin fer no faviors. No charity, thankee, this side o' th' poor-farm 'n' the grave! No matter if ye hev growed till ye 're most aout o' sight fr'm th' road!"

"Of course, of course! *I* know one man 's as good as another!"

"Yew bet he is!"

"And mebbe better."

"Like enough!"

"But then, business is business. You and the boys can haul right smart more corn to apply on what ye owe me, pilin' fifty bushels onto a wagin-load, than you can at twenty-six bushels."

"When we don't pay what we owe, ye 've got yer legle remedy. As fer business — this ain't business, 'n' yew know it."

"Wal, its owin' t' how ye look at it. What d' ye say to taking the wagon at a hunderd and giving me yer note for it?"

"'N' s'cure th' note ontew th' ol' morgidge?"

"Yes, of course."

"Why did n't ye say so fust off?"

"Oh, my foot slipped. I was coming to it afterwards."

"Wal, I dunno but whut I kin 'fford a hunderd fer the wagin. It seems a pootty good of a wagin."

By this transparent subterfuge Zury gained his

object (as usual) and the Ansteys drove home in the splendid new wagon after all, each nearly tumbling out on his or her side in enjoying the entrancing view of their new property.

As Zury and Anstey approached the homestead the old man said, —

"Th' ol' log shanty 's a-stan'in' yit, I see."

"Oh, yes indeed! Anne won't never hear o' gittin' shet o' that!"

"Tew handy, I reck'n."

"N — no, ye know women's kinder — sentimental-like. Ye 'member th' ole newspapers I papered it with — thirty years ago or so?"

"Ya-as. My ole woman tol' me haow th' wuz a story ye read aouter them papers, 't ye could n't never git th' eend on it; 'n' haow Anne Sparrow promised ye she 'd tell ye the rest."

"Jesso-jesso! Wal, she 's up 'n' soaked off that thar paper, 'n' cleaned off the sutt 'n' flyspecks, 'n' got it pasted inter a portfolio!"

"Law suz! 'N' made off the nub of th' story fer ye?"

"No. I would n't let her."

"Why not?"

"Wal, fer one thing — she 's kinder told it tew me."

"So! Haow wuz it? All O. K."

"All happy! This is it I 'm a livin' aout t'-day! That 's happy enough, ain't it?"

"Yew bet!"

"'N' then, she says she 'll write it all daown

afore she dies; 'n' I b'lieve her, 'n' so I wanter put it off till arter I 'm dead."

"Oh yew, sho! Zury Praouder! *Yew* won't never go t' Congress!" (And he never did.)

After early tea, a marvel of almost sinful luxury to the old folks, Zury must needs mount his horse again to see them safe home and afterward ride on to Wayback for the mail — perhaps a letter from Sister Meg!

Then Anne sits once more alone by the open window-door, while "Boy" and Shep go on with their endless railroad-training on the porch. She listens, and reads, and pauses from both to dream, and look back and look forward.

So good-bye, all! If any patient reader remembers promises, expressed or implied, which we have put forth and now leave unfulfilled, and asks "how about those others?" we can only beg pardon, and urge that the book is so near its colophon that we have no room to make a fitting reply.

"Those others," their fortunes and misfortunes, must pass into obscurity and oblivion (save as cherished in living and loving sympathies), or — must furnish the matter for another book of chronicles.

Now a low, tuneful whistle comes out through Anne's window and floats on the sunset air.

"Don't whistle, momma! You mate Sep ront to do 'way!"

"But mamma, has n't had any little boy for a long, long while! She almost feels as if she never had any little boy! Does n't her own Willie want to come and visit his mamma for just a little while?"

"No I tan't. I tan't leave my end-thin — it'll yun away 'n' bate all the tars! Choo-choo-choo-chah: choo-choo-choo-chah: Oooooot!"

GLOSSARY.

Allow, *v.* To suppose, think, expect, intend, conclude. Also to say.

Ary, *art.* E'er a, ever a. (The reverse of "nary.")

Bedfast, *adj.* Confined to bed.

Blaze, *n.* A white patch, especially on the trunk of a boundary-tree. *v.* To make a white mark by stripping off bark.

Brashy, *adj.* Disintegrated, weak, useless.

Chink, *n.* An interstice between logs. *v.* To fill such interstices.

Chinking, *n.* Materials used to fill such interstices.

Chip in, *v.* To contribute to a common stock.

Chivaree, *n.* A burlesque serenade; usually given to a married couple by persons not invited to the wedding.

Chore, *n.* A small task about the house, usually outside.

Chuck-hole, *n.* A sudden depression in a road-rut.

Clamp down, *v.* To seize upon.

Clap-board, *n.* Roofing made by splitting logs.

Close call, *n.* A narrow escape.

Coon's age, *n.* A great, indefinite number of years.

Dog-gone, *exp.* The Western equivalent of "goll-darn." A mild malediction.

Do-good, *n.* An expedient. A makeshift.

Downcy, *adj.* Ailing.

Dozy, *adj.* Disintegrated, useless, tending to decay.

Favor, *v.* To resemble.

Fixed, *adv.* Provided with money.

Fyce, *n.* A small cur.

Galley-west, *adv.* To destruction.

Galoot, *n.* A common, uncultivated rustic.

Gear, *n. & v.* Harness.

Get, *v.* To succeed in; to achieve. Also to purchase on credit. To "get to get," is to succeed in purchasing on credit.

Get away with. To vanquish, conquer, excel, defeat, surpass, consume.

Got up, *n.* Spirit, spunk; pluck in action, motion, or appearance.

Give away, *v.* To betray. *n.* Betrayal.

Glut, *n.* A wooden wedge used in splitting logs.

Go, *n.* A bargain struck, a decision arrived at, a start (as distinguished from a false start). *v.* To proceed intentionally.

Good and, *adv.* Extremely, indubitably, unqualifiedly.

Great shakes, *n.* Esteem. To think great shakes of anything is to hold it in high estimation.

Grip, *n.* Holding and staying power. Perseverance.

Hard lines, *n.* Severe trials.

Hen on, *n.* Something of importance hatching out.

Hike out, *v.* To go away, clear out, depart.

Hog, *v.* To gather (a crop) by turning swine in to it.

Horse-shed, *v.* To propagate views or advance interest by private or quasi public talk.

Humbly, *adj.* Homely. Unhandsome.

Jimpson weed, *n.* Stramonium,

Jamestown weed. (From the desolation about Jamestown, Va., where the ruins of John Smith's colony were marked by this malodorous plant.)

Knock, *v.* To overcome.

Laylock, *n.* Lilac.

Lay down, *v.* To surrender one's self.

Lay low, *v.* To hide one's self.

Limb, *n.* A limb of Satan.

Lop-sided, *adj.* Misshapen. Unsymmetrical.

Main chance, *n.* Personal gain.

Mitten, *n.* Rejection. (Usually of a marriage proposal.)

Monkey, *v.* To waste time in foolish actions.

Nary, *art.* "Ne'er a." (Reverse of "ary.")

Near, *adj.* Stingy, mean, penurious.

Nigger, *v.* To burn logs into lengths.

Nip and tuck, *n.* or *adv.* Perilous position, alternating between hope and fear.

Offen, *adj.* or *adv.* Off from.

O. K., *adj.* or *adv.* All correct or correctly.

On it, *adv.* Ably and willing, prompt and ready.

On the job, *adv. of place.* In the vicinity.

Ornery, *adj.* Ordinary, low, mean, contemptible.

Ou' doors, *adv.* Out of doors, in the open air.

Out or Outing, *n.* Outcome, result.

Owing to, *adverbial expression.* Depending on.

Patch, *n.* Piece: generally of land.

Peart, *adj.* Bright, smart, pert, in good condition.

Peter out, *v.* To grow small by degrees, down to nothingness.

Piece, *n.* A luncheon. Also an indefinite distance.

Plum, *adv.* Entirely, completely, irrevocably.

Puncheon, *n.* The side-cut off a saw-log. A slab.

Ready, *n.* Ready money. Also preparedness, as "to get a good ready." "Ready john:" cash on the nail.

Right, *adv.* Very, extremely.

Right away, *adv.* Immediately.

Right smart, *n.* A considerable quantity. *adv.* Considerably.

Rive, *v.* To split.

Sand, *n.* Courage, determination, obstinacy, perseverance, grit.

Scrape, *n.* A serious predicament.

Show, *n.* An opportunity for action.

Shucks, *n.* A symbol of uselessness.

Shun 'round, *v.* To avoid.

Slab, *n.* A side-cut off a saw-log.

Slop over, *v.* To be carried away by sentiment or enthusiasm.

Slouch, *n.* A poor, slovenly thing.

Smart Aleck, *n.* A fool, whose acts contravene his intentions.

Smudge, *n.* A smoky fire to drive away insects.

Snake, *v.* To drag lengthwise.

Sock it to, *v.* To assail, injure, forcibly or fraudulently.

Stall, *v.* To stop progress.

Stand from under, *v.* To look out for surprising developments. To beware.

Swap, *v.* To exchange. (Aboriginal.)

Sweat, *n.* Unwise haste, hurry.

Swing, *v.* To hold up, sustain, succeed with; especially an enterprise or speculation.

Tackle, *v.* To undertake. To take hold of.

Take stock, *v.* To estimate. To "take much stock" is to value highly.

Talking or Talking steady, *v.* Speaking to the purpose.

Talk turkey, *v.* To speak to the purpose, to speak with due regard to the other side.

Teetotal, *adj.* Total, entire, complete, unmixed. Especially used to indicate the extreme of the temperance movement.

Tie to, *v.* To rely on.

Truck, *n.* Personal property.

Way-wonted, *adj.* Accustomed to the locality.

Whack, *n.* A bargain struck.

Whack up, *v.* To share.

Whale, *v.* To strike hard and rapid blows.